CHEMICAL PUBLICATIONS

This long-awaited revision of a standard text and reference book takes into account the many changes which have occurred in chemical literature during the last two decades. The book introduces students to the nature and extent of all this literature of chemistry and chemical technology and gives them personal experience in its use. As before, the strong points of the book are an over-all, balanced perspective of chemical publications of various kinds and library exercises to be used to introduce students to this literature.

The general outline of earlier editions (with some minor rearrangements) has been followed, and the nature of periodicals, patents, treatises, and most other kinds of publications, remains unchanged. The suggested library problems are essentially the same, except for the inclusion of new assignments. Experience over a quarter of a century with these kinds of problems has proved their general workability. The point is to get the student into the library and to introduce him to the different kinds of sources. To many students this is a new and interesting experience in chemistry.

In the third edition new titles have been substituted for older ones. This applies to periodicals, treatises, and various kinds of single-volume books. The chapter on governmental publications is entirely rewritten to take into account the many changes in administrative distribution of the various bureaus of interest. Also many changes in the publications from these bureaus are noted.

The chapter on patents is by Dr. Julian Smith, an acknowledged expert in chemical literature.

ABOUT THE AUTHOR:

M. G. MELLON is Professor of Analytical Chemistry at Purdue University, where, since 1922, he has been teaching the course in chemical literature which he organized.

His membership in scientific societies includes the American Chemical Society, the American Association for the Advancement of Science, the American Society for Testing Materials, the Optical Society of America, the Society for Applied Spectroscopy, the Association of Analytical Chemists, the New York Academy of Science, the Coblentz Society and others.

He has been Chairman of the Division of Chemical Literature (American Chemical Society) and was given the Austin M. Patterson Award in Chemical Documentation, primarily for his book CHEMICAL PUBLICATIONS, and some fifteen articles in technical journals on chemical literature. Prior to his receiving the award, it had been given to only four other men.

CHEMICAL PUBLICATIONS

CHEMICAL PUBLICATIONS

THEIR NATURE AND USE

M. G. MELLON, Ph.D., Sc.D.

Professor of Analytical Chemistry
Purdue University

THIRD EDITION

McGRAW-HILL BOOK COMPANY, INC.

New York   Toronto   London

1958

CHEMICAL PUBLICATIONS

THE MAPLE PRESS COMPANY, YORK, PA.

THE CHEMICAL LITERATURE

(With apologies to Kipling)

The Literature,

The chemical literature—

When in doubt look it up in the literature.

Every question that man can raise, every phrase of every phase of that question is on record

In the literature;

Thrashed out threadbare pro and con

In the literature.

Did the universe at large once carry a positive charge?

Why aren't the holes in macaroni square?

From Avogadro's number to the analysis of cucumber, if you're interested you'll find it, for it's there

In the literature.

In *Journal* this or *Zeitschrift* that, *Comptes rendus* or *Zentralblatt*,

It's somewhere

In the literature.

—*P. G. Horton*

Anyone who wants to use a library effectively must already have some knowledge of the same nature as that which he hopes to find there. If not, he does not know where or how to look; nor can he grasp fully what he finds, even if he happens to hit upon the right book.

—*Sir William L. Bragg*

PREFACE

Nearly two decades have passed since the information was collected for the second edition of this book. The intervening period brought many changes in the chemical literature. To take account of the new situation has been the dominant objective of the third edition.

Several influences have operated in producing the present situation. World War II had considerable effect in several directions. Chemical research reacted rapidly to the exigencies of war, and control of nuclear reactions brought essentially a new kind of chemistry. Publication, however, lagged in most areas. Old journals disappeared, some to reappear under new names and some to resume publication later. Compilation of the great treatises became difficult. Some died, some are still trying to recover, and some new ones have appeared.

A decade after the start of the war, the various fields of chemistry were well on their way to recovery. American industry, along with its publications, was booming. German industry was well on its way back, and German publications again began to flourish. Russian work in chemistry and publications about it were becoming ever more important. The rate of publication of chemical information in all areas was increasing rapidly. New journals flourished, and patents multiplied. Altogether, chemists were soon confronted with a vast amount of new information.

Developments arising from all these changes have been noteworthy. Terms such as *documentalist, literature chemist,* and *retriever* have come into use. Aroused and increased interest resulted in the formation in 1948 of the Division of Chemical Literature of the American Chemical Society. This group now has extensive semiannual programs in a wide variety of subjects. Many papers describing these programs have appeared in the *Advances in Chemistry Series.* Mechanical searching not only is of interest but in some cases has become almost a necessity to keep up with the industrial pace. Photoduplication has become commonplace.

To introduce students to the nature and the extent of all this literature of chemistry and chemical technology and to give them personal experience in its use remains the principal objective. This book therefore follows the general outline of earlier editions, with some minor rearrangements. Although the selection of illustrative examples and the order and manner of presentation are personal choices, the nature of periodicals, patents, treatises, and most other kinds of publications remains unchanged.

The suggested library problems have not been changed essentially, except for the inclusion of new assignments. Experience over a quarter of a century with this kind of problem indicates their general workability. No doubt, different ones would be equally effective. The important point is to get the student into the library and to introduce him to the different kinds of sources. To many students this contact is a new and interesting experience in chemistry. As Whitehead has stated, "Education is the acquisition of the art of the utilization of knowledge."

Grateful appreciation is hereby expressed to the many persons who so kindly furnished facts and made suggestions. For meticulous checking of countless details special thanks are due the author's colleague, James van Luik, chemistry librarian (with the rank of assistant professor), and Ruth T. Power, chemistry librarian, associate professor of library science at the University of Illinois. In Chapter 4 advantage has been taken of the vast experience and knowledge of Julian F. Smith.

Considerable care has been taken to achieve reliability, but the star of infallibility is elusive. Reports of errors will be appreciated. Inaccurate assignments especially are depressing to the morale of a class.

M. G. Mellon

CONTENTS

CHAPTER 1

INTRODUCTION AND GENERAL OUTLINE

Very little advance in culture could be made, even by the greatest
man of genius, if he were dependent for what knowledge he might acquire upon his own personal observations. Indeed, it might be said that
exceptional mental ability involves a power to absorb the ideas of others,
and even that the most original people are those who are able to borrow
most freely.—*Libby*

Someone has stated that information of a scientific nature can
be obtained, in many cases at least, by one or more of the following procedures: first, by inquiring of the individual who knows;
second, by performing the experimental investigations necessary
to ascertain the desired facts; and, third, by consulting the scientific literature, where a record may be found of the published
reports of others' work upon the subject in question.

Although it may be taking the path of least resistance to resort
to the first possibility, provided an individual possessing the
information is available, and although it is frequently very desirable to obtain experimental facts first hand, there are many cases
in which recourse to either one of these alternatives is unnecessary
or impracticable. In such instances, the chemist turns to the
chemical library. The solubility data for sodium chloride in
water, for example, can probably be given by various individuals,
or it may be determined with fair precision by rather simple
means; but for ordinary purposes anyone requiring such information would consult solubility tables. It is a matter of utilizing
recorded chemistry.

Before beginning a journey to some distant point, one usually
gives at least passing consideration to his reason for going
and to the means to be employed in reaching the desired destina-
tion. Similarly, before taking up the question of how to use the
resources of a library, it seems desirable to give some attention
to the kind of inquiries which one takes to such a place and to

the nature of the sources to be examined when one arrives. Since our concern is with chemistry and, therefore, chemical or technical libraries, we should have in mind the kinds of questions which a chemist takes to the library. A searcher, having familiarized himself with the different sources of information relating to the several types of questions, is then in a position to make effective use of the material.

At this point, therefore, there is presented a classification of the types of questions for which the material in our various chemical publications may be expected to help in providing answers. The outline proposed[1] is based upon questions presented to the technological division of a large public library, where, for some 10 years, a record was kept of the more important inquiries submitted.

The inquirers ranged in their chemical interests all the way from commercial research and consulting chemists to boys seeking directions for some chemical trick or women requiring popular presentations of subjects for meetings of their clubs. Considering their source, it is not surprising that the questions varied widely in character, just as the questioners varied in their chemical interests. One individual wanted something very specific, such as the spectral transmission curve for a 10 per cent aqueous solution of cupric nitrate, while another wanted to know "all about cement." Some wanted only a popular article or book, while others were satisfied with nothing less than the latest technical data.

An examination of the hundreds of questions indicates that most of them fell readily into rather well-defined divisions. The scheme formulated for this purpose is given below. In it no particular significance is attached to the order in which the various divisions have been placed. There is included for each division a statement of the general nature of the inquiries belonging to it, together with several examples of typical questions.

TYPES OF QUESTIONS

A. Specific. Those in which the information desired relates to a single kind of chemical activity. The following areas are examples:

    1. *Bibliography*. Partial or complete lists of references, with or without annotations:

        References on the corrosion of alloys by ammonia

[1] Mellon, *Special Libraries*, **17**:275 (1926).

The literature on germanium

Popular articles on radiochemistry

2. *History and Biography.* Events in the life of an individual or in the development of an industry; the influences operating, and contributions made, during certain periods; the beginning and development of a theory or an industry:

Contributions of the alchemists

Life of Berzelius

Development of synthetic fibers

3. *Existence, Occurrence, and Source.* The location of raw material; its form; compounds which are known:

Occurrence of uranium in Canada

Commercial source of bromine

Fluorine substitution products of methane

4. *Composition.* Natural materials and artificial products; specifications and standards; formulas and workshop recipes:

Formula for automobile lacquer

Composition of electrolyte for Edison battery

Analysis of Pluto mineral water

5. *Methods of Production, Preparation, and Manipulation.* Laboratory and commercial processes; details of procedure; materials required; apparatus employed:

Manufacture of stainless steel

Preparation of mayonnaise

Fluorination of organic compounds

6. *Properties.* Physical and chemical (including physiological action); general and specific reactions:

Effect of carbon dioxide on individuals in closed rooms

Specific heat of calcium chloride brine of specific gravity 1.33

Action of charcoal as a purifying agent

7. *Uses.* Laboratory and industrial; general and special applications:

Uses of water glass (sodium silicate)

Industrial applications of silica gel

Employment of alkyl bromides in synthetic chemistry

8. *Identification, Testing, and Analysis.* Methods available; interpretation of results:

Detection of pasteurized milk

Testing of concrete

Analysis of flue gas

9. *Patents and Trade-marks.* Date of expiration; details of specifications; objects previously protected:

Details of a process for making synthetic methanol

Specifications for production of ascarite

Date of expiration of patent on Edison cell

10. *Statistical Data.* Production, consumption, cost, supply, price, market:

Production and supply of helium

Statistics on the lampblack industry

Foreign activities in the sulfur industry

B. General. Those in which the information desired relates to more than one of the above-mentioned classes. In this case we encounter two variations in the questions.

 1. Those in which there is clear indication of the particular classes which are involved:
      Preparation, properties, and uses of artificial stone
      Occurrence and composition of natural zeolites
 2. Those in which no such limitations are expressed or implied:
      Efflorescence on stone and brick
      Hydraulic cements

The Origin and Development of Chemical Literature

Having in mind the kinds of questions a chemist takes to the library, we are next interested in the sources available which are likely to contain information of value for answering these questions. In considering this part of our problem, attention may be directed briefly to the origin and development of those publications which have come commonly to be designated as the "chemical literature" and to certain points regarding the state of knowledge and the conditions prevailing at the time the publications appeared. Such an examination furnishes some perspective for judging the comparative value of the records for present-day work.

We find ourselves today in the midst of a great volume of published material of chemical importance. What was its origin? Why do we have it? Who was responsible for it? How did it reach its present form? These and similar questions probably do not often disturb the average chemist. They do have some interest, however, in spite of the fact that often there are not definite answers.

Numerous works have been published dealing with the historical aspect of various phases of chemistry. Some publications have been devoted to the activities and contributions of a certain individual; some deal only with the origin, development, and significance of an idea or theory; some deal with special industries, with divisions of chemistry, or with countries; and some aim to present a more or less comprehensive view of the whole field. But, curiously, none seems to be available having as its primary aim the presentation of an account of the development of chemical publications as such.[1] In most works of a historical nature,

[1] W. Ostwald, "Handbuch der allgemeinen Chemie," vol. I, "Die

at least occasional references are found to a considerable number of publications. Usually, however, the aim is to direct attention to some individual's idea or contribution rather than to the publication itself.

Even a superficial examination of the material available indicates a long story which recounts the course of man's development to the point of appreciating the significance of the modern scientific method and of applying it to a study of himself and of his environment. Even now, in the words of Millikan:

Man himself is just . . . emerging from the jungle. It was only a few hundred years ago that he began to try to use the experimental and the objective method, to try to set aside all his prejudices and his preconceptions,[1] to suspend his judgment until he had all the facts before him, to spare no pains to see first all sides of the situation and then to let his reason and his intelligence, instead of his passion and his prejudice, control his decisions. That is called the scientific method.

We now realize that, as a result of the combined contributions of many individuals, there has been acquired a powerful tool in the scientific method, and there has been accumulated an enormous collection of facts, recorded in many places and touching many phases of human activities. The greatest number of significant contributions have been made in the fields of knowledge encompassed by the natural sciences, in which chemistry occupies a commanding position. The written records of these developments include a multitude of facts, experimentally determined, together with discussions and interpretations involving these facts.

At present our interest will center on *publications containing accounts of facts and theories,* rather than on the facts themselves; on the methods by which they were discovered or obtained; or on the ultimate effect of the theories developed to account for the facts.

When did man begin to apply to his ideas the test of experimental verification? The answer must remain uncertain. Perhaps it is even not significant. We are convinced, however, that the adoption of the experimental method marked a very impor-

chemische Literatur und die Organisation der Wissenschaft," Akademische Verlagsgesellschaft m.b.H., Leipzig, 1919, is of interest.

[1] As Hugh Black has said, "to reject the idolatry of the traditional."

tant advance in the attainments of the human race; and we are partially aware of the marvelous material changes that have accompanied and grown out of its application in industrial and scientific research work.

What disposal the first enthusiastic workers made of the results obtained by this method we can only guess. It seems entirely probable that no organized work, as we now undertake it, was done and that no written records were made, perhaps for centuries.

Historical records do not show the rate of this development, but we do know that Francis Bacon, about 1600, formulated a program for establishing research as a means of regenerating learning in the service of humanity. This included the foundation of a college of research, whose function was to foster the New Philosophy (the experimental and scientific method), and the provision for the publication of such discoveries as were to be revealed.

Although Bacon did not see his project actively undertaken, his work did produce noteworthy results. The trend of the times became directed more and more toward intelligent experimentation. His "New Atlantis" was an imaginary picture of his college of research in practical operation. This book, according to H. G. Wells, may be considered as one of the ten which have been most instrumental in shaping and directing human activities. Wells writes that it

formulated the conception of a House of Science, incessantly inquiring and criticising and publishing, that should continually extend the boundaries of human knowledge; it replaced unorganized by organized scientific research, and did so much to insure the unending continuity of scientific inquiries; and it contains the essential ideas of the modern scientific process—the organized collection, publication and criticism of fact. . . . Of the supreme importance of the book itself as the seed of the Royal Society and most European academies, there can be little dispute. Like the rod of Moses, it strikes the rock of human capacity, and thereafter the waters of knowledge flow freely and steadily.

According to Liddell,[1] about 15 years after Bacon's death a group of

divers worthy persons inquisitive into Natural Philosophy and other parts of humane learning, and particularly what has been called the

[1] Liddell, *Science*, **60**:25 (1924).

"New Philosophy" . . . began by agreement to meet weekly in London to treat and discourse of such affairs.

Out of the efforts of this group, meeting for the purpose of discussing and sharing their intellectual interests, there was founded the Royal Society. Commenting on the significance of this event, Strachey states:

> If one were asked to choose a date for the beginning of the modern world, probably July 15, 1662, would be the best to fix upon. For on that day the Royal Society was founded, and the place of science in civilization became a definite and recognized thing. The sun had risen above the horizon; and yet, before that, there had been streaks of light in the sky. The great age of Newton was preceded by a curious twilight period—a period of gestation and preparation, confused, and only dimly conscious of the end toward which it was moving.

The Royal Society stands first in at least two respects: it was the first society of its kind to survive, and it was the first to publish the proceedings of its meetings.[1] This publication was first printed in 1665 as the *Philosophical Transactions* of the Royal Society, and it has had a continuous existence since that date. Even today the first volume is interesting.

Of particular significance to chemists is the fact that Robert Boyle was one of the most active pioneer members. To quote again from Liddell,[2] Boyle

> refers to himself as a member of the Invisible College, composed originally of scientific men bound together as an esoteric sodality without name or meeting place and having for its sole end the alleviation of the physical and spiritual ills of humanity.

The time when Boyle and his associates formed the Royal Society may be taken as the date of the dawn of chemical literature as we now know it. A simple beginning it was, this first systematic recording of scientific papers and discussions, and the preservation of these contributions for posterity; but now the practice is so universal, and the contributions are so numerous,

---

[1] "The Accademia del Cimento, founded at Florence, in 1657, . . . was the first scientific society of any importance. . . . Although it lived but ten years, it enriched the world by leaving a volume of important records of experiments, chiefly in pneumatics."—*Mellor*

[2] *Loc. cit.*

that one is amazed to find more than 7,000 periodicals publishing information more or less closely related to the work of the individual engaged in chemical and related pursuits. Crane says:[1]

> Since 1665, when this first scientific journal put in its appearance there has been an accelerated increase in the number of journals of interest to the chemist, and the bulk of the accumulated material has become almost staggering in its proportions. . . . The vastness of the chemical journal literature, its rapid and continuous advance upon the frontiers of our knowledge, and its essentially unorganized state, are . . . arguments why the chemist should see to it that he learns how best to make use of the means which have been provided to make this sea of information navigable.

In 1650, then, there were no scientific journals. At present more than 7,000 are regularly abstracted by *Chemical Abstracts*. Let us examine some of the intervening developments in chemical publications.

It has already been noted that several methods of communicating ideas were probably used during the centuries preceding the appearance of the *Philosophical Transactions* of the Royal Society. Following the inception of this initial serial publication, however, the practice of making a permanent record of individuals' contributions started to spread.[2] Gradually, various European academies came into existence, each founding, sooner or later, its own publication.[3] The general condition of affairs during this period necessarily made progress slow. There was still much confusion in the ideas regarding chemical matters. Over a century had to elapse between the founding of the Royal Society and the work of Lavoisier. Following his discoveries, there appeared, in 1778, the first chemical journal, Crell's *Chemisches Journal*. Others followed some years later.

By 1820, the volume of the material appearing had reached a stage where it seemed desirable to collect and summarize the contributions for each year. Accordingly, in 1821, Berzelius began his famous *Jahresberichte über die Fortschritte der physischen*

---

[1] Crane, *Ind. Eng. Chem.*, **14**:901 (1922).

[2] Barnes, *Sci. Monthly*, **38**:257 (1934); Kilmer, *J. Am. Pharm. Assoc.*, **19**:587 (1930).

[3] See M. Ornstein, "The Rôle of Scientific Societies in the Seventeenth Century," Ph.D. dissertation, Columbia University, New York, 1913, for developments in England, France, Germany, and Italy; see also Moore, "The Rôle of the Scientific Society in Chemistry," *Chemist*, **16**:327 (1939).

Wissenschaften. This publication represents the first chemical-review serial.[1] Not long afterward, a journal seemed justified whose purpose would be the publication of short summaries of each article as soon as possible after the article appeared. *Pharmaceutisches Centralblatt* was begun in 1830 to meet this need.[2] Developments of the present century give ample proof of the vision which these early chemists had regarding the place for such publications.

With a place to publish articles of their own and a source for summaries of others' work, together with reports of yearly developments, the chemists' needs in this direction seemed to be supplied for the time being. But with the appearance of more and more journals and the constant accumulation of facts in the rapidly widening range of chemical activities, there arose the need for other types of publications. Not more or different journals were needed this time, but rather publications in which the material already published could be gathered together and arranged according to definite schemes. Reference works were the answer—digests and treatises, including indexes of known compounds, compilations of chemical properties, discussions of definite fields of the science, dictionaries, and other works.[3]

Early Books on Chemistry

One might well conclude from the preceding statements that there are no records of chemical matters available before the founding of the Royal Society. Such is not the case. Although this event did result in the establishment of the first scientific journal to survive, various textbooks or treatises on chemistry, pharmacy, and metallurgy were already well known.[4]

On considering that modern chemical ideas began with Lavoisier's work, it seems that before 1600 the state of chemical knowledge must have been such as to make these books of

---

[1] *Berlinisches Jahrbuch für die Pharmacie und die damit verbunden Wissenschaften* was started in 1795 and continued until 1840.

[2] *Journal de pharmacie et de chemie* and *Annales de chimie* had been doing some of this kind of work.

[3] H. P. Spratt, "Technical Science Libraries," Library Association, London, 1934; "Libraries for Scientific Research in Europe and America," Grafton & Company, London, 1936.

[4] See Ives and Ihde, *J. Chem. Educ.*, **29**:244 (1952), for a description of the books of alchemy and the history of chemistry contained in the Duveen Library.

doubtful value to anyone except the chemical historian.[1] Many facts mentioned stand out as accurate observations of the early worker; but the records of his processes are meager, and the recipes of the alchemist are often mysterious, inaccurate, and misleading, in the light of our present knowledge. Thus, Bergman wrote, "The history of chemistry is properly divided into the mythological, the obscure, and the certain."[2]

FIG. 1. Library of the Mellon Institute, Pittsburgh. It contains approximately 35,000 volumes, which deal especially with industrial chemical research.

For the purpose of reference there is included a list of some of these early publications.[3] The arrangement is based upon the divisions of chemical activity used by Brown.[4] The student

[1] See, however, Caley, *J. Chem. Educ.*, **3**:1149 (1926), and **4**:979 (1927), for English translations of two Greek papyri, which the translator describes as being by far the most ancient documents we possess dealing with chemical arts and operations as such. They appear to have been written about the end of the third century.

[2] "Disertatio gradualis de primordiis chemiae," Upsaliae, Sweden, 1779.

[3] See also J. W. Mellor, "Treatise on Inorganic and Theoretical Chemistry," vol. 1, pp. 19–73, Longmans, Green & Co., Inc., New York, 1922.

[4] J. C. Brown, "A History of Chemistry from the Earliest Times," The Blakiston Division, McGraw-Hill Book Company, Inc., New York, 1920.

should bear in mind that these works were textbooks or short treatises on chemical knowledge and practice of their day and not reports of experimental work and discoveries resulting therefrom.

Prehistoric Period (up to 1500 B.C.). As an art, chemistry dates far back of the Christian era. There are no records of chemical practice in this period, but we do find much definite information regarding certain chemical facts mentioned by various writers, as in the Bible. Among these writers may be mentioned the Chaldean, Egyptian, Byzantine, Persian, Indian (Hindu), Roman, and Greek.

Alchemical Period (1500 B.C. to A.D. 1650). The activity of this period was directed toward the search for gold and for the philosophers' stone, including the transmutation of the elements. Many practical facts were noted as a result of calcinations, sublimations, and distillations.

History indicates that the Egyptians acquired much knowledge from the Chaldeans. The Arabians appropriated what was known to the Egyptians and the Greeks. There are preserved several Latin translations of writings by Arabians and others of this period, such as "Aurifera artis quam chemiam vocant" (1572), "Artis chemicae principes" (1572), "Theatrum chemicum" (1659–1661), and "Bibliotheca chemica curiosa" (Magnet, 1702). These profess to be the teachings of Hermes, Ostanes, Plato, Aristotle, Morienus, Geber, Rhazes, Bubucar, Alpharabi, and Avicenna.

Among the Greek writers (speculative philosophers) should be mentioned Heraclitus (540–475 B.C.), who declared, like Bergson, that "becoming," or eternal change, is the sole actuality; Aristotle (384–322 B.C.), who formulated the laws of deductive reasoning, that is, from the general to the specific; and Pliny (23–79), who wrote the "Historia naturalis," of 160 books, the last 5 volumes of which are an account of the chemical knowledge of the time.

Alchemistic writers include Zosismos, Albertus Magnus, Vincent de Beauvais, Thomas Aquinas, Arnoldus Villonovanus, Raymond Lully, and Roger Bacon (1214–1284). Bacon advocated the inductive system of philosophy (that is, reasoning from the specific to the general) and noted the importance and significance of experiment as a tool of research.

Iatrochemical Period (1500 to 1700). The preceding period included the time of the Middle Ages, while in this period we encounter chemistry during the Renaissance, when the search for new medicinal substances became the general aim. The following list includes the names of some of the contemporary writers and certain writings ascribed to them.[1]

Agricola, G. (1494–1555): "De re metallica libri XII," 1556.
Anthony, F. (1550–1623): "Medicinae chymicae et veri potabilis auri," 1610.
Baldwin, C. A. (1632–1682): "Aurum superius et inferius," 1675.
Barba, A. A. (1575–1650): "Arte de los metales," 1640.
Croll, O. (1580–1609): "Basilica chymica," 1609.
Glaser, C. (1615–1673): "Traité de la chymie," 1663.
Glauber, J. R. (1604–1668): "Operis mineralis," 1651.
Helmont, J. B. Van (1577–1644): "Opuscula medica inaudita," 1644.
———: "Ortus medicinae vel opera et opuscula omnia," 1648.
Kunckel, J. von L. (1630–1703): "Laboratorium chymicum."
Lemery, N. (1645–1715): "Cours de chymie," 1675; "Pharmacopeé universelle," 1697.
Libavius, A. L. (1540–1616): "Alchymia," 1597.
Mynsicht, A. von (1603–1638): "Thesaurus medico-chymicus," 1631.
Nicols, T. (1600–1660): "A Lapidary," 1652.
Paracelsus, P. T. A. B. (1493–1541): "Opera omnia medico, chemico, chirugica," 1558.
Plattes, G. (1575–1650): "Discovery of Subterranean Treasure," 1639.
Rolfinck, W. (1599–1673): "Chymia in artis formam redacta," 1641.
Sala, A. (1575–1640): "Opera medico-chemica," 1647.
Schrietman, C. (1525–1600): "Probenbüchlein frembde und subtile Künst," 1578.
Sennert, D. (1572–1637): "Epitome naturalis scientiae," 1618.
Webster, J. (1610–1682): "Metallographia," 1671.

Phlogiston Period (1650 to 1775). The aim of this period was directed toward the development of a rational theory of chemistry. The following list includes some of the writers and their contributions.

Becher, J. J. (1635–1682): "Metallurgie," 1660; also other works.
Boerhaave, H. (1668–1738): "Elementa chemiae," 1732.
———: "A New Method of Chemistry," 1727.

---

[1] The names, titles, and dates in these lists were taken from the following sources: "Catalogue générale des livres imprimes," Bibliothèque Nationale, Paris; "Catalogue of Printed Books" and "General Catalogue of Printed Books," British Museum, London; D. I. Duveen, "Bibliotheca alchemica et chemica," E. Weil, London, 1949; and J. C. Poggendorff, "Biographisch-literarisches Handwörterbuch zur Geschichte der exacten Wissenschaften," Barth, Leipzig, 1863.

Boyle, R. (1627–1691): "The Sceptical Chemist," 1680.

Geoffry, E. F. (1672–1731): "Des différents rapports observés en chimie entre différentes substances," 1718.

Hoffman, F. (1660–1742): "Opera omnia physico-medica," 1740.

———: "Opuscula physico-medica antehoc seorsim edita," 1725.

Hooke, R. (1635–1703): "Micrographia," 1665.

Juncker, J. (1679–1759): "Conspectus chemiae theoretico-practicae," 1730.

Macquer, P. J. (1718–1784): "Dictionnaire de chimie," 1766.

———: "Elemens de chymie pratique," 1751.

———: "Elemens de chymie théoretique," 1749.

Neumann, C. (1683–1737): "Lectiones chymicae," 1727.

Pott, J. H. (1692–1777): "Chymische Untersuchungen," 1746.

Stahl, G. E. (1660–1734): "Chymia rationalis et experimentalis," 1720.

———: "Fundamenta chymiae dogmaticae et experimentalis," 1723.

Quantitative Period (1775 to 1900). The aim of the period was to extend and apply chemical knowledge on the basis of the rational theory developed. The time included coincides with the development of modern chemistry. As we are often not aware of the books written during the earlier part of the period, the following list is included.

Berzelius, J. J. (1779–1848): "Föreläsurgar i Djurkemien," 1806.

———: "Lärbok i Kemien," 1808.

———: "Lehrbuch der Chemie," 1825.

Black, J. (1728–1799): "Lectures on the Elements of Chemistry," 1803.

Dalton, J. (1766–1844): "A New System of Chemical Philosophy," 1808.

Davy, H. (1778–1829): "Elements of Agricultural Chemistry," 1813.

———: "Elements of Chemical Philosophy," 1812.

Dumas, J. B. A. (1800–1884): "Traité de chimie appliquée aux arts," 1828–1846.

Faraday, M. (1791–1867): "Chemical Manipulation," 1827.

———: "Experimental Researches in Chemistry and Physics," 1859.

Fourcroy, A. F. C. (1755–1809): "Philosophie chimique," 1792.

———: "Systeme des connaissances chimiques," 1801.

Gmelin, L. (1788–1853): "Handbuch der theoretischen Chemie," 1817.

Klaproth, M. H. (1743–1817): "Beiträge zur Kenntnis der Mineralkörper," 1795.

———: "Chemisches Wörterbuch," 1807.

Lavoisier, A. L. (1743–1794): "Memoires de chimie," 1805.

———: "Opuscules physiques et chymiques," 1774.

———: "Traité élémentaire de chymie," 1789.

Mitscherlich, E. (1794–1863): "Lehrbuch der Chemie," 1829.

Morveau, G. de (1737–1816): "Elemens de chimie," 1771.

———: "Elemens de chymie théorique et pratique," 1777.

Richter, J. B. (1762–1807): "Anfangsgründe der Stöchymoetrie," 1792.

Rose, H. (1795–1864): "Ausfuhrliches Handbuch der analytischen Chemie," 1829.

Thénard, L. J. (1777–1857): "Traité de chimie élémentaire, théorique et pratique," 1813.
Wenzel, C. F. (1740–1793): "Einleitung zur höhren Chemie," 1774.
————: "Lehre von der Verwandschaft der Körper," 1777.

Following these writers came von Liebig, Wöhler, Stas, Bunsen, Meyer, Mendeleev, Laurent, Gerhardt, Wurtz, and a host of others up to our own time.

Outline of Chemical Publications

With this brief indication of the origin and development of early chemical publications, next in order is an outline covering the material available at the present time. Subsequent chapters deal with the different kinds of publications and their use.

In a systematic study of the literature of chemistry and chemical technology, some classification is needed for the numerous sources comprising the published information relating to this area. The material may be classified either according to the nature of the subject matter, as is the system in *Chemical Abstracts*, or according to the nature of the publication in which the information appears. This second basis of classification seems the logical one to adopt for those who want practical assistance in using a chemical library, since periodicals, bulletins, patents, and books are the units of a library.

The arrangement of this book is one of publications rather than of information. However, the two bases of classification are combined in a way, as there is included a statement of the kind of information which each type of publication contains. Although an attempt has been made to define the different classes of publications to make them reasonably inclusive and exclusive, not all the different sections are differentiated from each other by sharp lines of demarcation. There is some overlapping and occasional gradual merging of one into the other.

For some time the author has divided publications into (1) those containing chiefly original contributions and (2) those containing chiefly compilations and discussions of facts already recorded.[1] Recently a third group has been suggested,[2] that is,

---

[1] Mellon, *Chem. Met. Eng.*, **33**:97 (1926).

[2] J. F. Smith and J. D. Scott, "Literature of Chemical Technology," in Kirk and Othmer (eds.), "Encyclopedia of Chemical Technology," vol. 8, pp. 418–467, Interscience Publishers, Inc., New York, 1952.

those containing lists of people engaged in the field of chemistry and guides, catalogues, and directories to their publications, laboratories, plants, products, and services. These three groups may be more definitely designated as indicated.

Primary Sources. These publications contain chiefly new material or new presentations and discussions of known material. In general, they contain the latest published information, which is essentially unorganized. Examples are most periodicals, governmental bulletins, patents, dissertations, and manufacturers' technical pamphlets.

Secondary Sources. These publications contain chiefly known material that is arranged and organized according to some plan. Thus, the physicochemical constants in the tables of Landolt-Börnstein are systematic compilations of data previously published but so widely scattered as to be of little practical use unless collected and classified. Examples of this kind of publication are a few periodicals; bibliographies; reference works, such as tabular compilations, dictionaries, encyclopedias, formularies, and treatises; and monographs and textbooks.

Tertiary Sources. These publications contain compilations of information about chemists and chemical technologists and what they do. Such sources are organized to aid the searcher in using both primary and secondary sources and in following the production of and trade in chemicals and chemical equipment. Examples of this kind of publication are library guides, trade catalogues, directories, and biographies.

CHAPTER 2

PRIMARY SOURCES—PERIODICALS

> By a fiction as remarkable as any to be found in law, what has once been published (no matter what the language) is usually spoken of as known, and it is often forgotten that the rediscovery in the library may be a more difficult and uncertain process than the first discovery in the laboratory.—*Lord Rayleigh*

The publications which contain new material relating to current technological practice and which are issued, in general, at regular intervals, are designated as "periodicals." Their contents ordinarily constitute the latest published information, although one finds occasionally in a book new theories or facts. It is largely from periodicals that the facts are gathered for the preparation of the various publications to be discussed later as secondary sources. These periodicals in many cases appear under such titles as "bulletin," "journal," "proceedings," and "transactions" (or the equivalent of these terms in other languages), particularly if they are the publications of scientific societies.

The amount of this journal literature has become enormous. The German periodical *Annalen der Chemie* alone has reached over 600 volumes. Starting with one journal in 1665, *Philosophical Transactions of the Royal Society (London)*, the introduction of others has followed so rapidly that now more than 7,000 are searched by abstractors for articles of chemical interest. Most of the titles of the present list are additions of the twentieth century. It is well to recall, also, that a complete chemical library would contain many more than those currently being published. Hundreds survived for a time and then were discontinued. In 1893 Bolton[1] listed over 400 periodicals of chemical

[1] H. C. Bolton, "Select Bibliography of Chemistry," sec. 1, Smithsonian Misc. Coll. No. 850, Smithsonian Institution, 1893.

16

interest. In 1927 Crane and Patterson[1] listed 1,889 periodicals, of which 1,263 were then appearing.

Producers of Periodicals. Practically all periodicals are produced by a scientific society, a private individual or company, or a commercial publishing concern.[2] The first of these producers includes a large number, while individuals' publications are rare. The general object of the first two has been to furnish a place for authors to publish their papers and to disseminate other information of interest to the subscribers or members of the societies. The ultimate aim of commercial publications is profits. With these objectives in mind, it is not surprising to find that the general trend of the latter publications is to cater to the industrial interests and that much of the material in the publications of societies is of a distinctly less practical nature.

A number of periodicals were started in the nineteenth century by individuals whose names became so closely associated with the publication that one finds, especially in the older literature, many references including these names, such as Liebig's *Annalen der Chemie*, Fresenius's *Zeitschrift für analytische Chemie*, and Hoppe-Seyler's *Zeitschrift für physiologische Chemie*. The man's name is usually that of the first editor. In the *Annalen der Physik*, however, the name changed with each new editor, which accounts for the large number of references such as *Gilbert Ann., Pogg. Ann., Wied. Ann.*, and *Drude Ann.*, referring respectively to Gilbert, Poggendorff, Wiedemann, and Drude, the early editors.

The number of scientific societies of one variety or another which have been formed is surprisingly large. Even those which may properly be designated as chemical make up a considerable group. Bolton's list[3] includes 56 such organizations. Reid[4] included a later list of chemical societies and their publi-

[1] E. J. Crane and A. M. Patterson, "A Guide to the Literature of Chemistry," appendix 6, John Wiley & Sons, Inc., New York, 1927.

[2] *Journal of Research of the National Bureau of Standards* is published by the United States government; *Canadian Journal of Chemistry* is issued by the National Research Council of Canada.

[3] H. C. Bolton, "Chemical Societies of the Nineteenth Century," Smithsonian Misc. Coll. No. 1314, Smithsonian Institution, 1902.

[4] E. E. Reid, "Introduction to Organic Research," p. 73, D. Van Nostrand Company, Inc., Princeton, N.J., 1924.

cations. Still more comprehensive are the lists of Crane and
Patterson[1] and Hull and Kohr.[2]

The first chemical society was founded in 1785 with the name
Edinburgh University Chemical Society. In the Western Hemisphere the first chemical societies originated in Philadelphia.[3]
They were the Chemical Society of Philadelphia, founded in 1792,
and the Columbian Society of Philadelphia, founded in 1811.

Frequency of Appearance. Chemical periodicals are published
at widely varying intervals of time, with individual examples
ranging from publications appearing annually to those issued
every week. Proceedings of annual meetings of societies are
examples of the former, while the latter include certain trade
journals and chemical news weeklies. In general, the publications
of national societies appear each month.

Promptness of publication is desired by editor, author, and
reader. Usually 2 to 6 months elapse in this country from the
time a manuscript is received until it appears in published form.
Many journals note the date a communication is received.
Publication at a considerably later date indicates revision of the
original material or failure to issue it promptly. In some periodicals provision is made for more prompt issuance by short
"notes" or "letters to the editor."

Distribution by Language and Country. There is little published information on the relative number of periodicals produced
in different countries in the various fields of chemistry, including
the distribution by languages. The few limited reports, such as
those by Gross and Gross,[4] Sheppard,[5] Boig,[6] and Croft,[7] deal
with the citations found in single periodicals.

In 1951 *Chemical Abstracts* was abstracting 5,236 journals.[8]
They came from 87 countries and were printed in 31 languages.
Significantly, 44.8 per cent were in English, and of course some

[1] *Op. cit.*, appendix 5.
[2] C. Hull et al. (part 1) and J. R. Kohr (part 2), "Scientific and Technical
Societies of the United States and Canada," National Academy of Sciences
and National Research Council, Washington, 1955.
[3] Miles, *Chymia*, **3**:95 (1950).
[4] *Science*, **66**:385 (1927).
[5] *J. Chem. Educ.*, **12**:472 (1935).
[6] *Chem. Analyst*, **38**(1):3 (1949).
[7] *J. Chem. Educ.*, **18**:315 (1941).
[8] Crane, *Chem. Eng. News*, **31**:864 (1953).

Belgium

1832– Bulletin de la classe des sciences, Académie royale de Belgique
1875– Annales de la société scientifique de Bruxelles

Brazil

1929– Anais da academia brasileira de ciencias

Canada

1882– Transactions of the Royal Society of Canada
1929–1950 Canadian Journal of Research

Denmark

1814– Kongelige Danske Videnskabernes Selskab, Det, Oversigt over Selskabets Virksomhed
1917– Kongelige Danske Videnskabernes Selskab, Det, Matematisk-fysiske Meddelelser

Finland

1909– Annales Academiae Scientiarum Fennicae

France

1795–1835 Procès-verbaux des séances de l'académie
1835– Comptes rendus hebdomadaires des séances de l'académie des sciences
1857–1926 Moniteur scientifique du Docteur Quesneville
1946– Journal des recherches du centre national de la recherche scientifique, Laboratoires de Bellevue (Paris)

Germany

1710– Sitzungsberichte der deutschen Akademie der Wissenschaften zu Berlin, Klasse für Mathematik und allgemeine Naturwissenschaften
1820–1931 Dinglers Polytechnisches Journal
1835– Sitzungsberichte der mathematisch-naturwissenschaftlichen Klasse der bayerischen Akademie der Wissenschaften zu München
1897– Umschau in Wissenschaft und Technik, Die
1913– Naturwissenschaften, Die
1946– Zeitschrift für Naturforschung

Great Britain

1665– Transactions of the Royal Society (London), Philosophical
1783– Transactions of the Royal Society of Edinburgh
1798– Philosophical Magazine, The
1820–1928 Transactions of the Cambridge Philosophical Society
1831–1938 British Association for the Advancement of Science, Report of the Annual Meeting
1832– Proceedings of the Royal Society of Edinburgh
1843– Proceedings of the Cambridge Philosophical Society
1854– Proceedings of the Royal Society (London), Series A
1869– Nature (London)

1925– Proceedings of the Leeds Philosophical and Literary Society,
     Scientific Section
1939– Advancement of Science, The

India

1914– Journal of the Indian Institute of Science
1932– Current Science (India)
1934– Proceedings of the Indian Academy of Sciences
1936– Proceedings of the National Academy of Sciences, India
1950– Journal of Scientific Research of the Benares Hindu University,
     The

Ireland

1836– Proceedings of the Royal Irish Academy
1877– Scientific Proceedings of the Royal Dublin Society, The

Italy

1847– Atti della accademia nazionale dei Lincei, Memorie, Classe di
     scienze fisiche, matematiche e naturali
1865– Atti della accademia delle scienze di Torino
1907– Scientia (Milan)
1907– Società italiana per il progresso delle scienze, Atti della riunione
1930– Ricerca scientifica, La
1937– Società italiana per il progresso delle scienze, Scienze e tec-
     nica

Japan

1887– Journal of the Faculty of Science, University of Tokyo
1911– Science Reports of the Tôhoku University
1912– Proceedings of the Japan Academy
1922– Journal of the Scientific Research Institute (Tokyo)
1930– Journal of Science of the Hiroshima University
1930– Science Reports of the Tokyo Kyôiku Daigaku
1949– Science Reports of the Research Institutes, The, Tôhoku
     University
1949– Journal of the Osaka Institute of Science and Technology
1952– Annual Report of Scientific Works from the Faculty of Science,
     Osaka University

Mexico

1887– Memorias y revista de la academia nacional de ciencias (antigua
     Sociedad científica Antonio Alzate) (Mexico)
1940– Ciencia (Mexico)

The Netherlands

1866– Archives néerlandaises des sciences exactes et naturelles [now
     Physica]
1898– Koninklijke Nederlandse Akademie van Wetenschappen, Pro-
     ceedings

New Zealand

1868– Transactions of the Royal Society of New Zealand

Norway

1761– Kongelige Norske Videnskabers Selskabs, Det, Skrifter
1926– Kongelige Norske Videnskabers Selskabs, Det, Forhandlinger

Poland

1889– Bulletin international de l'académie polonaise des sciences et des lettres
1946– Annales Universitatis Mariae Curie-Skłodowska, Lublin-Polonia

Russia

1836– Izvestiya Akademii Nauk Soyuza Sovetskikh Sotsialisticheskikh Respublik
1934–1947 Comptes rendus (Doklady) de l'académie des sciences de l'U.R.S.S.

South Africa

1909– South African Journal of Science

Spain

1904– Revista de la real academia de ciencias exactas, físicas y naturales de Madrid
1947– Revista de ciencia aplicada (Madrid)

Sweden

1739– Kungliga Svenska Vetenskapsakademiens, Handlingar

Switzerland

1846– Archives des Sciences (Geneva)
1945– Experientia

United States

1818– American Journal of Science
1826– Journal of the Franklin Institute
1838– Proceedings of the American Philosophical Society
1846– Proceedings of the American Academy of Arts and Sciences
1883– Science
1915– Proceedings of the National Academy of Sciences of the United States of America
       Proceedings of the academies of the various states in the United States

Journals of Nonchemical Science. The growth and development of the several sciences were accompanied, sooner or later, by the appearance of periodicals devoted to the interests of each of these sciences. As we now well know, none of these fields stands apart, unrelated to any of the others. Biology, for example, cannot detach itself from physics, nor physics from chemistry. It is only to be expected that a journal devoted primarily to some one of these fields other than chemistry is bound to contain occasional chemical articles as incidental contributions. Investigations carried on by physicists, with the results published in a physical periodical, are often of great importance to physical chemists.

The number of these borderline publications is so large that no effort has been made to compile a list. The individual making searches of the literature must use his judgment in deciding where articles will be found that might appear in various journals.

Journals of Chemistry. The remaining group of periodicals is devoted to chemistry and chemical technology. Chemistry, both scientific and technologic, has expanded to cover such a range of activities that we have now a basis for a further subdivision. Periodicals which are devoted to several or all phases of the science may be designated as "general journals"; the foremost of these include the main publications of the various general chemical societies scattered throughout the world. With the increasing development of specialized lines of chemical work, there have appeared, especially since 1890, a large number of periodicals devoted to special or limited fields. These may be designated as "specialized journals."

The names of some of the more important journals of these two general classes have been collected and arranged in the lists below. In this compilation the aim was to select a representative rather than a complete list.[1]

General Chemical Journals. In the case of the general journals the earliest ones available have been included, together with the more important later ones, particularly the publications of all the larger, general chemical societies. The dates included are of interest in showing how one after the other appeared and in indicating the mortality rate of such publications.

List of General Chemical Journals

1778–1781[2] Chem*isches* Journal *für die* **Freunde** *der Naturlehre.* Superseded by:

1781–1786 **Neues***ten* **Ent***deckungen in der* **Chem***ie*

1783–1784 **Chem***isches* **Arch***iv.* Superseded by:

1784–1791 **Neues chem***isches* **Arch***iv.* Superseded by:

1792–1798 **Neuestes chem***isches* **Arch***iv*

1784–1803 **Chem***ische* **Ann***alen für die Freunde der Naturlehre* (L. Crell)

1785–1795 **Beiträge** *zu den chemischen* **Ann***alen von Lorenz* **Crell**

1789–1815 **Ann***ales de* chim*ie.* Changed to:

---

[1] For a list of 93 obsolete chemical journals of the nineteenth century, see G. M. Dyson, *Advances in Chem. Ser. No. 4,* 96–103 (1951).

[2] Overlapping dates indicate change of name during the year.

1816–1913   Ann*ales de* chim*ie et de* phys*ique.* Split into:
1914–   Ann*ales de* chim*ie* (**Paris**)   and   **Ann***ales de* phys*ique*
1788–1795   **Bibl***iothek der neuesten* phys*ische-*chem*ischen, metallurgischen, technologischen, und pharmaceutischen* **Lit***eratur*
1809–1813   **Bull***etin des neuesten und wissenswürdigsten aus den* **Naturwiss***enschaften.* Superseded by:
1814–1818   **Museum** *des neuesten und wissenwürdigsten aus dem Gebiete der* **Naturw***issenschaft, der Künste, der Fabriken*
1790–1802   **Annali** *di* chim*ica e* stor*ia* nat*urale*
1794–1815   **Journal** *des* mines. Changed to:
1816–1851   **Ann***ales des* mines
1797–1813   **Journal** *of* **Nat***ural* **Phil***osophy,* **Chem***istry and the* **Arts** (Nicholson). Merged into:
1798–   **Phil***osophical* **Mag***azine, The*
1798–1803   **Allgem***eines* **J***ournal der* **Chem***ie* (Scherer). Changed to:
1803–1806   **Neues allgem***eines* **J***ournal der* **Chem***ie* (Gehlen). Changed to:
1807–1810   **Journal** *für die* **Chem***ie,* **Physik** *und* **Mineral***ogie.* Changed to:
1811–1833   **Journal** *für* **Chem***ie und* **Physik** (Schweigger). Changed to:
1834–   **Journal** *für* **prakt***ische* **Chem***ie* (Erdmann)
1800–1802   **Arch***iv* **für** theoretische **Chem***ie*
1803–1818   **Arch***iv der* **Agrikulturchem***ie* **für** denkende **Landw***irthe*
1809–1814   **Bull***etin de* pharm*acie et des* sci*ences* accessoires. Changed to:
1815–1841   **Journal** *de* pharm*acie et des* sci*ences* accessoires. Changed to:
1842–1942   **Journal** *de* pharm*acie et de* chim*ie.* Merged with:
            Bull*etin des* sci*ences* pharmaco*logiques.* To form:
1943–   **Ann***ales* pharm*aceutiques* **français***es*
1813–1814   **Mem***oirs of the* **Columbian** **Chem***ical* **Soc***iety of Philadelphia*
1823–1831   **Mag***azin* **für** **Phar***macie.* Merged with:
1822–1831   **Arch***iv des* **Apotheker-Vereins** *im nördlichen Deutschland.* To form:
1832–1839   **Ann***alen der* **Phar***macie.* Changed to:
1840–1873   **Ann***alen der* **Chem***ie und* **Phar***macie.* Changed to:
1874–   **Justus Liebig's** **Ann***alen der* **Chem***ie*
1835–   **Arch***iv der* **Phar***mazie*
1824–1833   **Giorn***ale di* farm*acia* chim*ica e scienze accessorie.* Changed to:
1834–1845   **Bibl***ioteca di* farm*acia, chimica, fisica, medicina.* Changed to:
1845–1882   **Ann***ali di* chim*ica* appl*icata alla medicina cioè alla farmacia.* Changed to:
1882–1884   **Ann***ali di* chim*ica* appl*icata alla farmacia ed alla medicina.* Changed to:
1885–1897   **Ann***ali di* chim*ica e di* farm*acologia.* Changed to:
1898–1900   **Ann***ali di* farm*acoterapia e* chim*ica* biol*ogica*
1825–1876   **Journal** *de* chim*ie* méd*icale, de* pharm*acie, et de* toxic*ologie*
1826–   **Bull***etin de la* soc*iété* ind*ustrielle de* **Mulhouse**
1828–1833   **Journal** *für* tech*nische und* ökon*omische* **Chem***ie*
1829–   **American J***ournal of* **Pharm***acy*
1831–1839   **Gazz***etta* eclet*tica di* chim*ica* farm*aceutica*
1840–1858   **Chemist,** *The*
1841–1843   **Proc***eedings of the* **Chem***ical* **Soc***iety of London.* Merged with:

1841–1848   Mem*oirs* and **Proc***eedings of the* **Chem***ical* **Soc***iety of London.*
               Changed to:
1849–1862   **Quart***erly* Journal *of the* **Chem***ical* **Soc***iety.* Changed to:
1862–   Journal *of the* **Chem***ical* **Soc***iety*
1842–1859   **Chem***ical* **Gaz***ette, The.* Changed to:
1859–1932   **Chem***ical* **News** *and* Journal *of Industrial Science, The*
1846–1887   **Chem***isch-***tech***nische* **Mitt***heilungen der* **neuesten Zeit**
1855–1875   **Chem***ische* **Ackersmann**
1858–1859   **Krit***ische* **Zeitschrift** *für* **Chem***ie,* **Physik** *und* **Math***ematik.*
               Changed to:
1860–1864   *Zeitschrift für* **Chem***ie und* **Phar***macie.* Changed to:
1865–1871   *Zeitschrift für* **Chem***ie*
1858–1863   **Rép***ertoire de* chim*ie* **pure** *et* **appl***iquée.* Merged into:
1858–1906   **Bull***etin de la* **soc***iété* chim*ique de* **Paris.** Changed to:
1907–   **Bull***etin de la* **soc***iété* chim*ique de* **France**
1862–1901   **Chem***isch-***tech***nisches* **Rep***ertorium* (Berlin)
1866–1880   **Boston** Journal *of* **Chem***istry* (Nichol). Changed to:
1881–1883   **Boston** Journal *of* **Chem***istry and* **Pop***ular* **Science** **Rev***iew.*
               Changed to:
1883–1902   **Pop***ular* **Science** **News** *and* **Boston** Journal *of* **Chem***istry*
1868–1945   **Berichte** *der* **deut***schen* **chem***ischen* **Ges***ellschaft.* Changed to:
1947–   **Chem***ische* **Berichte**
1869–1872   **Zhur***nal* **Russ***kogo* **Khim***icheskogo* **Obshchestva.** Changed to:
1873–1878   **Zhur***nal* **Russ***kogo* **Khim***icheskogo* **Obshchestva** *y* **Fizicheskogo**
               Obshchestva. Changed to:
1879–1930   **Zhur***nal* **Russ***kogo* **Fiz***iko-***Khim***icheskogo* **Obshchestva.** Con-
               tinued as:
1931–   **Zhur***nal* **Obshche***ĭ* **Khim***ii* and   **Zhur***nal* **Fiz***icheskoĭ* **Khim***ii*
1870–1877   **Amer***ican* **Chem***ist, The*
1871–1891   **Chem***ical* **Rev***iew* (London)
1871–   **Gazz***etta* chim*ica* ital*iana*
1877–1951   **Chemiker-Z***eitung.* Changed to:
1951   **Chemiker-Z***eitung mit "Chemie-Börse"*
1879–1913   **Amer***ican* **Chem***ical* Journal. Merged with:
1879–   Journal *of the* **Amer***ican* **Chem***ical* **Soc***iety*
1880–   **Mon***atshefte für* **Chem***ie und verwandte Teile anderer Wissen-*
               schaften
1882–   **Rec***ueil des* **trav***aux* chim*iques des Pays-Bas*
1887–1903   **Bull***etin de l'association* **Belge** *des* chim*istes.* Changed to:
1904–1927   **Bull***etin de la* **soc***iété* chim*ique de* **Belg***ique.* Changed to:
1927–1944   **Bull***etin de la* **soc***iété* chim*ique de* **Belg***ique et Recueil des travaux*
               chimiques Belges. Changed to:
1945–   **Bull***etin des* **soc***iétés* chim*iques* **Belges**
1889–   **Svensk Kem***isk* **Tidskr***ift*
1903–1928   **Anales** *de la* **sociedad española** *de* **fís***ica y* **quím***ica.* Changed to:
1929–1940   **Anales** *de la* **real** **sociedad española** *de* **fís***ica y* **quím***ica.* Changed
               to:
1941–1947   **Anales** *de* **fís***ica y* **quím***ica* (**Madrid**). Split into:

1948–	Anales *de la real* sociedad española *de* física *y* química. *Serie A.* Física and *Serie B.* Química
1903–1948	Arkiv *för* Kemi, Mineral*ogi och* Geol*ogi.* Split into:
1949–	Arkiv *för* Kemi and Arkiv *för* Mineral*ogi och* Geol*ogi*
1903–	Chem*ische* Weekblad
1917–1920	Can*adian* Chem*ical* Journal. Changed to:
1921–1937	Can*adian* Chem*istry and* Met*allurgy.* Changed to:
1938–1951	Can*adian* Chem*istry and* Process Ind*ustries.* Changed to:
1951–	Can*adian* Chem*ical* Processing
1918–	Helv*etica* Chim*ica* Acta
1921–	Roczniki Chem*ii*
1922–1947	Scientific Papers *of the* Inst*itute of* Phys*ical and* Chem*ical* Research (Tokyo). Changed to:
1948–	Journal *of the* Scientific Research Inst*itute* (Tokyo)
1923–	Revista *de la* facultad *de* cien*cias* quí*micas* (Universidad nacional *de La Plata*)
1924–1927	Quarterly Journal *of the* Indian Chem*ical* So*ciety.* Changed to:
1928–	Journal *of the* Indian Chem*ical* So*ciety*
1926–	Bull*etin of the* Chem*ical* So*ciety of* Japan
1929–	Collection *of* Czechoslova*k* Chem*ical* Communi*cations*
1934–1949	Australian Chem*ical* Inst*itute* Journal & Proc*eedings, The.* Changed to:
1949–1950	Roy*al* Australian Chem*ical* Inst*itute* Journal & Proc*eedings, The.* Changed to:
1951–	Proc*eedings of the* Royal Australian Chem*ical* Inst*itute*

Journals of Specialized Chemistry. In listing current journals which are devoted, wholly or in part, to special areas of chemistry, the classification follows the order of the 31 subdivisions of *Chemical Abstracts.* Also the titles of these 31 sections are employed.

Selections of titles to include were made in each case by someone competent in the respective field.[1] These journals are considered to be those more generally useful in the special area. It is recognized, of course, that what may be most important to one individual may not be to another. In case more were recommended than could be included, the number was rather arbitrarily reduced, usually to leave representatives of several different countries.

In many cases the present title of a journal is not the one originally used. In fact, some have had several changes. The date is that of the founding of the journal under its original title, in case there has been a change. The order in each subdivision is alphabetical by abbreviations.

[1] In most cases an assistant editor of *Chemical Abstracts.*

FIG. 3. Reading room of the Lavoisier Library, Experimental Station, E. I. du Pont de Nemours & Company, Wilmington, Del. (*Courtesy of du Pont.*)

Brown[1] has listed the 100 most-cited serials in chemistry, physics, and six other areas.

LIST OF SPECIALIZED CHEMICAL JOURNALS

1. Apparatus, Plant Equipment, and Unit Operations

Chem*ie*-Ing*enieur*-Tech*nik*, 1887
Instruments and Automation, 1928
Journal of the Amer*ican* Inst*itute of* Chem*ical* Eng*ine*ers, 1955
Review *of Scientific* **Instr***uments,* 1930

See journals on industrial chemistry and chemical engineering.

2. General and Physical Chemistry

Journal of Chem*ical* Educ*ation,* 1924
Journal of Chem*ical* **Physics,** *The,* 1933
Journal de chim*ie* **physique** *et de physico-chimie biologique,* 1903
Journal of **Colloid Science,** 1946
Journal of **Physical** Chem*istry, The,* 1896
Kolloid-*Zeitschrift,* 1906
Trans*actions of the* **Faraday** Soc*iety,* 1905
Zhur*nal* Fiz*icheskoĭ* Khim*ii,* 1930
Zeitschrift für physikalische Chem*ie,* 1887

[1] C. H. Brown, "Scientific Serials," Association of College and Reference Libraries, Chicago, 1956.

See also journals of the principal general chemical societies and similar journals of the physical societies. The following titles are examples.

Bulletin of the Chemical Society of Japan, 1926
Bulletin de la société chimique de France, 1858
Chemische Berichte, 1868
Gazzetta chimica italiana, 1871
Helvetica Chimica Acta, 1918
Journal of the American Chemical Society, The, 1879
Journal of the Chemical Society (London), 1841
Recueil des travaux chimiques des Pays-Bas, 1882

3. Electronic Phenomena and Spectra

Comptes rendus hebdomadaires des séances de l'académie des sciences, 1835
Journal of Chemical Physics, The, 1933
Physical Review, The, 1893
Proceedings of the Royal Society (London), Series A, 1854[1]

See also journals of the general chemical societies.

3A. Nuclear Phenomena

Helvetica Physica Acta, 1928
Journal of Chemical Physics, The, 1933
Nucleonics, 1947
Philosophical Magazine, The, 1798
Physical Review, 1893
Proceedings of the Physical Society (London), 1874
Proceedings of the Royal Society (London), Series A, 1854[1]
Zeitschrift für Physik, 1920

4. Electrochemistry

Electroplating and Metal Finishing, 1947
Electrical World, 1883
General Electric Review, 1903
Journal of the Electrochemical Society, 1902
Journal du four électrique et des industries électrochimiques, 1895
Proceedings of the Institution of Electrical Engineers, The (London), 1872

5. Photography

Journal of Photographic Science, 1853
Journal of the Society of Scientific Photography of Japan, The, 1939
Photographic Engineering, 1950
Photographische Korrespondenz, 1864
Photographic Science and Technique, 1935
Science et industries photographiques, 1921
Zeitschrift für wissenschaftliche Photographie, Photophysik und Photochemie, 1903

[1] This is vol. 7. Earlier volumes are abstracts of papers in *Transactions of the Royal Society (London)*.

6. Inorganic Chemistry

Journal of Inorganic and Nuclear Chemistry, 1955
Zeitschrift für anorganische und allgemeine Chemie, 1892

   See journals of the general chemical societies and various journals on
applied chemistry.

7. Analytical Chemistry

Analytical Chemistry, 1929
Analytica Chimica Acta, 1947
Analyst, The, 1877
Chimie analytique, 1896
Journal of the Association of Official Agricultural Chemists, 1915
Mikrochimica Acta, 1923
Zeitschrift für analytische Chemie, 1862
Zhurnal Analiticheskoĭ Khimii, 1946

8. Mineralogical and Geological Chemistry

American Journal of Science, 1819
American Mineralogist, The, 1916
Bulletin de la société française de minéralogie et de cristallographie, 1878
Chemie der Erde, 1914
Economic Geology and the Bulletin of the Society of Economic Geologists, 1905
Geochimica et Cosmochimica Acta, 1950
Mineralogical Magazine and Journal of the Mineralogical Society, The, 1876
Zapiski Vsesoyuznogo Mineralogicheskogo Obschestva, 1830

9. Metallurgy and Metallography

Acta Metallurgica, 1953
Journal of the Institute of Metals and Metallurgical Abstracts, 1909
Journal of the Iron and Steel Institute (London), 1871
Journal of Metals, 1949
Revue de métallurgie, 1904
Stahl und Eisen, 1881
Transactions of the American Institute of Mining, Metallurgical, and Petrole-
   um Engineers, 1871
Transactions of the American Society for Metals, 1920
Zeitschrift für Metallkunde, 1911

10. Organic Chemistry

Annalen der Chemie, Justus Liebigs, 1832
Journal of Organic Chemistry, The, 1936
Journal für praktische Chemie, 1834[1]
Makromolekulare Chemie, Die, 1947

   See many journals of the general chemistry societies and also journals of
applied organic chemistry.

   [1] Publication interrupted to some extent between 1943 and 1954.

11A. Biological Chemistry. General

Archives of Biochemistry and Biophysics, 1942
Biochemical Journal, The, 1906
Biochemische Zeitschrift, 1906
Biochimica et Biophysica Acta, 1947
Biokhimiya, 1936
Bulletin de la société de chimie biologique, 1914
Journal of Biological Chemistry, The, 1905
Zeitschrift für physiologische Chemie, Hoppe-Seyler's, 1877

11B. Biological Chemistry. Methods and Apparatus

Archives of Biochemistry and Biophysics, 1942
Biochemical Journal, The, 1906
Biochimica et Biophysica Acta, 1947
Journal of Biological Chemistry, The, 1905
Journal of Clinical Investigation, The, 1924
Proceedings of the Society for Experimental Biology and Medicine, 1903

11C. Biological Chemistry. Microbiology

Annales de l'institut Pasteur, 1887
Biochemical Journal, The, 1906
Canadian Journal of Microbiology, 1954
Enzymologia, 1936
Journal of Bacteriology, 1916
Journal of Biological Chemistry, The, 1905

11D. Biological Chemistry. Botany

American Journal of Botany, 1914
Comptes rendus hebdomadaires des séances de l'académie des sciences, 1835
Doklady Akademii Nauk S.S.S.R., 1922
Journal of the Science of Food and Agriculture, 1950
Nature, 1869
Planta, 1925
Plant Physiology, 1926

11E. Biological Chemistry. Nutrition

American Journal of Clinical Pathology, 1931
Archives of Biochemistry and Biophysics, 1942
Biochemical Journal, The, 1906
Journal of Biological Chemistry, The, 1905
Journal of Nutrition, The, 1928
Journal of Physiology, The (London), 1878

11F. Biological Chemistry. Physiology

Fiziologicheskiĭ Zhurnal S.S.S.R., 1917
Journal of Clinical Endocrinology and Metabolism, 1941
Journal of Clinical Investigation, The, 1924
Journal of Physiology, The (London), 1878

Klin*ische* Wochen*schrift*, 1922
Proc*eedings of the* Society *for* Exper*imen*tal Biol*ogy and* Med*icine*, 1903

11G. Biological Chemistry. Pathology

Acta Endocrinol*ogica*, 1948
Brit*ish* Journal *of* Exper*imen*tal Pathol*ogy, The*, 1920
Cancer Research, 1941
Journal *of* Clin*ical* Invest*igation, The*, 1924
Klin*ische* Wochen*schrift*, 1922
Proc*eedings of the* Society *for* Exper*imen*tal Biol*ogy and* Med*icine*, 1903

11H. Biological Chemistry. Pharmacology

Acta Pharmacol*ogica et* Toxicol*ogica*, 1945
Arch*iv für* experimen*telle* Pathol*ogie und* Pharmakol*ogie*, Naunyn-Schmiede-
    berg's, 1873
Arch*ives* intern*ationales de* pharmacodynamie *et de thérapie*, 1894
Brit*ish* Journal *of* Pharmacol*ogy and Chemotherapy*, 1946
Journal *of* Pharmacol*ogy and* Exper*imen*tal Therape*utics, The*, 1909

11I. Biological Chemistry. Zoology

Biol*ogical* Bull*etin, The*, 1899
Comp*tes* rend*us des séances de la* soci*été de* biol*ogie et de ses filiales*, 1849
Exp*erimen*tal Cell Research, 1950
Journal *of* Cellular *and* Comp*arative* Physiol*ogy*, 1932

   See periodicals in 11A above.

12. Foods

Anal*yst, The*, 1877
Cereal Chemistry, 1924
Food Research, 1936
Food Technol*ogy*, 1947
Journal *of* Agr*icultural and* Food Chem*istry*, 1953
Journal *of the* Assoc*iation of* Offic*ial* Agr*icultural* Chemists, 1915
Journal *of* Dairy Science, 1917
Mitt*eilungen* aus dem Gebiete *der* Lebens*mitteluntersuchung* und Hygiene,
    1910
Z*eitschrift für* Lebens*mittel-*Untersuch*ung* und Forsch*ung*, 1898

13. Chemical Industry and Miscellaneous Industrial Products

Society Journals:
Angew*andte* Chem*ie*, 1887
Chem*ical and* Eng*ineering* News, 1923
Chem*ical* Eng*ineering* Progress, 1908
Chem*ische* Ind*ustrie* (Düsseldorf), 1949
Chem*istry* & Ind*ustry* (London), 1923[1]
Chem*ische* Weekblad, 1903

   [1] Bound as part of *Journal of the Society of Chemical Industry* through 1943.

Chimica, *La*, e *l'*industria (Milan), 1919
Chimie & industrie (Paris), 1918
Ind*ustrial and* Eng*ineering* Chem*istry*, 1909
J*ournal of* Appl*ied* Chem*istry* (London), 1882[1]
J*ournal of the* Chem*ical* Soc*iety of* Japan (Ind*ustrial* Chem*istry* Sect*ion*), 1880
Tra*nsactions of the* Inst*itution of* Chem*ical* Eng*ineers* (London), 1923
Zhur*nal* Prikl*adnoĭ* Khim*ii*, 1928

Nonsociety Journals:
Can*adian* Chem*ical* Processing, 1917
Chem*ical* Eng*ineering with Chemical & Metallurgical Engineering*, 1902
Chem*ical* Eng*ineering* Science, 1952
Chem*ical* Products, 1938
Chemi*sche* Technik, *Die* (Berlin), 1949
Chemi*ker-Zeitung mit "Chemische Apparatur" und "Chemie Börse,"* 1877
Ind*ustrial* Chemist *and Chemical Manufacturer, The*, 1925
Materials & Methods, 1929
Re*vue des* produits chim*iques, La, et L' Actualité scientifique*, 1898

Many trade journals.

14. Water, Sewage, and Sanitation

Ame*rican* J*ournal of* Public Health *and The Nation's Health*, 1911
Eng*ineering* News-Record, 1874
J*ournal of the* Ame*rican* Water Works Asso*ciation*, 1914
J*ournal of the* Inst*itution of* Water Eng*ineers*, 1947
Sewage and Ind*ustrial* Wastes, 1928
Water and Water Eng*ineering*, 1899

15. Soils and Fertilizers

Agr*icultural* Chemicals, 1946
Agron*omy* J*ournal*, 1907
Farm Chemicals, 1894
Ind*ustrial and* Eng*ineering* Chem*istry*, 1909
J*ournal of* Agr*icultural and* Food Chemistry, 1953
Soil Sci*ence*, 1916
Soil Science Soc*iety of* America, Proc*eedings*, 1936

15A. Pesticides and Crop-control Agents

Agr*icultural* Chemicals, 1946
Ann*als of* Appl*ied* Biol*ogy, The*, 1914
J*ournal of* Agr*icultural and* Food Chemistry, 1953
J*ournal of* Econ*omic* Entomol*ogy*, 1908
Phytopathology, 1911
Plant Disease Repo*rter, The*, 1917

16. The Fermentation Industries

Ame*rican* J*ournal of* Enol*ogy*, 1950
Appl*ied* Microbiol*ogy*, 1953

[1] Appeared as *Journal of the Society of Chemical Industry*, 1882–1950.

Archives of Biochemistry and Biophysics, 1942
Biokhimiya, 1936
Journal of Agricultural and Food Chemistry, 1953
Journal of Bacteriology, 1916

17. Pharmaceuticals, Cosmetics, and Perfumes

American Journal of Pharmacy and the Sciences Supporting Public Health,
     1829
Annales pharmaceutiques françaises, 1943
Archiv der Pharmazie und Berichte der deutschen pharmazeutischen Gesellschaft,
     1822
Farmaco, Il (Pavia), Edizione scientifica,[1] 1946
Journal of the American Pharmaceutical Association, 1912
Pharmaceutical Journal, The, 1841

18. Acids, Alkalis, Salts, and Other Heavy Chemicals

Angewandte Chemie, 1887
Canadian Chemical Processing, 1917
Chemical Engineering with Chemical & Metallurgical Engineering, 1902
Chemical Engineering Progress, 1908
Chemistry & Industry (London), 1923
Chimie & industrie (Paris), 1918
Industrial and Engineering Chemistry, 1909

19. Glass, Clay Products, Refractories, and Enameled Metals

Glass Industry, The, 1920
Glastechnische Berichte, 1923
Journal of the American Ceramic Society, 1918
Journal of the Society of Glass Technology, 1917
Transactions of the British Ceramic Society, 1901
Zement-Kalk-Gips, 1911

20. Cement, Concrete, and Other Building Materials

Cement and Lime Manufacture, 1928
Concrete, 1904
Journal of the American Ceramic Society, 1918
Journal of the American Concrete Institute, 1929
Pit and Quarry, 1916
Rock Products, 1902
Zement-Kalk-Gips, 1911

21. Fuels and Carbonization Products

Brennstoff-Chemie, 1920
Coke and Gas, 1939
Erdöl und Kohle, 1948
Fuel, 1922

----

[1] Also an edizione pratica, with the same volume number.

Industrial and Engineering Chemistry, 1909
Journal of the Institute of Fuel, 1926

22. Petroleum, Lubricants, and Asphalt

Industrial and Engineering Chemistry, 1909
Journal of the Institute of Petroleum, 1914
Neftyanoe Khozyaĭstvo, 1920
Oil and Gas Journal, The, 1902
Petroleum Engineer, The, 1929
Petroleum Refiner, 1922

23. Cellulose and Paper

Canadian Pulp and Paper, 1948
Holzforschung, 1947
Paper Industry, The, 1919
Paper Trade Journal, 1872
Papeterie, La, 1878
Papier, Das, 1947
Pulp & Paper, 1927
Pulp & Paper Magazine of Canada, 1903
Southern Pulp and Paper Manufacturer, 1938
Tappi, 1918

24. Explosives and Explosions

Chemical and Engineering News, 1923
Journal of the American Rocket Society, 1930
Journal of Physical Chemistry, The, 1896
Mémorial des poudres, 1882
Ordnance, 1920

25. Dyes and Textile Chemistry

American Dyestuff Reporter, 1917
Journal of the Society of Dyers and Colourists, The, 1884
Melliand Textilberichte, 1920
Textile Recorder, 1883
Textile Research Journal, 1931

26. Paints, Varnishes, Lacquers, and Inks

American Paint Journal, 1916
Journal of the Oil & Colour Chemists' Association, 1918
Official Digest of the Federation of Paint & Varnish Production Clubs, 1919
Oil, Paint, and Drug Reporter, 1871
Paint Industry Magazine, The, 1885
Paint and Varnish Production, 1910

27. Fats, Fatty Oils, Waxes, and Detergents

Fette, Seifen, Anstrichmittel, 1894
Journal of the American Oil Chemists' Society, The, 1924

Journal of **Applied Chem**istry **(London),** 1882
Journal of the **Oil Chemists' Soc**iety **(Japan),** 1952
Oléagineux, 1946
Promyshlennost (*S.S.S.R.*), 1941
Revue fran*çaise des* **corps gras,** 1954
Seifen-Öle-Fette-Wachse, 1874

28. Sugar, Starch, and Gums

International **Sugar Journal,** *The,* 1899
Listy Cukrovarnické, 1882
Sakharnaya Promyshlennost, 1923
Stärke, Die, 1949
Sugar, 1914
Zeitschrift für die **Zuckerind**ustrie, 1876

29. Leather and Glue

Bulletin *de l'*asso*ciation* **fran**çaise *des* **chim**istes *des* **ind**ustries *du* **cuir et**
    doc*uments* scienti*fiques* **et tech**niques *des* **ind**ustries *du* **cuir,** 1939
Gesammelte **Abhandl**ungen *des* **deut**schen **Lederinst**ituts **Freiberg/Sa,** 1949
Journal of the **Am**erican **Leather Chem**ists' **Asso**ci*ation, The,* 1906
Journal of the **Soc**iety *of* **Leather Trades' Chemists,** 1917
Leder, Das, 1950

30. Rubber and Other Elastomers

Kautschuk und **Gummi,** 1948
Revue gé*nérale du* **caoutchouc,** 1924
Rubber Age, *The* **(N.Y.),** 1917
Rubber Chemistry **and Technolo**gy, 1928
Rubber World, 1889
Transactions **and Pro**ceedings *of the* **Inst**itution *of the* **Rubber Ind**ustry, 1925

31. Synthetic Resins and Plastics

Chemistry *of* **High Polymers (Japan),** 1944
Journal of **Polymer Sci**ence, 1946
Khimicheskaya **Prom**yshlennost, 1924
Kunststoffe, 1911
Makromolekulare **Chem**ie, *Die,* 1947
Materie plastiche, 1934
Modern Plastics, 1925
Plastics (London), 1937

Notes on Periodicals

In the use of periodicals there are a number of items of some importance.

Photoreproductions. Two methods of particular interest are being used for photoreproduction of periodical sets.[1] Each has certain merits.

Microfilm reproductions usually have a page of a journal (or book) per frame of 35-mm film. Complete sets of a number of periodicals are available in this form. However, it is inconvenient to search long rolls of film when one wants only certain pages, perhaps somewhere in the center of the film. Such a reproduction is very useful for obtaining a copy of some article without having to borrow the journal.

An interesting use of film frames or strips is the punched microfilm aperture cards or Filmsort-Keysort microfilm jackets. These are the same kinds of cards as those described in Chapter 7 for bibliographies, except that they provide for including film on the card.

Microprint[2] reproduction utilizes cards about 3 by 5 in., on each of which some 40 pages of ordinary-size printing can be reproduced. These cards, filed like library index cards, are easily handled. Thus, one may quickly locate the card for a particular article and remove it for examination in a microcard reader. Compared with books, they save some 95 per cent in space used. Recently, microcard editions have been issued for some United States patents.

Indexes. Most journals have annual subject and author indexes, arranged separately or in a combined index. In case several parts of a single year's issue of a journal are bound separately, the index is generally included in the final part. If there is no index, usually at the beginning of each volume there is a table of contents which lists the titles of the articles. Each issue of a journal carries a table of contents on the front or back cover or near the front. Many journals have collective or cumulative indexes covering various periods of time. The usual period is 5 years or some multiple of 5.[3]

[1] C. M. Lewis and W. H. Offenhauser, Jr., "Microrecording, Industrial and Library Applications," Interscience Publishers, Inc., New York, 1956; see also Kuipers, *Ind. Eng. Chem.*, **42**:1463 (1950), for the use of microcards and microfilm for a central reference file.

[2] Microcard Foundation, Madison, Wis.

[3] West and Berolzheimer's "Bibliography of Bibliographies on Chemistry and Chemical Technology," contains, in part 3, a partial list of such collective indexes. The inclusive volumes and years covered are given for each index. See also Chap. 7.

The searcher must guard against relying too heavily on the indexes. Too often they merely index titles or words, and at best they probably never contain entries for all the important points covered by the articles. Chemists, as a class, have not shown great aptitude for selecting adequate and effective titles for papers. Thus, such a title as "Chemical Affinity" reveals very little about the article's content. Occasionally persistent searchers have been amply rewarded for making page-by-page searches through sets of periodicals.

Abbreviations. The standard abbreviation for the name of a journal, as approved by the International Union of Pure and Applied Chemistry and used by *Chemical Abstracts*, may be found in the "List of Periodicals Abstracted by *Chemical Abstracts*."[1] The entries are in alphabetical order by *abbreviations*. The list includes primarily periodicals being issued at the time of publication of the list. There are, however, many entries for changes of name. Reid[2] and Crane, Patterson, and Marr[3] listed the titles of discontinued periodicals.[4] Many of those listed are changes of name.

For checking items on periodicals, such as places of publication and beginning dates, the following lists are also useful.

Bolton, H. C.: "A Catalogue of Scientific and Technical Periodicals," Smithsonian Institution, Washington, 1897.

Graves, E. C. (ed.): "Ulrich's Periodical Directory," R. R. Bowker Company, New York, 1956.

Gregory, W. (ed.): "Union List of Serials in Libraries in the United States and Canada," The H. W. Wilson Company, New York, 1927.

Smith, W. A., et al. (eds.): "World List of Scientific Periodicals Published in the Years 1900–50," Academic Press, Inc., New York, 1952.

Stewart, J. D., et al.: "British Union Catalogue of Periodicals," Academic Press, Inc., New York, 1955–

Citation of References. In periodicals the method of handling the references to other publications is an important detail. Generally the citations are (1) placed as footnotes at the bottom of the page to which they refer and in the order in which they are mentioned or (2) gathered together at the end of the article. In

[1] See Chap. 6, section on abstracting journals.

[2] *Op. cit.*, p. 82.

[3] E. J. Crane, A. M. Patterson, and E. B. Marr, "A Guide to the Literature of Chemistry," appendix 6, John Wiley & Sons, Inc., New York, 1957.

[4] See also G. M. Dyson, *Advances in Chem. Ser., No. 4*, pp. 96–103 (1951).

the latter case they may be arranged in the order cited, but usually it is preferable to have them arranged alphabetically by authors.

Volume-Year Data. Frequently it is desirable to know the volume number of a journal for a given year, or the reverse of this. Tables containing such synchronistic data for a limited number of periodicals are included in the following books.

Atack, F. W.: "The Chemist's Yearbook," Sherratt, Altrincham, England, 1954.

Bolton, H. C.: "A Catalogue of Scientific and Technical Periodicals," Smithsonian Institution, Washington, 1897.

Comey, A. M.: "A Dictionary of Solubilities," The Macmillan Company, New York, 1921.

Dyson, G. M.: "A Short Guide to Chemical Literature," Longmans, Green & Co., Inc., New York, 1951.

Friend, J. A. N.: "A Textbook of Inorganic Chemistry," Charles Griffin & Co., Ltd., London (only the later volumes).

Lange, N. A.: "Handbook of Chemistry," Handbook Publishers, Sandusky, Ohio, 1934.

Richter, F.: "Beilstein's Handbuch der Organischen Chemie," vol. I, p. xxvi, Springer-Verlag OHG, Vienna, 1918.

———: "Erstes Ergänzungswerk," vol. I, p. x, Springer-Verlag OHG, Vienna, 1928.

———: "Zweites Ergänzungswerk," vol. I, p. xxvii, Springer-Verlag OHG, Vienna, 1941.

Roth, W. A., and K. Scheel: "Landolt-Börnstein's physikalisch-chemische Tabellen," p. 1634, Springer-Verlag OHG, Vienna, 1923.

Seidell, A.: "Solubilities of Inorganic and Organic Substances," D. Van Nostrand Company, Inc., Princeton, N.J., 1940–1941.

Translations. Translations may be required for articles in unfamiliar languages. Large libraries and literature consultants usually can provide such service.[1]

There are two general sources of translations. For some years the Card Division of the Library of Congress issued the monthly *Bibliography of Translations from Russian Scientific and Technical Literature.* These translations were either deposited or held by agencies of the United States government, scientific societies, industrial organizations, or universities. This collection has been

[1] The Pergamon Press (New York) maintains a translation service for Russian science, technology, and medicine. *Technical Translations* is issued monthly by Henry Brutcher, Altadena, Calif. See O'Dette, *Science*, **125**:579 (1957), for a discussion of Russian translations; see "Scientific Translations: A Preliminary Guide to Sources and Services," Public Health Service Publication No. 514, Washington, 1957.

combined with the Crerar collection in the John Crerar Library in Chicago. This library maintains a translation pool for non-Russian articles for the Special Libraries Association. These translations may be borrowed or photocopies may be purchased. The *Translation Monthly* reports current accessions to the pool. The combined collections are to have an improved subject index.

Errata. When an error that escapes an author is detected, correction is usually made in a subsequent issue of the periodical. Frequently this issue is the last for the year. To guard against missing such corrections, the searcher should examine the table of contents and the index of the journal for a year or two after publication of the original article. Preferably librarians should enter such corrections at the appropriate place as published.

Other Data. In many periodicals the professional connection or address of the author(s) is given either at the beginning or at the end of the article. Often the date of receipt and/or acceptance of the manuscript for publication is given. This establishes priority.

CHAPTER 3

PRIMARY SOURCES—
INSTITUTIONAL PUBLICATIONS

There are many virtues in books, but the essential value is the adding
of knowledge to our stock by the record of new facts. . . . —*Emerson*

In recent decades there has been a great increase in publications which are nonperiodical in nature and which originate in
institutions of some kind. These irregular publications are issued
mainly by national, state, and municipal governmental agencies.
By far the greatest production is national. There are a few privately endowed, nongovernmental agencies.

PUBLIC DOCUMENTS

Various Federal and state scientific organizations have been
established for investigating those matters which concern the
common welfare[1] and for securing the desired publicity for the
results obtained. The government of the United States is the
greatest of all publishers of scientific works.[2] The publications
themselves include the results of the investigations of thousands
of governmental workers conducting researches in many divisions
of scientific endeavor.

Large commercial concerns carry on independent research
work, often on a large scale; but as such work is usually undertaken for gainful purposes, these concerns feel under no obligation
to reveal the results of their investigations. The governmental
bureaus, experiment stations, and laboratories aim to investigate
and solve problems for the benefit of a whole industry, frequently

[1] North, *Ind. Eng. Chem.*, **31**:574 (1939).
[2] See Bixler, Uncle Sam: Author, Printer, Bookseller, *Am. Scholar*, **8**:
494 (1939); Giegengack, Uncle Sam, Publisher, *Special Libraries*, **36**:297
(1945).

under a cooperative arrangement with representatives of the industry. Thus, the operator of limited means, the individual who cannot afford the experimentation necessary to demonstrate the advantages of adopting new procedures for his small-scale operations, has available for his use the results of various investigations. He has a place to take his difficulties where facilities and trained investigators may be able to offer valuable assistance.

Of great importance also are the collection and dissemination of statistics, such as those on production, sales, and uses of commodities.[1]

Nearly a century ago Disraeli spoke to the British House of Commons on the importance of public documents. "In my opinion," he said, discussing the money to be voted for official printing and publishing, "there is no vote to which the Committee has given its sanction which is more advantageous for the public service than the present one, which produces a body of information that guides the legislature and influences to a great degree the ultimate prosperity of the country."

Various countries are conducting this kind of governmental activity. It is believed, however, that the United States does far more in this direction than any other country; consequently, the present discussion is devoted largely to our own publications. It should not be forgotten, however, that very important contributions come from many foreign institutions.

The publications of these bureaus and laboratories are usually issued irregularly, except the annual reports, in the form of circulars, pamphlets, or bulletins. The material comprising the reports includes, for the most part, valuable results of investigations. Occasionally mere compilations of matter published elsewhere, but not readily available, make up the publication, such as bulletins containing the various state mining laws. Frequently the results of investigations carried on in these laboratories are published as articles in some of the journals.

Publications of Federal Institutions

The reports coming from Federal institutions are considered according to the divisions of the government under which the bureaus come. Nearly every change in administration brings

[1] See P. M. Hauser and W. R. Leonard, "Government Statistics for Business Use," John Wiley & Sons, Inc., New York, 1956.

some departmental reorganization. Old agencies are discontinued, and new ones are organized. Others are changed from one department to another, and still others are given different names. This makes it difficult to verify that a given bureau is in a given department and, of course, the bureau may no longer exist a few years after the statement is written. At the present time, however, the following departments maintain, among others, the following bureaus which may be of interest to the chemist:[1]

Department of Agriculture

Agricultural Research Service
Forest Service

Department of Commerce

Bureau of the Census
Bureau of Foreign Commerce
National Bureau of Standards
Patent Office[2]

Department of Health, Education, and Welfare

Food and Drug Administration
Public Health Service

Department of the Interior

Bureau of Mines
Geological Survey

Other Departments

Air Research and Development Command (Air Force)
Army Research and Development Program (Army)
Bureau of the Mint
Bureau of Narcotics (Treasury)
Office of Naval Research (Navy)

Independent Agencies

Atomic Energy Commission
Federal Trade Commission

[1] See "United States Government Organization Manual, 1956–1957," Government Printing Office, 1956. Appendix *A* lists changes in executive agencies and their functions, and appendix *B* lists representative publications of departments and agencies. See also "Organization of the Federal Government for Scientific Activities," NSF 56-17, Government Printing Office, 1956. This is an elaborate outline of the important role of the Federal government in scientific research and development.

[2] See Chap. 4 for a full discussion of the Patent Office.

General Services Administration
National Science Foundation
Smithsonian Institution
Tariff Commission
Tennessee Valley Authority

Depository Libraries. A considerable number of libraries have been designated by Congress to receive copies if desired, of publications issued by the government for public distribution. A list of these libraries will be found in the "List of Publications of the Department of Commerce." The libraries of all states, territories, land-grant colleges, and many others are included in this list.

Locating Desired Publications. Without some general sense of direction, one's search for Federal publications on a given subject may be tedious, or even fruitless, because of the amount of material available and the problem of finding it.

First of all, there are certain general compilations which serve as guides and indexes to all such publications. They are probably less widely used than the more specific sources mentioned below. Of the comprehensive indexes the following, arranged chronologically, are the most important:[1]

1774–1881   "Descriptive Catalogue of the Government Publications of the United States" (Poore)

[1] For more detailed information on government publications, see the following articles and books:

N. T. Ball and C. R. Flagg, *Advances in Chem. Ser.*, No. *4*, p. 70 (1951).

A. M. Boyd and R. E. Rips, "United States Government Publications," The H. W. Wilson Company, New York, 1949.

E. S. Brown, "Manual of Government Publications, United States and Foreign," Appleton-Century-Crofts, Inc., New York, 1950.

P. M. Hauser and W. R. Leonard (eds.), "Government Statistics for Business Use," John Wiley & Sons, Inc., New York, 1946.

F. Harden, The Use of Government Publications in Chemical Research, *J. Chem. Educ.*, **21**:326 (1944).

H. S. Hirshberg and C. H. Melinat, "Subject Guide to United States Government Publications," American Library Association, Chicago, 1947.

W. P. Leidy, "A Popular Guide to Government Publications," Columbia University Press, New York, 1953.

L. F. Schmeckebier, "Government Publications and Their Use," Brookings Institution, Washington, 1939.

J. K. Wilcox, New Guides and Aids to Public Document Use, *Special Libraries*, **40**:371 (1949).

C. M. Winchell, "Guide to Reference Books," p. 105, American Library Association, Chicago, 1951.

1789–1909	"Checklist of U.S. Public Documents," (U.S. Government Printing Office)
1881–1893	"Comprehensive Index to the Publications of the United States Government" (Ames)
1893–1940	"Document Catalogue" (catalogue of the public documents of Congress and of all the departments of the government)
1895–1933	*Document Index* (an index to the reports and documents of Congress)
1895–	*Monthly Catalogue of United States Public Documents*
	Biweekly List of Selected United States Government Publications

Rather than wait for the appearance of these comprehensive indexes and then relying upon finding information in them, the author prefers to deal with information available from the individual bureaus. Most of them have their own lists of publications. Also available are free price lists of the publications each bureau has in print. The following price lists are most likely to be of chemical interest: 11, Home Economics; 15, Geology; 37, Tariff; 38, Animal Industry; 43, Forestry; 44, Plants; 46, Soils and Fertilizers; 51, Health; 58, Mines; 62, Commerce; 64, Scientific Tests; Standards; 70, Census; 84, Atomic Energy.

Next to having these separate lists at hand, it is most helpful to have a knowledge of the kind of work being done in the individual bureaus. For example, one should refer to the Geological Survey for information on surface waters of the Southwest, to the Bureau of Mines Experiment Station at Pittsburgh, Pennsylvania, for information on coal, and to the Photometry and Colorimetry Division of the National Bureau of Standards for information on spectrophotometry.

To provide a general idea of the nature of the work covered by the different bureaus and to indicate the kinds of publications issued thereby, a brief statement follows concerning the activities and publications of the bureaus most likely to be the source of important chemical information. More details may be found by consulting either the annual reports of the directors or chiefs of the bureaus or the special pamphlets issued by some of the bureaus. The annual yearbooks of various departments are useful statistical compilations.

Department of Agriculture

AGRICULTURAL RESEARCH SERVICE

Activities. Most of the biological, chemical, physical, and engineering research activities in the Department of Agriculture are now consolidated in the Agricultural Research Service at the Agricultural Research Center at Beltsville, Md. The various branches include, among others, the following: Field Crops, Horticultural Crops, Entomology, Soil and Water Conservation, Agricultural Engineering, Animal Disease and Parasites, Dairy Husbandry, Animal and Poultry Husbandry, Human Nutrition, and Home Economics.

Primarily the work deals with broad, basic scientific and applied problems of national interest. There is much cooperation with state agricultural experiment stations on more localized problems.

Regional laboratories at Wyndmoor, Pa., New Orleans, La., Peoria, Ill., and Albany, Calif., specialize in industrial farm products in the respective sections of the country.

Publications. The publications have included many articles in appropriate journals and a large number of technical bulletins, circulars, and miscellaneous items.

See Price Lists 11, 38, 44, and 46 and "List of Publications of the U.S. Department of Agriculture."

Forest Products Laboratory

Activities. The Forest Products Laboratory, located in Madison, Wis., is operated by the Forest Service, in cooperation with the University of Wisconsin. Its object is to develop new and more efficient methods of converting standing trees into finished products, to increase the possibilities for utilizing both used and unused species, and to find ways of utilizing material which otherwise would be wasted. To the chemist the following technical sections are most important: timber processing (wood treatment, glue, and laminated construction), pulp and paper (manufacturing methods and suitability of various woods for pulp, paper, and special products), wood chemistry (chemical properties and uses of wood and chemical wood products, such as turpentine, methanol, and acetic acid), and wood preservation (decay of timber, molds, stains in manufactured products, and antiseptic properties of wood preservatives).

Publications. Many articles dealing with these subjects appear in technical journals. In addition, mimeographed reports, bulletins, and circulars are issued.

See "List of Publications of the Forest Products Laboratory" and Price List 43.

Department of Commerce[1]

Bureau of the Census

Activities. The first census of population in 1790 was broadened in 1810 to include manufactures. In 1902 the permanent census office was created. As the present major agency of the Federal government for gathering statistical facts, the Bureau provides information in the broad fields of population, housing, agriculture, governments, manufactures, business, and foreign trade.

[1] For a selected list of publications of the U.S. Department of Commerce since 1790, see "United States Department of Commerce Publications."

The present schedule of major regular censuses is as follows: population and housing, every 10 years, taken in years ending in 0; agriculture, twice each decade, taken in years ending in 0 and 4; manufactures, mining industries, and business, taken every 5 years, taken in years ending in 3 and 8 (except 1954); and government units, every 5 years, taken in years ending in 2 and 7. For selected subjects, current data are collected monthy, quarterly, and annually. Each census provides area data for states, counties, or other suitable bases.

In the annual survey of manufactures, statistics on 17 major lines of manufacturing activity include chemicals and allied products, petroleum and coal, primary metals, and instruments.

Publications. The information is issued in various ways, the form and frequency depending upon the census involved. Thus, there are monthly, quarterly, annual, quinquennial, and decennial reports. Various ones have already been indicated. The *Statistical Abstract of the United States* and the *Survey of Manufactures* are annual. The *Summary of Foreign Commerce of the United States* is monthly. *Facts for Industry,* including chemicals, pulp and paper, and primary metals, appears monthly and is cumulated quarterly and annually.

For the new type of census reports, begun in 1954, separate industry, state, and subject bulletins are being issued. Each of the sets will be assembled into separate volumes. The preliminary state reports include various industry groups, such as chemicals and products, petroleum and coal products, and ceramic products. Advance industry reports cover some 15 different kinds of products.

The "Catalog of United States Census Publications, 1790–1945," is supplemented by an annual current catalogue published monthly, quarterly, and annually.

See Price List 70 and "Catalog of United States Foreign Trade Statistical Publications."

BUSINESS AND DEFENSE SERVICES ADMINISTRATION

Activities. This agency is responsible for carrying out the department's programs relating to current defense production, long-range industrial preparedness, and service to the business community. There are 25 industry divisions, about one-third of which are chemical in nature, and more than 30 field offices.

The Office of Technical Services collects and distributes scientific and technical information important to development of new products and better production methods. It is the official agency for dissemination to the public of declassified and unclassified information of the governmental agencies. As such, it is the source of the Publication Board (PB) reports. Many thousands of scientific and technical reports were brought to this country after World War II. The processed material has been publicized in the "Bibliography of Scientific and Industrial Reports," which is now known as "Bibliography of Technical Reports."[1]

Publications. A variety of publications are being issued. Examples are the

[1] Annotated subject indexes for these reports are for sale by the Technical Information Service, Washington, D.C.

industry reports (such as *Chemical Industry Reports* and *Rubber Industry Reports*), *Copper, Distribution Data Guide, United States Research Reports, Technical Reports Newsletter,* and others. They range in publication schedules from monthly to annual.

See "Catalogs of Technical Reports."

BUREAU OF FOREIGN COMMERCE

Activities. The Bureau of Foreign Commerce aims to promote international trade. Business information is available through the field-office network of the Department of Commerce as well as in Washington. This information ranges from complete analytical and statistical reports on all phases of commerce, industry, and investment in specific countries to details on such matters as foreign tariff classifications and rates, mark-of-origin requirements, and the preparation of shipments.

Trade lists give the names and addresses of businessmen abroad who make, buy, or sell specific commodities. The "World Trade Directory" reports on individual business firms.

Publications. The principal publications are *Foreign Commerce Weekly,* which presents current information on business conditions abroad; reports in the "World Trade Information Series," a publication series in four parts; a series of investment handbooks, which outline the conditions and outlook for United States investors; and the "Comprehensive Export Schedule" with supplemental Current Export Bulletins, which provide information on export control regulations.

See "Catalog of United States Foreign Trade Statistical Publications" and *Business Service Checklist,* a weekly list of publications of the Department of Commerce.

NATIONAL BUREAU OF STANDARDS

Activities. The National Bureau of Standards was established in 1901 to serve the Federal government as a central scientific laboratory and to provide basic standards for science and industry. Its activities include chemistry, mathematics, physics, and various branches of engineering. Within the physical sciences, the Bureau is engaged in fundamental and applied research, development, calibration and testing, and a variety of scientific services. Much of the research program is concerned with the development of new and improved standards, development of methods and instruments for precise measurement, determination of physical constants, and studies of the basic properties of materials.

Scientific and technical activities are carried on by 18 divisions: Electricity and Electronics, Optics and Metrology, Heat and Power, Atomic and Radiation Physics, Chemistry, Mechanics, Organic and Fibrous Materials, Metallurgy, Mineral Products, Building Technology, Applied Mathematics, Data Processing Systems, Cryogenic Engineering, Radio Propagation Physics, Radio Propagation Engineering, Radio Standards, Weights and Measures, and Basic Instrumentation. Each of the divisions consists of several sections, which deal with definite classes of problems.

Although all divisions do some work of a chemical nature, chemical research is centered in four divisions: Chemistry, Organic and Fibrous Materials, Metallurgy, and Mineral Products. The branches of chemistry represented are analytical, inorganic, organic, physical, and surface chemistry; spectrochemistry; and thermochemistry. Applied research includes chemical metallurgy, electrodeposition, gas chemistry, organic coatings, pure substances, mineral products, and the chemistry and technology of the polymers—rubber, textiles, paper, leather, and plastics.

Fig. 4. Airplane view of National Bureau of Standards. (*Reproduced with permission from the National Geographic Magazine.*)

Publications. Results of the Bureau's work are reported both in its own series of publications and in scientific and technical journals of societies. Bureau publications include two periodicals, *Journal of Research of the National Bureau of Standards* and *NBS Technical News Bulletin.* The former publishes complete research papers, and the latter contains concise summary articles on both current and completed research and development at the Bureau. The latter publication lists all staff publications in outside journals as they become available.

There are five nonperiodical series. The "Applied Mathematics Series" (AMS) consists of mathematical tables, manuals, and studies. "Circulars" (C) contain information compiled on various subjects and bibliographies related to scientific and technical activities of the Bureau. "Building Materials and Structures Reports" (BMS) give results of Bureau investigations in building materials and techniques. "Handbooks" (H) present recommended codes of engineering and industrial practice developed in cooperation with industry, professional organizations, and regulatory bodies. "Miscellaneous Publications" (M) consist of annual and conference reports, charts, and administrative documents.

For complete information on publications, see NBS Circular 460, "Publications of the National Bureau of Standards," and Supplement to Circular 460; see also Price List 64.

Department of Health, Education, and Welfare

UNITED STATES PUBLIC HEALTH SERVICE

Activities. Since its creation by Congress in 1798, the Public Health Service has borne a steadily increasing responsibility for the nation's health. Today the many services and facilities of the Bureau of State Services, Bureau of Medical Services, and National Institutes of Health, all operating under the Surgeon General, form an important part of the country's public health resources. The research arm of the Public Health Service, the National Institutes of Health, supports research and training in the nation's medical schools, universities, and other non-Federal centers. It also conducts laboratory and clinical research in its own facilities at Bethesda, Md. The program areas include heart disease, cancer, mental illness, neurological disorders and blindness, arthritis and metabolic diseases, dental diseases, and microbiological problems. Serving the various Institutes is the Clinical Center, a 500-bed facility for clinical-laboratory research.

There are two extensive laboratories at Cincinnati, Ohio, the Robert A. Taft Sanitary Engineering Center and the Occupational Health Field Headquarters. The former is devoted to research, technical services, and training in water supply, water-pollution control, sewage and industrial-waste disposal, radiological health, air pollution, and milk and food sanitation. The latter deals with occupational health hazards.

Publications. Scientists of the Institutes publish in a wide variety of non-Federal journals. Annual bound collections of their papers, "NIH Collected Reprints," are distributed to some 50 large medical libraries throughout the world. Lists of nonperiodic publications and of health-information leaflets and pamphlets are available on request from the Public Health Service at Washington. *Public Health Reports* is issued monthly, and the *Journal of the National Cancer Institute* is bimonthly. Special publications of the Sanitary Engineering Center are the monthly *Public Health Engineering Abstracts* and the quarterly *Activity Report*.

See "List of Publications of the United States Public Health Service"; see also Price List 51.

FOOD AND DRUG ADMINISTRATION

Activities. The Food and Drug Administration is concerned primarily with enforcement of the Federal Food, Drug, and Cosmetics Act, the Tea Importation Act, the Import Milk Act, the Caustic Poison Act, and the Filled Milk Act. Consequently, it deals with certification of products and violations of the acts.

In addition to testing samples to carry out this program, the staff laboratories make researches to form a groundwork for enforcement policy. Included are evaluations of the safety and efficacy of medicines; the toxicity of ingredients in foods, drugs, and cosmetics; the safety of pesticidal residues on food crops; and the potency of drugs and vitamins. New drugs must be certified before distribution.

Publications. Scientific papers usually appear in professional journals. Other publications cover the laws enforced, regulations promulgated under them, and reports of the results of Federal court cases. Included are the definitions and standards for foods, drugs, and cosmetics.

Department of the Interior

Bureau of Mines

Activities. This technical agency was created by Congress in 1910 to conduct scientific and technological investigations concerning mining and the preparation, treatment, and utilization of minerals and mineral fuels; to increase safety, efficiency, and economy in the development of mineral resources and in every way promote their conservation; and to study economic factors affecting the mineral industries.

The Bureau performs research and investigations to determine the best techniques for utilizing and conserving mineral resources and disseminates the knowledge gained to industry, state and private research and educational institutions, and others interested in wise development of mineral resources.

Within the Bureau chemical studies are conducted by the following divisions: Anthracite, Bituminous Coal, Petroleum, Minerals, and Health and Safety. The headquarters are in Washington, but the investigations are carried on at the experiment stations and field offices serving specific areas in the United States. The more prominent stations and offices include (1955) Albany, Ore.; Bartlesville, Okla.; Berkeley, Calif.; Boulder City, Nev.; Bruceton, Pa.; College Park, Md.; Denver, Colo.; Grand Forks, N.D.; Laramie, Wyo.; Minneapolis, Minn.; Morgantown, W.Va.; Norris, Tenn.; Pittsburgh, Pa. (central laboratory); Reno, Nev.; Rolla, Mo.; Salt Lake City, Utah; San Francisco, Calif.; Schuylkill Haven, Pa.; Seattle, Wash.; Spokane, Wash.; Tucson, Ariz.; and Tuscaloosa, Ala.

Publications. The following publications are of chief interest to chemists: bulletins (results of major scientific investigations), reports of investigations (principal features and results of minor investigations and significant phases of major studies), information circulars (digests, reviews, abstracts, and discussions of activities and developments in the mineral industries), periodical reports, including *Mineral Trade Notes* (primarily statistical, with discussion of markets for various minerals). The annual "Minerals Yearbook" summarizes information on production and consumption of minerals and mineral fuels. A new publication, "Mineral Facts and Problems," presents a detailed report on 87 minerals in the United States. It is the most comprehensive ever prepared by the Bureau.

See Price List 58; see also "List of Publications of the Bureau of Mines."

Geological Survey

Activities. The principal objectives of the Geological Survey are the determination and appraisal of the nation's mineral and water resources and the supervision of leasing of minerals on Federal and Indian lands. This agency carries on important scientific and engineering functions under five field branches. Most important chemically are the Geologic Division and the Water Resources Division. The former investigates the geology and the mineral deposits of the United States and conducts researches in geology and related chemical and physical problems. The latter investigates the quantity, distribution, mineral quality, and utilization of surface and underground waters.

The chemical laboratories in Washington analyze and identify rocks and minerals, conduct special researches of chemical and physical processes that affect rocks and govern geologic processes, and determine the mineral qualities of waters with special reference to their use in irrigation and industry.

Publications. The most important publications may be grouped as follows: annual reports (review of the year's work); monographs (extensive reports on broad geologic problems or on the geology of particular regions); professional papers (shorter reports of a similar nature); bulletins (reports on economic geology and applied geology, including many chemical and mineralogical contributions); and water-supply papers (reports dealing with the general problem of water supplies and their uses).

See Price List 15; see also "List of Publications of the United States Geological Survey."

Other Departments

In several other departments there is considerable research and development work of chemical and technological interest. Examples are the Office of Naval Research; the Army Research and Development Program and the Chemical Corps; and the Air Research and Development Command. All these departments maintain chemical and physical research and testing facilities.

Somewhat different are the chemical activities of the Bureau of Customs, the Bureau of Engraving and Printing, the Bureau of the Mint, and the Bureau of Narcotics (all in the Treasury Department), and the Federal Bureau of Investigation (in the Department of Justice). Since much of the work of these laboratories is routine, ordinarily no publications are issued. Consequently, the primary concern with them is to know the kind of work carried on so that personal communication may be employed when knowledge is desired on items of interest.

In still other directions information on the chemical industry may be found. Two examples are the records of congressional hearings and of anti-trust cases.

Independent Agencies

There are many agencies not organized in any of the major divisions of the United States government. The few which seem of interest as sources of chemical information are considered briefly.

ATOMIC ENERGY COMMISSION

Activities. This Commission carries out the provisions of the Atomic Energy Act of 1946. Included are the securing of raw materials, the production of nuclear material, and the uses of the military and other products. Facilities for research, development, and production are operated largely by industrial concerns and by private and public institutions under contract with the Commission.

Publications. Only declassified matter is published. What is released is issued in the form of comprehensive reports or limited items. Some technical reports of research appear in non-Federal journals. An example of a very extensive report is the multivolume set "National Nuclear Energy Series."[1] It covers biology, chemistry, engineering, and physics of the general period of World War II. In contrast is the report "Raw Materials Development Handbook of Analytical Methods."[2] The key to all declassified and unclassified AEC reports is the semimonthly *Nuclear Science Abstracts*. Free price lists, entitled "Atomic Energy Commission Research Reports," are available from the Office of Technical Services of the Department of Commerce.

See "Twentieth Semiannual Report of the Atomic Energy Commission," appendix 6, for general material on the publications.

FEDERAL TRADE COMMISSION

Activities. Among its functions the Commission aims to prevent unfair or deceptive trade practices, to safeguard the consuming public, to enforce truthful labeling of wool and fur products, to prevent interstate marketing of dangerously flammable wearing apparel, and to gather and make available factual data concerning economic and business conditions for the guidance and protection of the public.

Publications. The principal publications are "Decisions of the Federal Trade Commission," "Annual Reports," and reports on individual commodities and industries.

See "List of Publications."

GENERAL SERVICES ADMINISTRATION

Activities. As one of its five units, the General Services Administration includes the Federal Supply Service. In this unit at least the following divisions are of interest: Standardization, National Buying, and Inspection.

These divisions are concerned with the purchase and handling of vast amounts of many commodities by the many agencies of the United States government. Specifications and standards and methods of testing are used in order to obtain the products desired for specific purposes.

Publications. This agency prepares and maintains the "Federal Standard

---

[1] Published by McGraw-Hill Book Company, Inc., New York.

[2] United States Atomic Energy Commission TID-7002 (TID indicates the source, Technical Information Division).

Stock Catalog" and its specifications. There are thousands of specifications and standards. They are listed alphabetically and by classes in "Index of Federal Specifications and Standards." There is also the restricted "Directory of U.S. Government Inspection Services and Testing Laboratories" for Federal purchasing officers, inspection officials, and government personnel requiring inspection or testing services.

NATIONAL SCIENCE FOUNDATION

Activities. In 1950 the Congress established the National Science Foundation to promote the progress of science; to advance the national health, prosperity, and welfare; and to secure the national welfare. Some aid is provided for publication of reference aids and for the study of processing, storing, and retrieving scientific information.

The Scientific Translation Center has been established at the Library of Congress. It collects, records, and duplicates translations of Russian scientific papers from many sources.[1]

The Office of Scientific Information maintains the Government Research Information Clearinghouse to assist in determining the existence, location, and availability of unclassified reports on government-sponsored basic scientific research.

Publications. The publications are chiefly reports on the various activities. See "Annual Reports."

SMITHSONIAN INSTITUTION

Activities. Established by the will of James Smithson, of England, the Smithsonian Institution operates under a Board of Regents headed by the Chief Justice of the Supreme Court. It was established "for the increase and diffusion of knowledge among men." Its bureaus include, among others, the National Museum and the Astrophysical Laboratory. Within the latter is the Division of Radiation and Organisms.

Publications. The publications cover a wide range of activities. The regular publications include Smithsonian Contributions to Knowledge, Smithsonian Miscellaneous Collections, and the "Smithsonian Annual Report." The first of these includes memoirs or records of extended investigations and researches. The miscellaneous collections were designed to contain reports of the present state of knowledge of particular branches of science,[2] instructions for collecting and digesting facts and materials for research, lists and synopses of species of the organic and inorganic world, museum catalogues, reports of explorations, and aids to bibliographic investigations.

See "List of Publications of the Smithsonian Institution."

TARIFF COMMISSION

Activities. In establishing tariff schedules the Tariff Commission collects statistics on the domestic production and sales of a wide variety of com-

---

[1] See O'Dette, *Science*, **125**:579 (1957).

[2] Fine examples are the bibliographies of J. L. Howe and H. C. Bolton (see Chap. 7).

modities, including many chemical products. There are surveys of domestic and foreign industries, including costs of production. Also there are studies of invoices and records of imports at the ports of entry. Investigations are made for the President and for Congress.

Publications. The annual publication "Synthetic Organic Chemicals," compiled from the Facts for Industry of the Tariff Commission, includes total production and sales for each compound listed. There is a directory of manufacturers. Also included are statistics on research personnel and expenditures.

Monthly statistics are issued on selected organic chemicals and plastics materials. The annual report "Imports of Coal-tar Products" contains summaries of investigations made on various commodities.[1]

See "Annual Report of the United States Tariff Commission"; see also "List of Publications of the Tariff Commission."

TENNESSEE VALLEY AUTHORITY

Activities. The Office of Chemical Engineering of the Tennessee Valley Authority carries on a program in chemistry, chemical engineering, and metallurgy to improve the use of natural resources and for national defense. It also operates plants for production of fertilizers and munitions materials.

Publications. Various reports on research and production have been issued.

See "Analytical Index of Chemical Engineering Publications, Patents, Reports."

Obtaining Federal Documents

Several arrangements may be used to obtain copies of United States public documents. Occasionally it is possible to secure them free by writing to one's congressman or to the person in charge of the division of work concerned. Such distribution generally applies only to the smaller publications, such as circular letters and pamphlets.

The other alternative is to buy the publications. Any of the following procedures is satisfactory.

1. Send check, postal money order, express order, New York draft, or currency (at sender's risk) in advance of shipment of publications, making payable to Superintendent of Documents, Government Printing Office, Washington, D.C. Postage stamps, foreign money, and smooth or defaced coins are not accepted.

2. Enclose coupons with the order. Coupons may be purchased (20 for $1) from the Superintendent of Documents and are accepted as cash for any requested publications.

[1] The Manufacturing Chemists' Association publishes a compilation of these various statistics. The first three editions were entitled "Chemical Facts & Figures." The fourth edition (1955) is "Chemical Statistics Handbook."

3. Use the deposit system, by depositing $5 or more, with the Superintendent of Documents. The cost of publications, as ordered, is charged against the deposit. This system avoids remittances with every order and delay in first obtaining prices.

4. Order publications sent C.O.D. if they are needed immediately and the price is unknown. Payment is made when they are received.

Free price lists of all government publications are available from the Government Printing Office, or the various departments and bureaus will supply their particular lists.

Publications of Foreign Governments

In various foreign countries scientific work comparable to that in the United States is being done under government supervision. In general, such activities are not as extensive as our own. The present discussion is limited to sources of further information.

Great Britain

"Government Publications." See sectional lists, such as Department of Scientific and Industrial Research, Chemical Research Board, Forest Products Research Board, National Physical Laboratory, and Scientific Research in British Universities. See also reports of Medical Research Council.

Consult British Library of Information, 270 Madison Avenue, New York, N.Y.

Canada

"Canadian Government Publications"
"Publications of the National Research Council of Canada"
"Technical Information Service Reports"
"Information Notes"
"Sources of Information on Canada"

Consult Technical Information Service, National Research Council, Ottawa, Canada.

France

"Bibliographie de la France," Supplement F, Publications officielles

Germany

"Monatliches Verzeichnis der reichdeutschen amtlichen Druckschriften"

Publications of the United Nations

Activities. As part of its activities, the United Nations maintains the Statistical Office, which publishes various periodicals containing official quantitative information of many nations on various subjects.

Publications. Two publications contain the most useful detailed statistics on international trade. The *Directory of International Trade* is a quarterly, with monthly supplements, which summarizes trade from the viewpoint of countries. In contrast, the quarterly *Commodity Trade Statistics* presents full statistical information on the imports and exports for each of some 150 commodity groups.

Publications of State Institutions[1]

In addition to the extensive list of public documents issued by the several Federal departments, we have, in the aggregate, a large number of publications coming from similar institutions which are under the control of the state governments. As intimated, these publications are not essentially different in character from those already considered. Frequently the subjects treated have a distinctly local significance; but probably just as often the subject matter is of more general interest than many productions of the Federal bureaus.

Two of the main sources of these publications are the state engineering experiment stations and agricultural experiment stations, which are located in many cases at the state universities. The general function of the first of these stations is to conduct investigations along various lines of engineering and to cooperate with engineering societies in pursuing industrial investigations, particularly for the engineering interests of the states. The agricultural investigations bear a similar relationship to the agricultural interests of the states.

One of the functions of these institutions is to publish the results of their work. This usually takes place in the form of bulletins. One may secure lists of available publications by writing the directors of the various stations, and ordinarily copies of the bulletins may be secured in a similar manner, without charge.

Certain other state institutions issue publications which are less numerous but often of value, such as the annual reports of the state boards of health and the bulletins of the state geological surveys.

Many publications of state institutions, such as experiment stations, geological surveys, boards of health, and similar organizations, are listed in the *Monthly Check List of State Publications*, Superintendent of Documents, Washington, D.C., $1.50 per year.

---

[1] For state sources of market information, see J. D. McPherson and E. D. Simpson, *Advances in Chem. Ser.*, No. 4, pp. 14–21 (1951).

REPORTS OF NONGOVERNMENTAL INSTITUTIONS

Publications are also issued from several institutions whose financial status is such that they should hardly be included among those already discussed as governmental projects. These institutions are maintained, or were started at least, by private endowments. They may be under the general supervision of some governmental agency. The nature of the publications themselves does not differ from that of public documents. Two typical institutions of this kind will be considered briefly.

CARNEGIE INSTITUTION OF WASHINGTON

Activities. The corporation endowed by Andrew Carnegie and incorporated as the Carnegie Institution of Washington has for its object "to encourage in the broadest and most liberal manner investigation, research and discovery and the application of knowledge to the improvement of mankind." Accordingly, means are provided to undertake large problems within the institution itself, and to help individual investigators, in other institutions, where elaborate facilities are not required.

"The institution aims to lend its work, whenever possible, to advance fundamental research in fields not normally covered by the activities of other agencies, and to concentrate its attention upon specific problems, with the idea of shifting attack from time to time to meet the more pressing needs of research as they develop with the increase of knowledge."

The projects carried on within the institution are scattered among several laboratories. The ones of chief chemical interest are the Laboratory of Plant Physiology at Tucson, Ariz.; the Nutrition Laboratory at Boston, Mass.; and the Geophysical Laboratory at Washington, D.C.

Publications. Many of the contributions coming from these laboratories are published in scientific journals. Others are issued under the title of "Carnegie Institution Publications."

See "Price List of Publications."

BATTELLE MEMORIAL INSTITUTE

Activities. This institute was founded "for the purpose of education . . . the encouragement of research . . . and the making of discoveries and inventions for industry." The sponsored research is in industrial science, agriculture, and many specialized technologies.

Publications. Many technical articles appear in appropriate journals. The institute publishes the monthly *Battelle Technical Review*, which includes an extensive abstract section.

CHAPTER 4

PRIMARY SOURCES—
LITERATURE ON PATENTS[1]

For words, like Nature, half reveal and half conceal the Soul within.—
Tennyson

The subject of patents is narrowly specialized, and the sources of information relating to it are such that a special chapter has been devoted to its consideration. One might, of course, group the publications coming from the various patent offices along with public documents, in view of the fact that these offices are governmental institutions.

The patent literature began in 1617 with the granting of the first British patent. Now the total number issued by all countries granting patents has become very large. Thus, the United States alone has issued 2,818,566 patents between July 28, 1836, and December 31, 1957.[2]

Because of the number of countries involved and of the variance in their patent practices, only United States patents are considered here.

In considering the patent literature, we are concerned with at least three questions: "(1) Of what value is it to the chemist? (2) What are the significant publications? (3) What are the methods and facilities for using those publications?"

The Chemist's Interest in Patents

An alert and competent chemist or chemical engineer should be a potential inventor. If he possesses an imaginative temperament and an analytical mind, he should be capable of detecting defects

[1] Contributed by Julian F. Smith, Lenoir-Rhyne College.
[2] The first United States patent, issued July 31, 1790, relates to chemicals. Its title is "Making Pot and Pearl Ashes."

in old procedures and of devising preferable alternatives. If he is endowed with creative or inventive capacity and he is trying to develop a new process or product or to improve a process or product already being used or manufactured, he is very likely to have an interest in those objects which are patentable.

Information regarding patents which have been issued or which are under litigation in the courts or patent offices is often of great importance, particularly to the industrial chemist.[1] The vast number of chemical patents deal not only with a great variety of industrial activities but also with laboratory developments merely having possibilities of commercial exploitation.

In the following statement Barrows[2] has given a good summary of the general significance of patents to chemists:

> Patents, from their very nature, require consideration from various aspects other than as a part of the chemical literature. Thus, the patentability of inventions, the filing and prosecution of applications for patents, the construction, validity, and scope of issued patents, questions of infringement of unexpired patents, patent litigation, property rights in patents, the rights and obligations of patentees, etc., are matters primarily involving patents as patents rather than as publications, and are matters requiring consideration from the standpoint of the relevant principles of the patent law applicable thereto, as well as from the standpoint of the chemical principles that are involved.
>
> Patent searches or investigations may thus be of a special character. In considering questions of infringement, for example, the primary search extends only through the United States patents granted during the last seventeen years and requires consideration of the invention claimed rather than, or in addition to, the invention described; but inasmuch as the claims of a patent may require to be construed by the accompanying description and in the light of the Patent Office proceedings leading up to the grant of the patent, as well as in view of the prior state of the art disclosed by prior patents and publications, and in accordance with relevant principles of the patent law, a more extended search to include expired United States patents and other patents and publications may be important or even essential.
>
> Investigations of the patentability of inventions, such as are made to determine the advisability of making application for a patent, or by the Patent Office examiners in determining the patentability of inventions

---

[1] Brown, *Ind. Eng. Chem.*, **31**:580 (1939).
[2] *Chem. Met. Eng.*, **24**:517 (1921).

set forth in patent applications, as well as investigating the scope and validity of issued patents, may likewise require an extended search of the prior patents and publications, to determine whether the invention is new and whether it is a patentable invention or discovery, within the meaning of the patent law.

Patent investigations thus include both investigations of patents as patents, and investigations or searches of patents as publications and as a part of the chemical literature.

FIG. 5. Building containing U.S. Patent Office.

Considered as a part of the chemical literature, the patent literature furnishes one of the most important fields of search, inasmuch as it records the inventions and improvements, and hence the progress, made in almost all fields of chemical industry. Not infrequently inventors have patented their inventions without having published any descriptions of them elsewhere and without any abstracts or digests of their inventions appearing in the periodical literature. The patent literature, therefore, contains much that is not available elsewhere.

In order to take advantage of his possibilities the potential chemical inventor should understand what patents are and something of what can and cannot be done with them. Three items of major importance are the nature of a patent, the kinds of items which are patentable, and the requirements for patentability.

Nature of Patents. When we state that an individual has a patent, we refer to the letters patent issued to the patentee by the United States or other government. *Letters patent* is a legal term meaning "open (i.e., public) documents." Such a document consists of the grant, the specification, and the drawing(s), if any, including complete and full disclosure of the invention.

The grant in the United States is a paper containing a short title of the invention and purporting to grant "to the patentee, his heirs and assigns, for a period of 17 years from the date of issue, the exclusive right to make, vend, or use the invention throughout the United States and the territories thereof." What really is granted is the right to prevent others from *making*, *using*, or *selling* the invention.

The specification is the information furnished by the patentee regarding the object or process patented. This section of the letters patent consists, in addition to any drawings, of two parts, as follows:[1]

The *description* is a disclosure of the invention, and of the manner or process of making, constructing or compounding, and using it, in such full, clear, concise, and exact terms as to enable any person skilled in the art or science to which it appertains, or with which it is most nearly connected, to make, construct, or compound, and to use the same. . . . The function of the *claims* is to define the exact limits of the invention, and no matter what has been described in the body of the specification, or illustrated in the drawings, the invention patented is the invention set forth in the claims—nothing more. The patentee is bound by his claims, and these will not ordinarily be enlarged by reference to the specification. Failure to claim described matter dedicates it to the public use, unless claimed in other applications which should be properly referred to.

Items Patentable. There is frequent misunderstanding of just what is patentable. If the chemist is to take advantage of his inventive possibilities, he should have clearly in mind what can be patented. Thus, a new analytical balance might be patentable, but a new law for the absorption of radiant energy would not. Six distinct types of patents are recognized:

1. *A Machine.* To a chemist, a machine is most likely to be a mechanical, electrical, or optical device of some kind. Laboratory

[1] O. A. Geier, "Patents, Trade-marks, and Copyrights: Law and Practice," p. 11, privately published, 1930.

apparatus, such as balances and spectrophotometers, or plant equipment, such as stills and centrifugals, are examples.

2. *A Process.* This is an art or means of doing something. In organic chemistry a method of synthesizing a compound, such as cyclopropane, is an example. Other examples are methods of extracting gold or of tanning leather. Recently methods of making chemical analyses have been patented.

3. *A Composition of Matter.* There are two types of composition-of-matter patents. One is represented by a new compound. The other is represented by a combination of substances which, when combined, possess properties not attributable to the sum of the properties of the substances combined. Many alloys are of the latter type.

4. *A Manufacture.* This refers to an article for use produced from raw or prepared materials by giving them new forms, qualities, properties, or combinations. Glidden's patent on barbed wire (U.S. 157,124) is an example. Others are the patents on expanded metal and excelsior.

5. *A Plant.* This type includes (botanical) plants, such as roses, pears, and hybrid corn. It is the most recent type recognized by the Patent Office.

6. *A Design.* A design patent covers new, original, and ornamental appearance of articles of commerce. Examples are radiator shells of automobiles, wedding rings, and playing cards. Interesting new designs appear in every issue of the *Official Gazette*, discussed below.

The first three of these six types are of principal concern to chemists and chemical engineers. In avocational projects, plant and design patents might be of interest. Likewise, trade-marks and copyrights may have interest. Examples of trade-marks are "Ivory" soap and the "Quantometer" direct-reading emission spectrometer.

Requirements. There are three general requirements which must be met to secure a patent. Court interpretation at times may have left uncertainty about the interpretation of these requirements, but they may be summarized as indicated here.

1. *Novelty.* The invention must be new. The item must not have been patented anywhere previously nor the idea for it published anywhere more than 1 year before application is made for a patent. Obviously, a decision on novelty puts great responsibility upon a patent examiner in the Patent Office.

This requirement also makes it imperative that a prospective patentee keep adequate and reliable dated records to support his application for a patent. Issuance of a patent, and also defense of one issued, may depend upon proof of priority of novelty of the idea.

2. *Utility.* In theory, at least, to be patentable the item must be useful. Otherwise presumably there would be no point in patenting it. Actually, there seems to have been some laxity in adhering to this requirement, and probably with some justification. For example, it seems likely that some new chemical compound may not at once be recognized as useful for anything but later may be found very useful in some particular application.

3. *Completeness of Disclosure.* The courts have recognized a broad, general test here. In brief, the description must be adequate to enable "one skilled in the art" to make and/or use the item. That is, an organic chemist, competent in synthetic work, should be able to apply in the laboratory a process patent for making some new organic compound. Decisions in famous patent cases have hinged upon demonstration of this requirement.

The Patent Literature

Although over 100 countries grant patent protection[1] and a considerable number issue official publications from their patent offices, this discussion is confined for the most part to the practice followed in the United States and to the publications of the U.S. Patent Office. These publications are considered under three divisions.

Letters-patent Documents. These are copies of the original patents. They include the description and claims, in addition to the heading, which gives the date the patent is issued, its number, the name and address of the patentee, the title of the patent, the date of application for the patent, the name of the assignee (if any), and the class number. As an example, a typical United States chemical-process patent is given here.[2]

---

[1] Smith, *Ind. Eng. Chem.*, **16**:527 (1924).

[2] The following examples give an idea of the range in size of United States patents: (1) D. Isenberg, U.S. 1,650,071, on paint, consisting of one-third page of description, including one claim; (2) W. S. Gubelman, U.S. 1,817,451, on a calculating machine, consisting of 40 sheets of drawings and 205 pages of description, including 975 claims (a champion number); and (3) J. H. Voss,

UNITED STATES PATENT OFFICE   2,702,824

Patented Feb. 22, 1955

LIQUID-VAPOR PHASE METHOD FOR PRODUCING LOWER DIALKYL SULFOXIDES

Gustav Allan Wetterholm and Kåre Ragnvald Fossan, Gyttorp, Sweden, assignors to Nitroglycerin Atkiebolåget, Gyttorp, Sweden, a company.

Application August 18, 1952, Serial No. 305,044

6 Claims. (Cl. 260—607)

The present invention relates to a method for producing low-molecular dialkyl sulfoxides which is characterized therein that the corresponding dialkyl sulfides are oxidized in the liquid phase by means of an oxygen or a gas mixture containing oxygen under catalysis of nitric oxides which here include NO, NO_2, N_2O_3, N_2O_4 and HNO_3 of at least 99% concentration.

It is known to produce dimethyl sulfoxide by oxidizing dimethyl sulfide in the gaseous phase with oxygen or air while employing nitric oxide and/or other oxygen-transmitting nitric oxides as catalysts. In this process the dimethyl sulfide must be converted into the gaseous form prior to oxidation which does not involve any difficulties in itself owing to the volatility of the sulfide, but the carrying out of the process on a commercial scale is rendered difficult on account of the large volumes that have to be handled. Moreover, if in said process a surplus of oxidizing gas is employed, N_2O_4-losses will occur during condensation, owing to the solubility of this substance in the dimethyl sulfide–methyl sulfoxide mixture. If on the other hand the process is carried out with a deficit of oxidizing gas in which case the nitric oxide is present as NO, which is not appreciably soluble in said reaction mixture, losses of sulfide will occur, if the gases are not recirculated which is possible with pure oxygen but scarcely so with air.

Experiments have now shown surprisingly enough that the oxidizing process takes place so easily that it can even be carried out in the liquid phase in the manner indicated, and this applies not only to dimethyl sulfide but also with other low-molecular dialkyl sulfides. It is thus possible to carry out oxidation by introducing oxygen or air, for example, into the liquid dialkyl sulfide together with one or more of the said catalysts, which may be mixed with the oxidizing gases or added to the liquid separately. A condition for carrying out the process is, of course, that the rate of adding the oxidizing gases and the reaction path, the concentration of the catalysts and the temperature must be in suitable relation to the rate of oxidation, under which assumption the oxygen is entirely consumed during the passage through the liquid and the oxida-

U.S. 2,320,548, on a telephone system, consisting of 174 sheets of drawings and 220 pages of specification, including 209 claims (a champion in length).

tion of the dialkyl sulfide takes place exclusively in the liquid phase. Under these conditions the gas bubbles which pass through the liquid consist of nitric oxide and—when air is used—also of nitrogen, etc., but not of any higher nitric oxides, and the capacity of these gases to oxidize dialkyl sulfide to the corresponding sulfoxide is entirely exhausted.

The method is preferably carried out in a closed system with circulation and re-introduction into the process, either entirely or partly, of the escaping gases which may also contain vaporized dialkyl sulfide.

As indicated above, instead of adding nitric oxides as such, nitric acid of at least 99% concentration may also be added primarily as a catalyst. In this connection it is preferable to proceed in such a way that a few per cent of the acid are added in the beginning and the reaction zone is heated up to a temperature above 30° C., whereby the nitric oxides necessary for the catalysts are visibly formed directly in the liquid. If on the other hand, NO_2, N_2O_3, or similar nitric oxides are added as such it is not necessary to heat the liquid and the reaction can commence at room temperature (20–25° C.) in which case the temperature of the reaction mixture will subsequently rise to 35° C. or higher, according to the dialkyl sulfide being treated, whereupon cooling may take place, if necessary. As the reaction progresses, the nitric oxide passing off must be replaced which may be effected by the re-introduction of nitric oxide into the process as described above, or by the addition of fresh nitric oxide or nitric acid. The concentration of the catalysts is successively increased to enable the reaction to continue until it is completed, so that the whole quantity of the dialkyl sulfide is converted to dialkyl sulfoxide. During the latter part of the process the temperature may also suitably be raised slightly but should always be kept below the boiling point of the reaction mixture.

The process may either be carried out interruptedly or continuously, that is, under continual addition of both dialkyl sulfide and oxidizing gas and continual removal of the dialkyl sulfoxide formed.

The process is preferably carried out in a reaction column which may suitably be filled with filling material, such as Rasching rings or the like, containing dialkyl sulfide in liquid form into which the gases are introduced at the bottom of the column which is provided with suitable pipe coils conveying a heating or cooling medium for regulating the temperature, arrangements also being made for the circulation of the gases. In a reaction column of this kind the reaction conditions can be conveniently regulated and controlled in the manner described. Thus, incomplete oxidation in the solution which may produce oxidation in the gaseous phase secondarily, is recognized in the following manner:

The gaseous phase is heated.

Condensation of the sulfoxide takes place and may be observed in the unfilled part of the column above the surface of the liquid.

As the atmosphere above the surface of the liquid is normally filled with NO and the dialkyl sulfide, an oxygen bubble, should one pass through the solution unconsumed, will momentarily colour the layer above the surface brown owing to the formation of NO_2 which will then react with dialkyl sulfide under discolouration.

The process according to the invention is more particularly described below with reference to the accompanying drawings which in Figs. 1–5 illustrates various forms of construction of suitable apparatus for carrying out the process.

In all the figures A is the reaction column which may be provided with a filling material as indicated in the drawing, or without such material, B indicates the pipe-coils for the heating or cooling medium, D is the circulating pump, E is the piping for supplying the oxidizing gases, H is the supply pipe for dialkyl sulfide, and I is the piping for drawing off the dialkyl sulfoxide. In Figs. 1–4 the piping E is combined with a shunt connection with a vessel C for supplying catalysing gases, while Fig. 5 shows an arrangement for supplying nitric acid as the catalysing agent, from the vessel K.

In the arrangement according to Fig. 1 it is assumed that oxidation will take place with a supply of oxygen gas as the oxidizing agent. The oxygen is partially saturated in the vessel C by the catalysing gas. The pipe coil for regulating the temperature is located in the lower part of the zone of the main reaction, and the gas flowing out which consists chiefly of NO, is circulated and forced into the system again.

In the arrangement according to Fig. 2 it is assumed that oxidation will be effected by a gas mixture such as air which is supplied saturated with catalysing gases in the same manner as in Fig. 1. Here, however, an effective cooler F is required to reduce the quantities of dialkyl sulfide carried along by the gases passing off which in addition to NO contain large quantities of nitrogen. For drawing off a part of the quantities of gas passing off, the circulating piping is here provided with a draw-off pipe, as indicated in the drawing.

In the forms of construction shown in Figs. 3 and 4 it is assumed that the process is carried on continuously. The reaction zone is here divided into two sections, namely, the primary zone A_1 and the secondary zone A_2, which are connected to one another by a throttle passage G, as may be seen in Fig. 3. In this case the main reaction takes place in the primary zone A_1, with the heating-cooling coil B_1, while the last part of the oxidation is carried out with fresh gas under heating by means of the coil B_2 in the secondary reaction zone. The dialkyl sulfide is supplied continuously at H.

The arrangement according to Fig. 4 is based on the same principle as the arrangement shown in Fig. 3, but has a slightly varied form for the separation of the two reaction zones. Finally, as stated above, the ar-

Feb. 22, 1955   G. A. WETTERHOLM ET AL   2,702,824
LIQUID-VAPOR PHASE METHOD FOR PRODUCING
LOWER DIALKYL SULFOXIDES
Filed Aug. 18, 1952

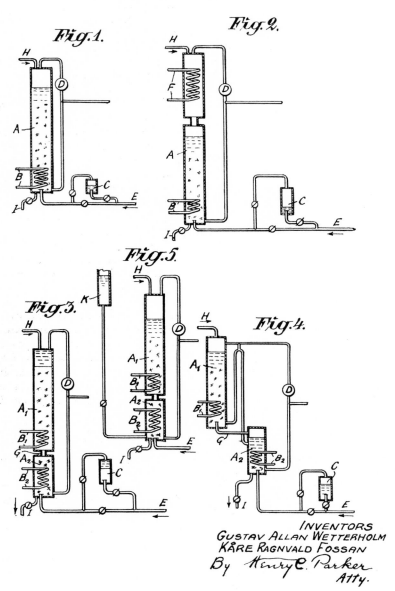

INVENTORS
GUSTAV ALLAN WETTERHOLM
KÅRE RAGNVALD FOSSAN
By   Henry C. Parker
                    Atty.

rangement according to Fig. 5 is intended for supplying nitric acid as a catalysing agent, but is similar in all other essential respects to the arrangement according to Fig. 3.

Instead of dividing the reaction zone into two sections as shown in Figs. 3–5, it is also possible to employ more than two reaction zones, if desired.

Example 1

Into a column 13 cm. long and 4.5 cm. in diameter provided with a gas inlet pipe at the bottom and a gas distributing plate, 800 g. of dimethyl sulfide were introduced. The lower half of the tube was filled with a filling material to increase the reaction surface. The upper part of the column was provided with a good cooler cooled by means of a cooling liquid of $-10°$ C. From the beginning so much NO_2 was supplied to the solution that its concentration became $\frac{1}{2}\%$. Initial temperature 20–25° C. In this case the oxidizing mixture consisted of oxygen containing 12–15% NO_2. The NO_2 concentration was regulated from time to time so that complete absorption of the oxygen was effected. Rate of oxygen 6–10 liter per hour. Higher gas velocities may also be adopted if desired. With higher temperatures a lower NO_2 concentration may be employed without unconsumed oxygen passing through the liquid. As the reaction progressed the temperature was raised slightly, up to 40–45° C. final temperature. The yield of dimethyl sulfoxide was 95% of the theoretical value.

Example 2

Into a column approximately 15 cm. long with a 3-necked $\frac{1}{2}$ lt. retort at the bottom and a gas supply pipe inserted into one of the necks of the retort passing through it, and provided with a gas distributing plate, 884 g. of dimethyl sulfide were introduced. The upper part of the pipe was provided with a good cooler. One of the remaining necks of the retort was employed as a supply pipe for highly concentrated (at least 99%) nitric acid. It is advantageous to use fuming nitric acid containing NO_2. Through the third neck a thermometer was inserted and samples could be drawn off by means of a T-pipe and cock.

At the beginning of the experiment so much nitric acid was added that a 1% total concentration was obtained. At the same time the solution was heated to 35° C. and the introduction of oxygen was begun at a rate of 8–9 liter per hour (11.2–12.6 g.). Every second hour 5 g. of concentrated acid were added to replace the loss of nitric oxide and accelerate the reaction. As the experiment progressed, the temperature was also raised slightly to finally reach about 50° C. in the reaction zone. The temperature was considerably lower in the upper part of the column. The introduction of oxygen was continued for 20 hours after which oxidation was found to be complete. Tests by mixing with water then exhibited complete miscibility. The total content of nitrogen compounds towards the end corresponded to 1.59% nitrogen. Yield of dimethyl sulfoxide 4087 g. or 90% when the nitrogen is calculated as nitric acid and the total weight is corrected accordingly.

Example 3

In an apparatus consisting of a glass tube 30 cm. long and 3 cm. in diameter, a cooler, thermometer and a gas distributor, 200 g. of diethyl sulfide were introduced. A mixture of oxygen and NO_2 was then led into the apparatus, the composition of the mixture being so regulated that the oxygen was entirely consumed during its passage through the diethyl sulfide. Hereby the content of NO varied between 5 and 15%. Owing to the low solubility of the nitric oxide in the reaction mixture, a part of the catalysts was lost so that a certain quantity of NO_2 had to be added throughout the whole of the experiment.

Oxidation took place very readily and under considerable development of heat, but the reaction temperature was maintained at 40–50° C., when necessary by external cooling with water.

After the greater part of the diethyl sulfide had been converted to diethyl sulfoxide the mixture was neutralized with gaseous ammonia. On distillation in vacuum (15 mm.) the diethyl sulfoxide passed over at 92° C. Melting point 17° C.

In an analogous manner dipropyl sulfoxide, melting point 21° C. (somewhat undefinite), dibutyl sulfoxide, melting point 30° C. and ethylpropyl sulfoxide, melting point 19° C., were produced.

It will be noted from the above specific examples that the oxygen-containing gas used in our process is initially passed through a body of liquid consisting of liquid dialkyl sulfide. No extraneous solvent is added and, even when 1% of 99% nitric acid is added, as in Example 2, no more than a trace of water is present in the reaction zone.

We claim:

1. In the manufacture of low-molecular dialkyl sulfoxide, the process which comprises establishing and maintaining in a reaction zone a body of liquid which at the start of the process consists of a liquid of low-molecular dialkyl sulfide; this liquid dialkyl sulfide being converted into liquid dialkyl sulfoxide during the course of the reaction; introducing a small amount, sufficient only to catalyze the oxidizing reaction, of a catalyst, selected from the group consisting of NO, NO_2, N_2O_3, N_2O_4, and HNO_3 of at least 99% concentration, maintaining the liquid reaction mixture at a temperature below the boiling point of the liquid reaction mixture while passing therethrough an oxygen-containing gas at a rate below that causing discoloration of the vapor above the reaction liquid, whereby the oxidation of the dialkyl sulfide takes place exclu-

sively in the reaction liquid, and recovering the resulting dialkyl sulfoxide.

2. The process of claim 1 wherein the dialkyl sulfide is dimethyl sulfide.

3. The process of claim 1 wherein the process is conducted in two reaction zones, one being positioned above the other, the liquid dialkyl sulfide being passed into the upper reaction zone and the dialkyl sulfoxide being drawn off from the bottom of the lower reaction zone.

4. The process of claim 1 wherein at least part of the gases escaping from the body of the liquid dialkyl sulfide is recycled and re-introduced into the process.

5. The process of claim 1 wherein highly concentrated nitric acid of at least 99% concentration is the catalyst, a few per cent of this acid being introduced into the body of liquid dialkyl sulfide at the start of the process, the body of liquid being heated to a temperature above 30° C. to start the reaction and cause the formation of nitrogen oxides in the liquid.

6. The process of claim 1 wherein the catalyst is a nitrogen oxide higher than NO and the reaction zone is at room temperature at the start of the process.

References Cited in the file of this patent

UNITED STATES PATENTS

2,581,050   Smedslund...............Jan. 1, 1952

FOREIGN PATENTS

442,524   Great Britain............Feb. 10, 1936

As the United States alone has issued more than 2,800,000 patents in the present series (beginning July 28, 1836),[1] a large number of which relate to chemistry and allied subjects, it is evident that this part of the literature is enormous. Interesting statistics are shown in the table on page 74.

Various schemes of classification, differing in different countries, have been devised to aid the searcher in locating particular patents or in assuring himself that none exists covering a prospective invention. An inspection of the United States system[2] will convince the chemist that the arrangement is less than satisfactory for his use. The system is described in the "Manual of Classification," the semiannual bulletins, and the "Definitions of

[1] For the first series, covering 1790–1836, see "List of Patents Granted by the United States, Apr. 10, 1790, to Dec. 31, 1836."

[2] Van Doren, *J. Chem. Educ.*, **6**:536 (1929); Geier, *op. cit.*, p. 46.

NUMBER OF UNITED STATES PATENTS, BY DECADES

Decade	Years	First patent number	Number during decade
1	1836–1845	1	4,347
2	1846–1855	4,348	9,661
3	1856–1865	14,009	37,775
4	1866–1875	51,784	119,857
5	1876–1885	171,641	161,853
6	1886–1895	333,494	219,008
7	1896–1905	552,502	256,116
8	1906–1915	808,618	357,801
9	1916–1925	1,166,419	401,621
10	1926–1935	1,568,040	458,476
11	1936–1945	2,026,516	365,340
12	1946–1955	2,391,856	337,057
13	1956–1965	2,728,913	

Revised Classes and Sub-classes," all published by the U.S. Patent Office. Two aids for using the "Manual of Classification" are the "Classification Bulletin of the United States Patent Office" and the "United States Patent Office Index to the Classification."

The specification of a United States or foreign patent, including the claims, constitutes the information one generally desires. If the patent files are not available, copies of patents may be obtained from the sources, and at the prices, indicated below.[1]

Australia

Commissioner of Patents, Department of Patents, Canberra, A.C.T.; 5 shillings per copy, post-free.

Austria

Osterreichisches Patentamt, Druckschriftenverschleiss, Kohlmarkt 8–10, Vienna 1; 10 Austrian shillings per copy (photocopies, 4.50 Austrian shillings per page, after original edition is exhausted).

Belgium

Service de la Propriété industrielle, 19 rue de la Loi, Brussels; 20 francs per copy, beginning with patent 493,079, January, 1950 (9.50 francs per page plus 15 francs postage for photocopies of previous patents).

Canada

Commissioner of Patents, Ottawa; 50 cents per copy for patents 445,931 to

[1] *Chem. Abstr.*, **51**:v (1957).

450,789 (1948) and all patents issued beginning Jan. 1, 1949 (estimates of cost of typewritten or photostatic copies of patents issued before that date can be obtained).

Czechoslovakia

Dr. Jaroslav Tušek, Advokátní poradna č. 10, Štěpanská 16, Pragua II; 7.40 koruny per copy.

Denmark

Direktorat for Patent-og, Varemaerkevaesenet,Nyropsgade 45, Copenhagen V; 3.00 kroner per copy.

France

Service d'Edition et de Vente des Publications Officielles, 39 rue de la Convention, Paris 15; 100 francs per copy plus 45 francs postage for one copy, 60 francs for two to five copies, and 90 francs for five to ten copies.

Germany

Deutsches Patentamt, Museuminsel 1, Munich 2 (marked "Girokonto bei der Landeszentralbank München Nr. 6/154"); 1.50 Deutsche marks per copy. An account can be maintained if an initial deposit is made of 50 Deutsche marks or more.

Great Britain

Comptroller, The Patent Office, Sale Branch, 25 Southampton Buildings, London W.C. 2; 3 shillings per copy, by international money order (photocopies of out-of-print patents not more than 50 years old are available for the same price).

Hungary

Országos Talámányi Hivatal, Sztálintér 4, Budapest V; 5 forint per copy (photocopies according to special rates).

India

Patents 1 to 45,000: Controller of Patents and Designs, 214 Lower Circular Road, Calcutta 17. Patents 45,001 and higher: Officer-in-charge, Government of India Book Depot, 8 Hastings St., Calcutta. Printed specifications published before Nov. 1, 1950, 1 rupee per copy; those published on or after that date, 2 rupees per copy.

Italy

Libreria dello Stato, Piazza G. Verdi, 10, Rome; 100 lire per copy.

Japan

Hataumei-Kyokai (Invention Association), c/o Patent Office, No. 1 San-nen-cho, Chivodaku, Tokyo; 10 yen per copy (photocopies are also available, the cost being determined for each application).

Netherlands

The Patent Office (Octrooiraad), Willem Witsenplein 6, The Hague; 1 florin per copy.

Norway

Styret for det Industrielle Rettsvern, Middelthuns gate 15b, Oslo; 1.50 kroner per copy plus postage (0.20 krone for ordinary mail, 0.75 krone registered).

Spain

Printed copies not available; send inquiries to Director, Registro de la Propriedad Industrial, Patio Atocha 1, Madrid.

Sweden

Kungl. Patent-och Registreringsverket, Stockholm 5; 2.00 kronor per copy if the patents contain drawings, otherwise 1.50 kronor (no charge for postage unless air mail is requested).

Switzerland

Bureau fédéral de la propriété intellectuelle, Berne; 1.50 francs for the first eight sheets plus 1.50 francs for the next twelve sheets, 1.50 francs for the next ten sheets, and 0.20 franc for each additional sheet (the cost is 1.00, 1.00, 1.00, and 0.20 franc, respectively, if a deposit is maintained).

U.S.S.R.

Our abstracts are obtained from *Byulleten Izobretenii,* where abstracts only appear (no more information than *Chemical Abstracts* gives). No information is available concerning the procurement of patent specifications.

United States

Commissioner of Patents, U.S. Patent Office, Washington 25, D.C.; 25 cents per copy. Payment must be made in United States specie, treasury notes, national-bank notes, post-office money orders, or certified checks.

Often the quickest way to get a copy of a foreign patent is to purchase a photoprint from the U.S. Patent Office, Washington, D.C. Photostatic copies of foreign patents, publications, and exhausted United States patents are furnished at the rate of 30 cents per print, small or large.

In purchasing copies of patents issued by the United States, it is convenient to buy and use coupons, procurable from the Commissioner of Patents, Patent Office, Washington, D.C., at 25 cents each, on which may be written the necessary data, such as the number of the patent. An account may be opened, or estimates may be obtained in advance.

Bound certified copies of the specifications and drawings of United States patents, as well as patents of certain foreign countries, may be found in some of the larger libraries outside Washington, as noted later.

Periodicals.[1] Summarized or abridged information regarding objects or processes patented is issued in a number of periodicals. These periodicals may be classified in three groups.

General Abstracting Journals. These include abstracts of many chemical patents (unfortunately, not all), in addition to other abstracts, giving the name of the patentee, the number of the patent, the country, the date, and the general nature of the patent. This often constitutes the only information regarding a patent which is published in a chemical journal. If details are desired, one must obtain a copy of the original patent. *Chemical Abstracts, Chemisches Zentralblatt, British Abstracts* and its predecessors, and *Chemiker-Zeitung* are examples of such publications.

In *Chemical Abstracts* (see discussion of this periodical in Chapter 6) the patents are included in the appropriate sections according to the subjects. The countries whose patents are covered (up to 1956) are shown in the directions above for obtaining copies.

All British, French, German, and United States patents of chemical interest are covered either by abstracts or by titles and references to previous abstracts (used when the subject has been previously patented in another country and an abstract published). For each of the other countries listed, only those chemical patents are reported which have been issued to individuals or companies resident in that country or in a country not in the list and which have not been found to correspond to patents previously issued in any country in the list.

The dates which accompany abstracts of United States and foreign patents are for the most part those used by the U.S. Patent Office in citing patents as references. These are: Australia* (accepted); Austria (*ausgegeben*); Belgium* (*brevet publié*); Canada* (issue); Czechoslovakia (*vydáno*); Denmark (*offentliggjort*); France (*publié*); Germany (*ausgegeben*); Great Britain (complete specification published); Hungary (*megjelent*); India (sealed); Italy (*concesso*); Japan (granted); Netherlands (*uitgegeven*);

---

[1] Von Hohenhoff, *J. Patent Office Soc.*, **17**:971 (1935), and **18**:49, 139 (1936), contains a bibliography of journals, books, and compilations which list and abstract patents.

Norway (*offentliggjort*); Spain (*concedida*); Sweden (*publicerat*); Switzerland (*veröffentlicht*); United States (issue).

These are for the most part actual or approximate publication dates. For the countries marked with an asterisk, the publication date is not conveniently ascertainable (e.g., it does not appear on the face of the patent); the date used, however, is usually not far from the publication date. Date of issue and date of publication are identical, or nearly so, for most countries. Application dates were used in abstracts for certain countries up to July 20, 1933. The dates given are useful for reference purposes (especially in working in the library and in ordering specifications).

The class is indicated for German, Austrian, and Swiss patents because otherwise it would be especially difficult to locate patent specifications in libraries.

In *Chemical Abstracts* each patent gives, in sequence, a short descriptive title, name(s) of the inventor(s), assignee (if any), and the date of issue, followed by the abstract. Patent abstracts were mostly very brief in the early years of *Chemical Abstracts*, but the present trend is toward more detail.

Chemical Abstracts contains the following abstract for the patent quoted earlier in this chapter:

Dialkylsulfoxides. Gustav A. Wetterholm and Kåre R. Fossan (to Nitroglycerin Aktiebolåget). U.S. 2,702,824, Feb. 22, 1955. See Brit. 737,575 (C.A. **50**, 9942*d*).

The reason for the omission of a detailed abstract in this case is that the following two abstracts had already been issued for equivalent patents granted in England and Sweden.

Dimethyl Sulfoxide by Oxidation of Dimethyl Sulfide. Nitroglycerin Aktiebolåget (G. A. Wetterholm and K. R. Fossan). **Swed.** 151,609. Sept. 27, 1955. The oxidation of dimethyl sulfide to dimethyl sulfoxide is performed with oxygen or oxygenous gas mixture under catalysis with nitrogen oxides, such as NO, NO_2, N_2O_3, N_2O_4, HNO_3 in liquid phase. The reaction is done in a column of which different examples are shown in the specification.

Dialkyl Sulfoxides. G. A. Wetterholm and K. R. Fossan (to Nitroglycerin Altiebolåget). **Brit.** 737,575, Sept. 28, 1955. Into a column 13 cm. long and 4.5 cm. diameter (packed with a material to increase the surface area) provided with a gas inlet tube at the bottom, dimethyl sulfide was introduced and a mixture of N_2O_3 and N_2O_4 was introduced at a rate to keep its concentration at 0.5%. The product was dimethyl sulfoxide. Similarly diethyl sulfoxide, dipropyl sulfoxide, and ethylpropyl sulfoxide were prepared. Drawings of the apparatus are included.

Journals on Industrial Chemistry. These contain notices, abstracts, or reviews of the more important patents, together with occasional discussions of general interest in patent practice.[1] In this case not all chemical patents are included but only those considered as being of most importance; the information given for each patent is correspondingly fuller. Such periodicals are not numerous.

Special Journals on Patents. These are made up of material devoted exclusively to patents, designs, trade-marks, and matters relating to them. Sources of such information include the official publications of the various patent offices.[2]

The *Official Gazette* of the U.S. Patent Office, which was first issued in 1872 and appears on Tuesday of each week, may be taken as an example. Government-depository libraries receive it. In it may be found the following items: condition of pending applications; decisions in patent and trade-mark cases; notices concerning patent suits; interference notices; abridgments of all patents, including classification and one or more claims; patentee and patent classification indexes; and trade-marks issued during the week. Wherever possible, drawings are shown. In addition, monthly alphabetical lists of patentees are published. Particulars for the year's patents are given in the annual report of the Commissioner of Patents, with which is included an index of patentees and inventions (now published separately). The invention index is far from being an adequate subject index, since the alphabetical list is based on titles of patents rather than on their contents.

For the patent quoted earlier, the following abridgment appeared in the *Official Gazette* in the issue containing the list of patents granted Tuesday, February 22, 1955:

2,702,824. Liquid-Vapor Phase Method for Producing Lower Dialkyl Sulfoxides. Gustav Allan Wetterholm and Kåre Ragnvald Fossan, Gyttorp, Sweden, assignors to Nitroglycerin Aktiebolåget, Gyttorp, Sweden, a company. Filed August 18, 1952. Serial No. 305,044. 6 Claims. 5 Figures.

[1] E. J. Crane, A. M. Patterson, and E. B. Marr, "A Guide to the Literature of Chemistry," p. 171, John Wiley & Sons, Inc., New York, 1957.

[2] See Smith's bibliography for a list, *Ind. Eng. Chem.*, **16**:527 (1924).

1. In the manufacture of low-molecular dialkyl sulfoxides, the process which comprises establishing and maintaining in a reaction zone a body of liquid which at the start of the process consists of a liquid low-molecular dialkyl sulfide; this liquid dialkyl sulfide being converted into liquid dialkyl sulfoxide during the course of the reaction; introducing a small amount, sufficient only to catalyze the oxidizing reaction, of a catalyst, selected from the group consisting of NO, NO_2, N_2O_3, N_2O_4 and HNO_3 of at least 99% concentration, maintaining the liquid reaction mixture at a temperature below the boiling point of the liquid reaction mixture while passing therethrough an oxygen-containing gas at a rate below that causing discoloration of the vapor above the reaction liquid, whereby the oxidation of dialkyl sulfide takes place exclusively in the reaction liquid, and recovering the resulting dialkyl sulfoxide.

The British *Official Journal* (1889–   ), supplemented by the *Illustrated Abridgements*, the German *Patentblatt* (1877–   ), with its supplement *Auszüge aus den Patentschriften* (1880–   ), and the French *Bulletin officiel de la propriété industrielle et commerciale* (1884–   ) are similar publications differing somewhat in details.[1]

Court Records. Barrows states:[2]

Valuable information may likewise be obtained from many of the court records of patent cases and even from the court decisions in such cases, inasmuch as a consideration of the patentability, in view of prior patents and publications, is almost always raised in such cases. Extended searches are usually made in connection with such litigation and the pertinent results thereof made a part of the record of the cases. The testimony forming a part of the court records may likewise contain valuable information.

These cases generally involve patentability, infringement, interference, and injunctions.

Lists of Patents. In addition to the publications just described, there are available several works which are either indexes to or lists of chemical patents. Of these the following are probably most important:

1. *Census Bulletin* 210, U.S. Patents prior to 1902. This was also issued as Special Reports on Selected Industries, *Census Reports*, vol. 10, Twelfth Census of the United States, Manufactures, part 4.

[1] For further information concerning foreign patents, see A. D. Roberts, "Guide to Technical Literature," chap. 6, Grafton & Company, London, 1939; and B. Severance, "Manual of Foreign Patents," Washington Patent Office Society, Washington, 1935.

[2] *Chem. Met. Eng.*, **24**:517 (1921).

2. "U.S. Patents Granted to Germans and Austrians," yearbook for 1918 of the *Oil, Paint and Drug Reporter*.

3. Doyle, "Digest of Patents Relating to Coal Tar Dyes and Allied Compounds," Chemical Publishing Co., New York, 1926. This set, planned to be five volumes, covers "All U.S. Patents (to 1924) not only dyes and intermediates, but on methods of dye application as well. A selected group of finished products, other than dyes is also included. Under it are listed explosives, flavors and perfumes, medicinals, photochemicals, plastics and tanning."

4. Friedlander, "Fortschritte der Teerfarbenfabrikation und verwandter Industriezweige," Springer-Verlag OHG, Berlin, 1888–1942. This work covers all branches of synthetic coal-tar chemistry for German patents issued since 1877. The complete text is given, including subject, patentee, and numerical indexes, together with a collective numerical index of preceding volumes in each of the later volumes beginning with vol. 4. Twenty-five volumes cover the period 1877 to 1942.

5. Winther, "Patente der Organischen Chemie," Topelmann Verlag, Giessen, Germany, 1908–1910. This work includes German patents from 1877 to 1905 on dyestuffs and other organic chemicals along with separate lists of patents on organic chemistry from 1895 to 1908 for the United States, Great Britain, France, Austria, and Russia.

6. Bräuer and D'Ans, "Fortschritte in der anorganisch-chemischen Industrie," Springer-Verlag OHG, Berlin, 1921–1939. For inorganic chemistry this work is comparable to Friedlander's, covering the period 1877 to 1940, in five volumes.

7. Worden, "Chemical Patents Index," Chemical Catalog Co., New York, 1927–1934. Worden's compilation, in five volumes, includes the chemical subject matter of the 398,377 United States patents granted during the 10-year period 1915 to 1924, of which 22,882 patents have been exhaustively indexed, together with the reissues.

8. "Patents Owned by the Chemical Foundation, Inc. . . . grouped according to the classification adopted by the U.S. Patent Office," the Chemical Foundation, Inc., New York, 1925. The Chemical Foundation made available an index of 40,000 references to its patents. These include patentees, assignees, chemicals, processes, apparatus, uses, and patents of this and other countries.

9. Lange, "Die Zwischenprodukte der Teerfarbenfabrikation," O. Spamer, Leipzig, 1920. This is a summary of the patented methods for making aromatic intermediates.

10. Randall and Watson, "Finding List for United States Patent, Design, Trade-mark, Reissue, Label, Print, and Plant Patent Numbers," University of California Press, Berkeley, Calif., 1938.

11. Other lists. A number of additional lists are available in books, periodicals, and other publications in the form of bibliographies, as part of the discussion of some special topic. Examples of these may be found in the following works: C. W. Bedford and H. A. Winkelmann, "Systematic Survey of Rubber Chemistry," Chemical Catalog Company, New York, 1923; C. Ellis, "Synthetic Resins and Their Plastics," Chemical Catalog

Company, Inc., New York, 1923; E. Hemming, "Plastics and Molded Electrical Insulation," Chemical Catalog Company, Inc., New York, 1923; and E. C. Worden, "The Technology of Cellulose Ethers," Worden Laboratory and Library, Millburn, N.J., 1933.

Making Patent Searches

The various indexes and lists of patents just described, together with the various abstracting journals (see Chapter 6) and publications of the patent offices, are very valuable for making patent searches. From abstracts located through patentee, subject, and numerical indexes one can very often determine whether a patent is of interest. Copies can then easily be obtained from the U.S. Patent Office. There are probably just as many cases where an abstract is too brief to reveal the significance of the patent.

The United States patents are arranged in some 300 classes, identified by number and title. Then there are more than 50,000 subclasses, which form the basic units for searching.[1] For the patent quoted earlier, the class number is 260-607. The class, 260, is "Chemistry, carbon compounds"; and the subclass, 607, is "Sulfur, selenium, or tellurium containing."

One may order from the Patent Office, at a cost of 25 cents per sheet, copies of the lists (numbers) of original patents contained in the subclasses comprising the field of search and inspect printed copies of the patents in any of the following libraries:

Albany, N.Y., University of the State of New York
Atlanta, Ga., Georgia Institute of Technology
Boston, Mass., Public Library
Buffalo, N.Y., Grosvenor Library
Chicago, Ill., Public Library
Cincinnati, Ohio, Public Library
Cleveland, Ohio, Public Library
Columbus, Ohio, The Ohio State University
Denver, Colo., Public Library
Detroit, Mich., Public Library
Kansas City, Mo , Linda Hall Library
Los Angeles, Calif., Public Library
Madison, Wis., State Historical Society Library
Milwaukee, Wis., Public Library
Minneapolis, Minn., Public Library
Newark, N.J., Public Library

[1] See "Manual of Classification" and the indexes of classes and subclasses, Government Printing Office, Washington, D.C.

New York, N.Y., Public Library
Philadelphia, Pa., Franklin Institute
Pittsburgh, Pa., Carnegie Library
Providence, R.I., Public Library
St. Louis, Mo., Public Library
San Francisco, Calif., Public Library
Seattle, Wash., Public Library
Toledo, Ohio, Public Library

If a really comprehensive search of the patent literature is to be made, however, it is probably best to utilize the facilities of the U.S. Patent Office itself. This, of course, necessitates a visit in person by the inquirer or the agent to whom he delegates the search. One well-known chemist has stated that

it is, as a rule, advisable to confide this (the search) to some well-known reputable patent attorney, not only versed in patent law, but also possessing more than a passing acquaintance with chemistry, since the methods employed for locating foreign and other patent references call for specialized training.

Searching Facilities at the U.S. Patent Office. In an article discussing the patent literature as a source of information Smith states:[1]

For searching purposes, the most important patents are those of the United States, Great Britain, Germany and France. Switzerland and Austria come next. Dutch, Scandinavian, British colonial and Japanese printed specifications are less important but not to be forgotten. They are given a minor rating for two reasons: first, they are not numerous, and second, many of them are duplications from larger countries. The common practice of patenting valuable inventions in many countries is responsible for much duplication.

To the searcher, the one vital feature of patent publications is the manner in which they are classified or indexed. The U.S. Patent Office has an elaborate classification which is constantly being revised. It is essentially a functional classification; that is, first consideration is given to the function performed by a device and not to its structural, physical or chemical features. The classification of a given patent is based solely on the claims; but there is a system of copious cross references to guide the searchers to like patents in other classes and to matter appearing in specifications but not in claims.

Searchers in the U.S. Patent Office have access to files of printed specifications arranged according to this classification. The *Annual*

[1] *Chem. Met. Eng.*, **34**:160 (1927).

Report of the Commissioner of Patents includes an index of patentees and assignees, and a title index in which entries are made from the leading word of the patent title. As a subject index, this is worth hardly anything. Therefore, as far as Patent Office publications are concerned, the searcher must rely on classification. This has its advantages, and searching is greatly facilitated by the cross references; but there is the inherent disadvantage of all classifications in the fact that many patents are capable of being classified in more than one way. This compels the searcher to go through all the subclasses in which his topic might appear.

The British classification is much simpler. It also is largely functional but does not adhere strictly to that idea. To search British patents solely by classes would be comparatively tedious; but the Office has been diligent in providing other searching aids. These include the "Subject Matter Index," going back to 1617; the numbers prior to 1884 are mostly out of print and can be consulted only in libraries. Then there is the "Fifty Years, Subject Index," from 1861 to 1910, in 271 parts for the 271 sub-classes. These may be had at 6d. each. From 1911 on there are annual subject indexes, not classified; and in each current year quarterly subject indexes are issued. An additional searching aid is the series of "Illustrated Abridgments of Specifications." For each of nine periods from 1855 to 1908, these occupy 146 volumes corresponding to the 146 divisions of the old classification. The revised classification is in 271 parts, so there are 271 volumes after 1908. Classified abridgments are easier to search than complete specifications; but the limitations imposed by the necessary omission of detail must be duly considered.

The German classification is somewhat more elaborate than the British, but much simpler than the American. It has been adopted by several patent offices in the smaller countries. A translation appeared some years ago as a U.S. Government document; and the British Patent Office has published a "Key to the Classifications of the Patent Specifications of France, Germany, Austria, Netherlands, Norway, Denmark, Sweden and Switzerland."

In reviewing official journals, such as the U.S. *Official Gazette,* to find patents of probable interest, the reviewer must keep in mind the universal desire of inventors to get as much protection as possible. This desire gives rise to the custom of couching patents in general terms, in order to cover all the ground the Patent Office will allow. Thus, a jointed doll becomes an articulated toy; a vacuum tube is an electron discharge device; a child's scooter is a two-wheeled vehicle, etc. By reason of this custom, the specific purpose of a patent is often totally concealed in the title, and may be difficult or impossible to find in the abridgment. Sometimes the illustration tells the secret; or there may be a clue in the name and business of the assignee, or even in the inventor's address. Thus, a patent from Detroit is likely to have an automotive slant; and one from Akron is almost sure to have some relation to rubber, oatmeal or fishing tackle. When the official journal gives no clue, it becomes necessary to refer to the printed specification and drawings to ascertain the specific nature of the invention.

For some special fields of invention there are unpublished unofficial guides which supplement the functions of the official publications. Chemical technology is particularly well equipped in this respect. In the field of mechanical inventions, on the other hand, the main reliance must be placed on searching the classified specifications, or the indexed abridgments themselves. As pointed out by a former patent examiner, this difference is a natural consequence of the inherent difficulty of searching chemical patents which, unlike mechanical inventions, cannot be illustrated by drawings.

One of the principal aids to chemical searching is to be found in the U.S. Patent Office. This is the chemical card index, started in 1899 by Dr. A. E. Hill of the corps of examiners. It contains over a million cards, from patents and the general literature of chemistry, divided into a subject index and a formula index. Unfortunately it was discontinued in 1919.[1]

In addition to the classified patents, other valuable facilities are available at the Patent Office. Concerning these, Barrows states:[2]

In making searches at the Patent Office at Washington, not only does the searcher have available the classified patents (U.S.), but he has access to the files of such patents containing the various Patent Office proceedings leading up to the irgrant, including the original application papers and amendments thereto, and the official communications of the examiners who examined the application, in which are references to the prior patents and publications which the examiners found on their search and considered relevant to the invention sought to be patented. By examining the files of U.S. patents which are of nearest subject matter to the investigation in question, it may be possible to obtain reference to prior patents or publications which are of particular interest and which would not be readily available elsewhere.

A further value of the patent files is the indication therein of the classification of the respective patents and the indication in the various official actions of the classification of the prior patents which are referred to therein. Attention may thus be directed not only to prior

---

[1] The cards have been donated to the University of Illinois Library, Urbana, Ill. See Chap. 8.

[2] *Op. cit.*, p. 518.

patents of relevant subject matter, but even to other classes of the Patent Office which might otherwise have been overlooked but which may contain patents of interest. The number of classes and subclasses is so great and the classification of patents is in many instances so complex that relevant classes or subclasses may well be overlooked unless special precautions are taken to insure their proper consideration.

Likewise available at the Patent Office (in addition to approximately three million patents of about fifteen other countries), are the records of interference proceedings in which issued patents have been involved— records which in some cases contain lists of prior patents and publications relating to the same subject matter as the patent, in others testimony of interest in connection with the patented invention.

In conclusion, Smith states:[1]

The searcher who can go to the Patent Office has every advantage. The large and comprehensive library of the Patent Office provides the necessary technical literature and works of reference; complete classified files of United States patents are available; and there is a nearly complete collection of the printed specifications and official publications of all the patent offices of the world. The chemical card index has already been mentioned. Experienced translators are at hand, to iron out difficulties with foreign patents, even in the uncommon and lesser known languages. And last but not least, the searcher has at his service one of the leading technical libraries of America. When a desired reference is not to be found in the Patent Office, it can generally be located in one of the numerous scientific and technical libraries of government departments and bureaus in Washington.

Excepting for the classified files of United States patents, searching facilities are nearly as good in and around New York City. The New York Public Library has the printed specifications of several countries, and official journals of several more. It also has a splendid reference library; and so have the Chemists' Club and the Engineering Societies.

ADDITIONAL REFERENCES ON PATENTS

Allis-Chalmers Company: "Patent Background for Engineers," Allis-Chalmers, Milwaukee, Wis., 1955.

Amdur, L. H.: "Patent Fundamentals," Chemical Publishing Company, Inc., New York, 1948.

Baker, B.: "Outline of Patent Office Interference Practice," 1955.

Berle, A. K., and L. S. de Camp: "Inventions and Their Management," International Textbook Company, Scranton, Pa., 1951.

Biesterfeld, C. H.: "Patent Law for Lawyers, Students, Chemists, and Engineers," John Wiley & Sons, Inc., New York, 1949.

[1] *Op. cit.*, p. 161.

Callman, R.: "The Law of Unfair Competition and Trade-marks," Callaghan, Chicago, 1950.

Calvert, R. P.: "Patent Practice and Management for Inventors and Executives," Reinhold Publishing Corporation, New York, 1950.

Fleischer, J.: Exploring United States Chemical Patent Literature and Exploring Foreign Chemical Patent Literature, *Advances in Chem. Ser. No. 4*, pp. 61, 81 (1951).

Hayes, J. E. R.: "The Nature of Patentable Inventions, Its Attributes and Definition," Addison-Wesley Publishing Company, Cambridge, Mass., 1948.

Hoar, R. S.: "Patent Tactics and Law," The Ronald Press Company, New York, 1950.

"Information for Patentees," Patent Office, London.

"Instructions to Applicants for Patents," Patent Office, London.

Keiper, F.: "Pioneer Inventions and Pioneer Patents," privately published, 1923.

Lanham, B. E.: Chemical Patent Searches, *Ind. Eng. Chem.*, **43**:2494 (1951).

————: Services Available from the Patent Office, *Special Libraries*, **46**:25 (1955).

Laughlin, M. P.: "Money from Ideas: A Primer on Inventions and Patents," Popular Mechanics Press, Chicago, 1950.

Lindenmeyer, H. F.: What Does the Patent Office Scientific Library Have to Offer the Chemist? *J. Patent Office Soc.*, **36**:463 (1954).

Marx, C.: Chemical Patent Searches, *Chem. Age*, **31**:393 (1923).

Michel, A. J.: "Dictionary of Intellectual Property," Research Patent and Trade-marks, New York, 1954.

Muller, E.: "Chemie und Kontinental Patentrecht," Verlag Chemie, G.m.b.H., Weinheim, Germany, 1932.

————: "Chemie und Patentrecht," Verlag Chemie, G.m.b.H., Weinheim, Germany, 1928.

Potts, H. E.: "Patents and Chemical Research," University Press, Liverpool, 1921.

————: "Patents, Invention and Method," Open Court Publishing Co., London, 1924.

Rivise, C. W.: "The Preparation and Prosecution of Patent Applications," Michie Company, Charlottesville, Va., 1933.

————: What Is Patentable in Industrial and Engineering Chemistry, *Ind. Eng. Chem.*, **23**:580 (1931).

Rivise, C. W., and A. D. Caesar: "Interference Law and Practice," Michie Company, Charlottesville, Va., 1940–1948.

Rossman, J.: "The Law of Patents for Chemists," Inventor's Publishing Co., Washington, D.C., 1934.

————: What the Chemist Should Know about Patents, *J. Chem. Educ.*, **9**:486 (1932).

Sadtler, R. E.: Foreign Patents on Foreign Inventions, *Ind. Eng. Chem.*, *News Ed.*, **16**:190 (1938).

Schapp, A.: "Patent Fundamentals: A Textbook for Inventors, Executives, and Students," The Industrial Press, New York, 1939.

Smith, J. F.: Patent Literature as a Source of Information, *Chem. Met. Eng.*, **34**:160 (1927).
———: Patent Reference Sources, *Ind. Eng. Chem.*, **16**:527 (1924).
Thomas, E.: "Chemical Inventions and Chemical Patents," Clark Boardman Company, Ltd., New York, 1950.
Toulmin, H. A.: "Handbook of Patents," W. H. Anderson Co., Cincinnati, Ohio, 1954.
U.S. Patent Office: "General Information Concerning Patents," 1956.
———: "Manual of Patent Examining Procedure," 1949.
———: "Patent Laws," 1955.
———: "Rules of Practice," 1955.
———: "Story of the Patent Office, 1790–1956," 1956.
Untiedt, F. H.: Some Aspects of Chemical Patent Searches, *Ind. Eng. Chem.*, **21**:689 (1929).
Van Doren, L.: Organization of the Patent Office, *J. Chem. Educ.*, **6**:536 (1929).
Vaughn, F. L.: "The United States Patent System," University of Oklahoma Press, Norman, Okla., 1956.
Vojacek, J.: "A Survey of the Principal National Patent Systems," Prentice-Hall, Inc., Englewood Cliffs, N.J., 1936.
Wade, W.: "Patents for Technical Personnel," Chemonomics, New York, 1957.
White, W. W., and B. G. Ravenscroft: "Patents throughout the World," Trade Activities, New York, 1948.
Wise, J. K.: "Patent Law in the Research Laboratory," Reinhold Publishing Corporation, New York, 1955.
Woodling, G. V.: "Inventions and Their Protection," Clark Boardman Company, Ltd., New York, 1954.

CHAPTER 5

PRIMARY SOURCES—
MISCELLANEOUS CONTRIBUTIONS

Those who cannot remember the past are condemned to repeat it.—
Santayana

There are two other types of publications hardly belonging in the previous chapters. Their total number is not large, and often the material in an individual publication is not extensive; but the information may be important, and they should not be overlooked.

Dissertations

For many years candidates for the doctoral degree in philosophy or science were usually required to publish their dissertations and to deposit a specified number of copies in the library of the institution granting the degree. Most of the copies were distributed to important libraries. In some cases an entire dissertation was published in a journal. Then reprints of the article were accepted as fulfilling the deposition requirement. In these instances the information may be found in the appropriate journal.

Very often, however, a detailed account of the work is so long that only lengthy abstracts or abridgments, giving the most important contributions, are published in journals. Then one must obtain a copy of the dissertation to consult details of the work.

Until recently these publications have not been easy to locate. As far as the author is aware, no general list of all dissertations is available, even by title. Since 1938 *Chemical Abstracts* has been including titles of dissertations issued by University Microfilms.[1]

The service of University Microfilms was begun in 1938, and

[1] Ann Arbor, Mich.

now nearly 70 graduate schools are cooperating. The author of a dissertation writes a summary of not over 600 words. This summary is printed in *Dissertation Abstracts*, published monthly by University Microfilms and distributed on a subscription basis. At the same time that the abstract is printed, the complete dissertation is microfilmed. This provides for reproduction of positive copies, which may be purchased from University Microfilms.[1]

Locating dissertations written before the establishment of this abstracting and reproducing service may be a real problem. If a copy is in a given library, it will be shown, of course, by the card catalogue of the library. Frequently, in such cases, one learns of the existence of the dissertation through references to it in articles or bibliographies.

The Library of Congress accumulated many thousands of dissertations from European universities. These publications are now in the Midwest Inter-Library Center in Chicago.

There have been some compilations of dissertation titles, and in recent years some effort has been made to publish annual lists. Generally such lists give only the title, and every experienced searcher knows how ambiguous titles can be. At best a brief abstract or digest may be included. Some dissertations are listed under the name of the institution granting the degree.

The following sources are of some use.

Canada

"Canadian Theses: A List Accepted by Canadian Universities," National Library, Ottawa, 1952.

France

"Catalogue des thèses et écrits académiques," Ministère de l'instruction publique, 1885–   . This is the annual official French list. Apparently it was discontinued in 1929, to be superseded by "Bibliographie de la France; ou, Journal générale de l'imprimerie et de la librairie," Paris, 1930–   .

Germany

"Bibliographischer Monatsbericht über neuerschienene Schul-, Universität- und Hochschulschriften," Fock, Leipzig, 1889–   . A classified list, with indexes.
"Deutsches Bücherverzeichnis," Börsenverein der deutschen Buchhändler, Leipzig, 1915–   . Printed dissertations listed by author, with subject index.

---

[1] The current price per page is $1\frac{1}{4}$ cents for a microfilm copy, or 10 cents for a paper enlargement.

"Jahres-verzeichnis der an den deutschen Universitäten und Hochschulen Erschienenen Schriften," Börsenverein der deutschen Buchhändler, Leipzig, 1885–   . In this standard official German list the arrangement varies somewhat with each issue.

Mundt, H.: "Bio-bibliographisches Verzeichnis von Universitäts- und Hochschuldrucken vom Ausgang des 16 bis Ende des 19 Jahrhunderts," Carlsohn, Leipzig, 1934–   . Chiefly German universities are included, but some Swedish and Netherlands universities are also listed.

Great Britain

"Index to Theses Accepted for Higher Degrees in the Universities of Great Britain and Ireland," Aslib, London, 1950–   . This is an annual list.

Switzerland

"Jahresverzeichnis der schweizerischen Hochschulschriften," Verlag der Universitätsbibliothek, Basel, Switzerland, 1897–   . The list is arranged by universities.

United States

"A List of American Doctoral Dissertations," U.S. Government Printing Office, 1912–1938. This is an annual list of publications acquired by the Library of Congress.

"ACS Directory of Graduate Research," American Chemical Society, Washington, D.C., 1955. Faculties, publications, and doctoral theses are listed for departments of chemistry, chemical engineering, and biochemistry at universities in the United States.

"Doctoral Dissertations Accepted by American Universities," The H. W. Wilson Company, New York, 1933–   . An annual list arranged alphabetically by subjects and, under subjects, by institutions and authors.

Doctorates Conferred in Sciences by American Universities, *Bull. Natl. Research Council; Reprint and Circ. Ser.*, no. 12 (1920); no. 26 (1921); no. 42 (1922);[1] no. 75 (1926); no. 80 (1927); no. 86 (1928); no. 91 (1929); no. 95 (1930); no. 101 (1931); no. 104 (1932); no. 105 (1933). The listing is alphabetical by subjects and, under subjects, by institutions and authors.

Bolton, H. C.: A Select Bibliography of Chemistry, 1492–1897, sec. 8, Academic Dissertations, *Smithsonian Inst. Publs. Misc. Collections*, no. 1253 (1901). The list contains the printed dissertations of France, Germany, Russia, and the United States, by authors, with subject index.

Marr, E. B.: Theses and Dissertations, *Advances in Chem. Ser. No. 4*, p. 51 (1951).

[1] For the years 1922–1926, see Hull and West, *J. Chem. Educ.*, **3**:77 (1926); **4**:99 (1927).

Palfrey, T. R., and H. E. Coleman, Jr.: "Guide to Bibliographies of Theses, United States and Canada," American Library Association, Chicago, 1936. Included are a general list, lists for special fields, and lists for institutions.

Manufacturers' Technical Publications

Many manufacturers of materials and equipment used in scientific and technical work issue pamphlets or circulars dealing with the construction and use of new apparatus, appliances, materials, and processes. These bulletins serve partly as advertising but more as technical information. Often there is included a summary of the theory of the construction and operation of scientific apparatus, together with instructions for using the apparatus for its intended purpose. Accompanying the description may be a bibliography of references relating to the apparatus and its applications. Along with current advertising, these publications constitute the latest published announcements of producers.

Many of these publications are quite technical in nature. Many more are designed to acquaint the public with the product described. They are of particular value to teachers of undergraduate students as an authoritative statement concerning the nature and applications of new products.[1]

As an example of the activities of one firm in this direction, the Leeds and Northrup Company issues such publications on the theory, design, and use of their instruments. Folders, data sheets, catalogue excerpts, reprints, and technical publications are included. Three such publications are "Temperature Measurement with Rayotubes," "Thermoelectric Thermometry," and "New Horizons with Speedomax."

Another example is the series of Solvay technical bulletins issued by the Solvay Process Division of the Allied Chemical and Dye Corporation. Typical titles are "Soda Ash," "Liquid Chlorine," "Water Analysis," and "Calcium Chloride."

Various names are used for this kind of publication. Examples are "trade literature,"[2] "house organs,"[3] "data sheets," "package circulars," and "sales-development brochures." "Customer magazines" is another name employed.

[1] See Kessel, *J. Chem. Educ.*, **31**:255 (1954), for a list of such literature.

[2] See L. V. E. Cheyney, *Advances in Chem. Ser. No. 4*, pp. 126–131 (1951).

[3] See L. F. Lederman, *Advances in Chem. Ser. No. 4*, pp. 104–111 (1951).

If these publications are filed at all in libraries, usually the collection is small. Ordinarily the best way to obtain late copies is to write the concerns advertising in periodicals or taking space in trade catalogues. Some companies maintain a permanent mailing list upon which one may have his name placed, thus ensuring the receipt of the latest bulletins. For convenience some periodicals include with their advertising cutout or tear-out mailing cards for use in sending for such industrial literature. Each notice or advertisement is numbered so that one has only to encircle the appropriate numbers and mail the card. Thus, *Chemical and Engineering News* maintains a readers' information service for such purposes.

A systematic scheme has been suggested for cataloguing such engineering trade literature according to unit operations.[1]

[1] Vilbrandt, *J. Chem. Educ.*, **10**:354 (1933).

CHAPTER 6

SECONDARY SOURCES—
PERIODICALS AND SERIALS

All that mankind has done, thought, gained or been—it is lying, as in magic preservation, in the pages of books.—*Carlyle*

The various types of publications already considered constitute the primary sources of chemical information. This does not imply that they are of greater importance than those which remain to be discussed. Such publications, as a rule, contain material that is new, or at least previously unpublished. From our consideration of the nature, number, and variety of these primary sources, it is evident that the facts relating to some given subject will, in all probability, be widely scattered and, as a consequence of this, be difficult to locate when needed. The material included in them is necessarily unorganized. At the present time the separate and distinct published chemical items of some significance— that is, papers, bulletins, patents, and others—must number millions, when we reflect that *Chemical Abstracts* contained about 100,000 abstracts in 1957.

The publications considered in this chapter, together with several more following, have been termed "secondary sources," since they contain information compiled from one or more of the primary sources and arranged according to some definite plan. This material, then, is essentially organized in its nature. The general object in issuing such publications is to provide means for collecting, classifying, arranging, and discussing the scattered myriads of facts already recorded, so that the most efficient use may be made of the results of others' work. These secondary sources consist of periodicals or serials, bibliographies, reference works, monographs, and textbooks. Those appearing periodically are considered in this chapter.

Periodicals and Serials

With the rapid increase in the number of primary sources, together with the accompanying extension in the amount included in them, it became very desirable to have some agency for collecting, classifying, and summarizing this material as soon as possible after its appearance. No individual or small group of individuals is capable of performing such a task. Comprehensive efforts in this direction are limited mostly to scientific societies.

Depending upon the information furnished and upon the method of arrangement used, the periodicals supplying this kind of information have been grouped under the headings of index serials, abstracting journals, and review serials.

Index Serials

Index serials contain compilations of references only, including the author's name, the title of the article, and the citation to the original. Their general function is to serve as an index by means of which one may easily find scientific papers.

Some individuals may be inclined to put index serials and bibliographies in the same class. In the sense that they are both lists of references, this is justified. The two have been separated, however, upon the general basis that index serials are periodical publications and are devoted to some general field of scientific endeavor. Bibliographies, on the other hand, are not periodical publications, and they relate to some specific subject in one field of science.

There seems to be no index serial devoted to chemistry alone. Since the boundaries of chemistry, as well as other sciences, are more or less vague and since these publications cover science in general, or some broad technical field, a search through them may be valuable when made in connection with a search in abstracting journals. Several index serials will be considered briefly.

J. D. Reuss, *Repertorium commentationum a societatibus litterariis editarum* . . . , t. 3. *Chemia et res metallica* Dieterich (1803). This work is an index to the publications of the learned societies of various countries from the founding of the society to 1800.

Catalog of Scientific Papers (1800–1900; name changed in 1900 to *International Catalog of Scientific Literature*). The Royal

Society had under way what was termed the "most comprehensive index to general science ever attempted." Although a number of volumes were issued, publication of the work ceased.

Repertorium der technischen Journal-literatur. Appearing first as an annual publication in 1874, the *Repertorium der technischen Journal-literatur* had been issued previously, under the name of *Repertorium der technischen Literatur* prior to 1879, in three volumes covering the period back to 1823. The German Patent Office issued it from 1877 to its discontinuance in 1908. Many references were included. The arrangement is alphabetical by subjects.

Engineering Index (1884–   ). In *Engineering Index*[1] papers are listed by title. It is valuable for information on costs and finance and management of industrial concerns. Its particular interest is technical and engineering subjects, so that one may expect to find some information relating to certain phases of applied chemistry.

From 1884 to 1905 four volumes were issued; since that time the index has been an annual publication. Most of the approximately 1,200 journals covered are in the English language.

For some years the purely indexing function has been extended by Engineering Index Service. This is really an abstracting service. For each article indexed there is prepared a 3- by 5-in. card carrying essentially the same kind of information as an abstract in *Chemical Abstracts*. One may then subscribe to the whole service or to any one of more than 300 subdivisions. About 60 of these are of definite chemical interest. This method of operation is relatively expensive.

Industrial Arts Index (1913–   ).[2] The *Industrial Arts Index* is issued in magazine form as an indexing service to over 200 technical journals, mostly American, which are selected by the subscribers as the leaders in their respective fields. The entries deal with technical articles and descriptions of new apparatus and machinery relating to engineering, electrical appliances, chemistry, business, printing, and textiles and are arranged alphabetically by subject under sufficient subject headings to bring out the points of interest.

[1] Different names have been used.

[2] In 1958 to be divided into *Applied Science and Technology Index* and *Business Periodicals Index.*

Agricultural Index (1916–   ). The *Agricultural Index* is a monthly subject index to over 115 agricultural periodicals, publications of the U.S. Department of Agriculture and of American state and foreign agricultural experiment stations, and, occasionally, other literature.

Current Chemical Papers (1954–   ). This new periodical is intended to inform chemists of new work more quickly than an abstract journal. It is designed to serve as a guide to a chemist's reading. The titles are classified in 13 sections. The entries are obtained by scanning some 300 periodicals.

Index Medicus (1879–   ). In 1879 the librarian of what is now the National Library of Medicine[1] started the *Index Medicus* as a current index of periodical publications on medicine. A *Current List of Medical Literature* is issued monthly to cover periodical articles. It is now running more than 100,000 titles annually. There are semiannual cumulative subject and author indexes. An annual catalogue is issued for the book accessions to this great library.

Reader's Guide (1900–   ). Articles of a popular nature, appearing in more than 115 nonchemical periodicals, may be found through the *Reader's Guide*.

Abstracting Journals

Abstracting journals contain contemporaneous, concise summaries of the various articles, bulletins, patents, and other contributions already mentioned.

Each abstract ordinarily furnishes the following information: title of original contribution abstracted, author's name, original reference (that is, number and designation of a bulletin; abbreviation, series, volume, page, and year of journal; name of patentee, country, date, and number of a patent; or other suitable means to enable one to locate the original), and usually a brief summary of the main points or results brought out in the paper.[2]

Crane, Patterson, and Marr state:[3]

---

[1] Formerly Library of the Surgeon General's Office.

[2] For the relation of an abstract to its original, see G. M. Dyson, *Advances in Chem. Ser. No. 4*, pp. 26–29 (1951).

[3] E. J. Crane, A. M. Patterson, and E. B. Marr, "A Guide to the Literature of Chemistry," p. 124, John Wiley & Sons, Inc., New York, 1957.

The ideal abstracting journal (1) covers its field completely (2) publishes good annual and collective indexes (3) maintains a high quality in its abstracts, and (4) keeps its service prompt. All are important but it is believed that completeness and the publication of good indexes are of the most consequence.

There are two rather distinct types of abstracts.[1] The *indicative type* may either elaborate the title or describe the scope of a publication and its significant contributions. The *informative type* gives the information itself.

Publications constitute not only a means of communicating ideas but also a barrier between a discoverer and the potential user of the discovery. Generally the discoverer, as author, bears the responsibility of describing adequately his contribution. At this point the abstractor begins. Assuming that he fully comprehends the significance of the publication, the quality or value of the abstract depends very largely upon his skill in preparing an adequate summary.[2] In many cases he decides that the title is sufficient to indicate the probable value of the reference. Papers in foreign languages, and especially those in rare and inaccessible periodicals, are usually abstracted in more detail.

Next, the indexer has an important function to perform, for the compilation of an adequate and accurate index for the abstract is second only in importance to the preparation of the abstract itself.[3] Since one depends so much upon indexes in looking for material, an index must be dependable if nothing is to be missed. Finally the searcher must have the perseverance and ingenuity to find what has been written, abstracted, and indexed. His problem is discussed more fully in Chapter 11.

One very serious, and possibly insurmountable, difficulty connected with all abstracting journals is the failure to list or index what may be termed hidden facts. Unfortunately, titles and indexes often give no adequate indication of the nature of the material presented in a publication, and one is dependent upon the abstractor's judgment about what should be mentioned in

---

[1] M. Fleisher and M. Hooker, *J. Chem. Educ.*, **33**:27 (1956).

[2] See Crane, "In the Abstract," *Ind. Eng. Chem., News Ed.*, **16**:353 (1938). For the aid of abstractors, *Chemical Abstracts* provides detailed directions, available in pamphlet form, covering the preparation of abstracts.

[3] Bernier and Crane, *Ind. Eng. Chem.*, **40**:725 (1948).

the abstract. It frequently happens that dependence upon indexes causes one to miss important points. This will be mentioned again in a later section. But so far as their indexes are accurate, abstracting journals do enable one to ascertain what general references are available upon a given subject and where the original may be found, if details are desired. Frequently, of course, the information contained in the abstract is all that is required.

In connection with abstracts, borderline publications present at least two problems. The first concerns the editor of the abstracting periodical, who must decide whether the publication has sufficient chemical interest to warrant abstracting and indexing. The second concerns the searcher, who obviously cannot find the item in a given abstracting journal if no abstract was prepared. As an example we may consider analytical balances and spectrophotometers, both instruments being the product of the physicist and of primary theoretical interest to him from the standpoint of mechanics and optics, respectively. Probably all new items on balances will be abstracted, since every chemist is familiar with the instrument. Certain analysts may be just as much interested in a new spectrophotometer, but until recently there was no assurance a publication on it would be included. The worker in this field had to watch suitable sources in physics as well as chemistry.

Abstracting all publications of chemical interest, or even most special fields, has become an undertaking of such magnitude that only an organization, such as a chemical society, can do it. Some of the larger chemical manufacturing firms have their library operate a private abstracting service. Generally such internal abstracts include only those thought (usually by the librarian) to be of interest to the research staff, and they are likely to be more detailed than those otherwise available.

Between the time of publication of an item in an original source and the appearance of an abstract of it there is an inevitable time lag, usually not less than 2 to 3 months or more than 1 year. Most delay is likely to be encountered in the rarer foreign periodicals. Abstract editors strive for promptness, but the distribution, writing, and printing processes take time.

Journals Publishing Abstracts. Abstracts appear in two kinds of journals: those devoted exclusively to abstracts and those whose contents consist partly of abstracts and partly of other items, mentioned when discussing periodicals in Chapter 2. The second type is found particularly in publications devoted to special fields; here, as one might expect, the abstracts are selected upon the basis of their importance to those engaged in the special work. Some of the more important general abstracting periodicals will now be considered briefly.

Chemical Abstracts. The American publication *Chemical Abstracts* will be considered first as it is devoted exclusively to this type of publication, and it is the most comprehensive periodical of its kind now appearing, considered from the standpoint of the number of abstracts and the sources of abstracts covered. Started in 1907 by the American Chemical Society to replace *Review of American Chemical Research* (published from 1897 to 1906), it appears on the 10th and 25th of each month, with the issues of December 10 and 25 devoted to the annual indexes. In 1920 an empirical formula index was added, covering both inorganic and organic compounds, and in 1935 a numerical patent index was added. Now a collective formula index covers the years 1920 to 1946. Collective patent-number indexes cover the periods 1907 to 1936 and 1937 to 1946, the patents being listed by countries. Individual issues carry author and numerical patent indexes.

At the time of this writing (1956), the staff of *Chemical Abstracts* consists of 1 editor, 20 associate editors, 50 assistant editors and advisers, 51 section editors, and nearly 1,500 abstractors. *Little C.A.* is issued several times a year as a family morale builder for this group.

Every 5 years since 1926 *Chemical Abstracts* has published a list giving the sources searched for abstracts. In 1956 this list[1] contained more than 7,000 entries. As far as possible there is included for each publication the name,[2] frequency of appearance, number of volumes per year, volume number for 1956, price, place of publication, and libraries in this country and Canada where it may be found.

In compiling the material, the field of chemistry is divided, as shown in the table on page 102, into 33 classes, for each of which one or more assistant editors is responsible. This enables one having special interests to locate easily the main references bearing upon his specialty. In each section appear, in the order given,

[1] See *Chem. Abstr.*, **51**:1$_J$ (1957).
[2] Many changes in title are included.

general abstracts, cross references to other sections, notices of new books, and patents. To facilitate finding a reference upon a given page[1] which has been located in the index, a small numerical or letter superscript is given for each page or column indicated. This superscript shows the nearest ninth of the page, counting downward, on which the abstract will be found. Abbreviations used may be found at the end of the subject-index volume.

FIG. 6. Home of *Chemical Abstracts*, Columbus, Ohio.

Decennial indexes have appeared regularly, the fifth covering the period 1947 to 1956. Users should familiarize themselves with the introductory sections of the decennial and subsequent annual subject indexes being examined. In addition to the general explanatory material, any changes from previous practice are given.

The rather special significance of abstracts of patents is considered in Chapter 4, under the heading "General Abstracting Journals."

Since 1950 the Japanese Patent Office has published only *Tokkyo Koho*, which gives the numbers of patents granted each year starting from 1. Sometime later this patent office plans to issue a supplementary index which will provide continuous patent

---

[1] Since 1934 a two-column page has been used. The superscripts refer to the separately numbered columns.

STATISTICS FOR 1955

	Number of abstracts	
	Papers	Patents
Apparatus, plant equipment, and unit operations......	1,514	309
General and physical chemistry.....................	7,400	
Electronic phenomena and spectra.................	3,712	56
Nuclear phenomena...............................	2,934	19
Electrochemistry.................................	1,338	326
Photography.....................................	332	216
Inorganic chemistry..............................	1,027	
Analytical chemistry.............................	2,812	16
Mineralogical and geological chemistry..............	2,149	
Metallurgy and metallography.....................	2,556	672
Organic chemistry................................	9,798	3,162
Biological chemistry..............................	22,710	32
Foods..	1,693	159
Chemical industry and miscellaneous industrial products	598	287
Water, sewage, and sanitation.....................	715	67
Soils and fertilizers...............................	1,206	55
Pesticides and crop-control agents..................	1,162	177
Fermentation industries...........................	751	59
Pharmaceuticals, cosmetics, and perfumes............	1,773	355
Acids, alkalies, salts, and other heavy chemicals.......	260	398
Glass, clay products, refractories, and enameled metals	739	189
Cement, concrete, and other building materials........	343	95
Fuels and carbonization products...................	1,011	316
Petroleum, lubricants, and asphalt.................	1,014	739
Cellulose and paper..............................	953	244
Explosives and explosions.........................	213	42
Dyes and textile chemistry........................	721	644
Paints, varnishes, lacquers, and inks................	454	201
Fats, fatty oils, waxes, and detergents..............	831	260
Sugar, starch, and gums..........................	425	53
Leather and glue................................	269	45
Rubber and other elastomers......................	589	145
Synthetic resins and plastics......................	662	588
Totals....................................	74,664	9,926
Books..	1,732	
New journals....................................	68	

numbers to replace or supplement the annual numbers. To avoid considerable delay, *Chemical Abstracts* uses the form "Japan. No. 4520 ('52), Dec. 12," which means that Japanese patent 4520 is granted on December 12, 1952.

Chemisches Zentralblatt. Because of the length of time covered, the *Zentralblatt* is probably the most important general abstracting journal. It started in 1830 as *Pharmaceutisches Zentralblatt*, changed to *Chemisch-Pharmaceutisches Centralblatt* in 1849, to *Chemisches Centralblatt* in 1856, and finally to *Chemisches Zentralblatt* in 1897. Publication lapsed in 1945 because of the war. Various efforts were later made to reestablish the journal, including a German and a Russian edition. Normal publication was resumed in 1952. The breaks are now covered by supplementary volumes.[1]

The journal was long published by the Deutsche Chemische Gesellschaft. In 1950 it became a joint project of the Deutsche Akademie der Wissenschaften (Berlin), the Chemische Gesellschaft (Soviet East Zone), the Akademie der Wissenschaften (Göttingen), and the Gesellschaft Deutscher Chemiker.

The abstracts as a whole are likely to be more detailed than those in *Chemical Abstracts*. Special features are the use of italics for the names of new compounds, a brief outline at the beginning of the volume for each division of chemistry covered, a list of numbers of patents mentioned, and statistical data on the abstracts included in the various divisions. A valuable feature is the list of equivalent patents for different countries.

References to the *Zentralblatt* usually have the form "*Chem. Zentr.* 1928 II, 789," which indicates year, part, and page (there being no volume number). Simply "*C*" may replace "*Chem. Zentr.*" "*D.R.P.*" means "*Deutsches Reichs-Patent.*"

Before 1919 no attempt was made to cover applied chemistry thoroughly, because early industrial abstracts appeared in *Angewandte Chemie* and the *Chemisch-technische Übersicht* of *Chemiker-Zeitung*.

Collective indexes are shown in a combined table for the three general abstracting journals. Since the formula indexes use the Richter system, only organic compounds are included.

---

[1] See Pflücke, *Chem. Tech. (Berlin)*, **6**:125 (1954), for a brief history of this famous periodical. For a list of periodicals abstracted, see M. Pflücke and A. Hawelek, "Periodica Chimica," Verlag Chemie, G.m.b.H., Weinheim, Germany, 1952.

British Abstracts. The two journals just described are the main current ones devoted entirely to general abstracts, but many others contain abstracts along with other material. Two of these deserve special attention because of their general nature. They are the *Journal of the Chemical Society* (London) and the *Journal of the Society of Chemical Industry* (London). Abstracts appeared first in the former journal in 1871, and a separate volume was devoted to them first in 1878. From then until 1926 the even-numbered volume for each year was devoted to abstracts on general, organic, and physical chemistry. The latter journal was started in 1882 and from the beginning included abstracts on all aspects of applied chemistry.

Beginning in 1926 the abstracting work of the two journals was combined in *British Chemical Abstracts*, Part *A*, pure chemistry, bound separately, and Part *B*, applied chemistry, bound as part of the *Journal of the Society of Chemical Industry* (name changed to *Chemistry and Industry*). Later the abstracting name was changed to *British Chemical and Physiological Abstracts*, and finally, in 1945, to *British Abstracts*. In 1944 Part *C*, Analysis and Equipment, was added. All the parts had subparts, generally paged separately. Finally, in 1953, this fine abstracting service was terminated.

The general quality of these English abstracts was high. Together they enable one to follow abstracts in the English language back to the dates given. *Chemical Abstracts* has consistently covered more periodicals. The indexes available are shown in the accompanying table. A list of periodicals abstracted was published in 1949.

Since 1953 what is left of *British Abstracts* appears in the following two journals:

1. *Journal of Applied Chemistry.* The abstracts are classified under (1) Chemical Engineering; (2) Fuel and Fuel Products; (3) Industrial Inorganic Chemistry; (4) Industrial Organic Chemistry; (5) Fats, Waxes, Detergents; (6) Fibres; and (7) Apparatus and Unclassified.

2. *Analytical Abstracts.* The abstracts are classified under (1) General Analytical Chemistry, (2) Inorganic Analysis, (3) Organic Analysis, (4) Biochemistry (five subdivisions), (5) General Technique and Laboratory Apparatus (four subdivisions).

Bulletin de la société chimique de France. This journal first included abstracts in 1863. From 1892 to 1933 even-numbered volumes contained the abstracts. Since that time this volume has been known as the "documentation volume." Since 1918

IMPORTANT CUMULATIVE INDEXES OF ABSTRACTS

Years covered	Kinds of indexes		
	Subject-Author	Formula	Patent
Chemical Abstracts:			
1907–1916	X		
1917–1926	X	X	X
1927–1936	X	X	X
1937–1946	X	X	X
1947–1956	X	X	X
Chemisches Zentralblatt:			
1870–1881	X		
1889			
1897–1901	X		
1902–1906	X		
1907–1911	X		
1912–1916	X		
1917–1921	X		
1922–1924	X	X	X
1925–1929	X	X	X
1930–1934	X	X	X
1935–1939	X	X	X
1940–1944	X	X	X
1945–1949	X	X	X
British Abstracts:			
1848–1872	X		
1873–1882	X		
1883–1892	X		
1893–1902	X		
1903–1912	X		
1913–1922	X		
1923–1932	X		
1933–1937	X		
1946		X	

French abstracts on applied chemistry have appeared in *Chimie & industrie* (Paris).

Referationyi Zhurnal, Khimiya. In 1952 Russia established the Institute of Scientific Information of the Academy of Sciences of the U.S.S.R. It publishes abstract journals on exact natural sciences and engineering covering publications of the world. The abbreviated name is *RZhKhim.*

Separate abstract journals are issued from a central office on the following subjects: astronomy and geodesy, biochemistry, biology, chemistry (established in 1953), geology and geography, mathematics, mechanics, and physics. To be added are electrical engineering, mechanical engineering, and metallurgy.

Practices of *Chemical Abstracts* have been followed somewhat, including use of the Hill system for formula indexes. The indexes include author and patent index for each issue; annual indexes for authors, subjects, patents, and formulas; and an annual index of organic reactions.

Other Sources of Abstracts. The publications mentioned above are considered best for general work. Abstracts are widely scattered, however, since many periodicals have contained such information for at least part of the period covered by the journals. In case the periodical was not restricted in its field, its abstracts are general in nature; but if it pertained to some special field, the abstracts are confined to this and closely related fields. The latter arrangement is the more common and forms a desirable combination for the individual who wishes to watch developments only in his own limited field.

These sources go back to the first continuous chemical journal, *Annales de chimie*. In fact, it carried some abstracts from 1789 to 1870. The previous edition of this book[1] included a selected list of such periodicals with their starting dates. For searches before 1875 these sources may be of some value.[2]

Of more importance today are the journals currently carrying such abstracts. Bassett's list[3] is the most recent. He included

[1] 2d ed., pp. 85–87, 1940.

[2] For a more extensive list of sources of early and specialized abstracts, see the following publications.

Periodical Bibliographies and Abstracts for the Scientific and Technological Journals of the World, *Bull. Natl. Research Council U.S.*, vol. 1, no. 3, 1920.

"Technical Indexes and Bibliographies Appearing Serially," Carnegie Library, Pittsburgh, Pa., 1910.

Crane, Patterson, and Marr, *op. cit.*, pp. 139–150.

E. E. Reid, "Introduction to Organic Research," p. 92, D. Van Nostrand Company, Inc., Princeton, N.J., 1924.

C. J. West and D. D. Berolzheimer, "Bibliography of Bibliographies on Chemistry and Chemical Technology," p. 12, National Research Council, Washington, 1925.

[3] Paper presented before the Division of Chemical Literature of the Ameri-

periodicals carrying more than 100 abstracts per year. The following titles were selected because they carry more than 700 abstracts per year. They are classified only roughly.

Agricultural and Food Chemistry

Baking Abstracts, sec. B
British Food Manufacturing Industries Research Association Abstracts from Current Scientific and Technical Literature
Current Abstracts
Dairy Science Abstracts
Food Science Abstracts
Journal of the Science of Food and Agriculture
Milchwissenschaft
Nutrition
Research Association of British Flour Millers, Cereals Research Station, Bimonthly Summary of Literature
Soils and Fertilizers, Commonwealth Bureau of Soil Science

Analytical Chemistry

Analytical Abstracts
Annales des falsifications et des fraudes
Chimie analytique
Spectrochimica Acta
Zeitschrift für analytische Chemie

Biological Chemistry

Abstracts of World Medicine
Archiv für die gesamte Physiologie des Menschen und der Tiere
Archives of Industrial Hygiene and Occupational Medicine
Berichte über die gesamte Physiologie und experimentelle Pharmakologie
Biological Abstracts
British Abstracts of Medical Sciences
Bulletin of Hygiene
Excerpta Medica
International Abstracts of Biological Sciences
Nutrition Abstracts and Reviews

Ceramic Chemistry

Berichte der deutschen keramischen Gesellschaft
Ceramic Abstracts (Great Britain)
Ceramic Abstracts (United States)
Glastechnische Berichte
Journal of the Society of Glass Technology

---

can Chemical Society at Atlantic City, N.J., Sept. 20, 1956. See also Bradford, *Chem. & Ind. (London)*, **56**:947 (1937); Landuyt, "Bibliography of Engineering Abstract Services," Special Libraries Association, 1955; and Singer, *Ind. Eng. Chem., News Ed.*, **18**:541 (1940).

National Glass Budget
Silicates industriels
Telescoping the Technical News

Fuels and Petroleum

API Technical Abstracting Service
British Coal Utilization Research Association Monthly Bulletin
Combustible e combustione
Fuel Abstracts
Gas Abstracts
G.R.B.[1] *Digest* (general and research editions)
Journal of the Institute of Petroleum
Lubrication Engineering
Petroleum and Natural Gas Digest
Petroleum Processing
Petroleum Refiner
Synthetic Liquid Fuel Abstracts
Technical Press Review

General Chemistry

Bulletin analytique
Indian Science Abstracts
Nippon Kagaku Soran

Geology and Mineralogy

Geophysical Abstracts
Mineralogical Magazine
Zeitschrift für Mineralogie

Metallurgy

Abstract Bulletin of the Aluminum Laboratories, Ltd.
ASM Review of Metal Literature
Bibliographic Survey of Corrosion
Bulletin of the British Non-ferrous Metals Research Association
Bulletin and Foundry Abstracts of the British Cast Iron Research Association
Crerar Metals Abstracts
Diduminium Abstract Bulletin
Electroplating and Metal Finishing
Jernkontorets Litteraturöversickt
Journal of the Institute of Metals
Journal of the Iron and Steel Institute
Light Metals Bulletin
Metallurgia e meccanica
Metals Review
Nickel Bulletin
Stahl und Eisen
Werkstoffe und Korrosion
Zeitschrift für Metallkunde

[1] Gas Research Board.

Paper

Bulletin of the Institute of Paper Chemistry
Paper Trade Journal
Pulp and Paper Manufacture

Photography

Ansco Abstracts
Monthly Abstract Bulletin (Eastman Kodak Company, Inc.)
Photographic Abstracts

Physical Chemistry

Physics Abstracts
Physikalische Berichte
Revue d'optique théorique et instrumentale

Plastics

British Plastics Federation Abstracts
Industrie des plastiques modernes
Modern Plastics
Plastics Newsletter

Rubber

India Rubber World
Revue générale du caoutchouc
Rubber Abstracts
Rubber Age
Rubber Formulary
Rubber Patent and Trade Mark Review

Textiles

Bulletin de l'institut textile de France, documentation et recherche
Journal of the Textile Institute
Textil-Rundschau
Textile Technology Digest

Miscellaneous Technological Fields

Abstract Review
American Dyestuff Reporter
Battelle Technical Review
British Leather Manufacturers' Research Association Monthly Bulletin
Building Science Abstracts
Buletin de documentare technica
Bulletin of the British Scientific Instrument Research Association
Bulletin of the International Institute of Refrigeration
Carrier Corporation Engineering Library Monthly Bulletin
Chemical Market Abstracts
Chimica e l'industria
Chimie et industrie (Paris)

Commercial Fisheries Abstracts
Engineering Index Service
Explosivstoffe
Facts for Industry
Fats, Oils, Detergents
Hungarian Technical Abstracts
Ion. Revista española de quimica applicada
Journal of the American Oil Chemists' Society
Journal of the Society of Dyers and Colourists
Naval Research Laboratory Library Bulletin
Nuclear Science Abstracts
Oléagineux
Paint Technology
Polish Technical Abstracts
Prevention of Deterioration Abstracts
Public Health Engineering Abstracts
Refrigeration Abstracts
Review of Current Literature Relating to the Paint, Colour, Varnish, and Allied
    Industries
Sugar Industry Abstracts
Water Pollution Abstracts

Review Serials

A third type of periodical is given over to brief accounts of the developments in various fields for some given period of time. These accounts are really annual reviews of progress, and the publications are known as "review serials." The method of compilation usually consists in having someone familiar with a given field examine the papers and other contributions relating to this field and then prepare a summary stating the general trend indicated by the developments during the year and noting any particular advances made. References to the more important papers are usually given.

That the significance of such reviews was realized early in the development of modern chemistry is indicated by the establishment of such a publication in 1795. With the facilities now available, one familiar with index serials and abstracting journals should be able to compile his own report of progress, or at least a noncritical summary; but it is often a very distinct advantage to be able to find such a review already written.

Several sources of reviews are available. A few of them will now be considered, the order being based upon the time of their appearance.

1821–1849, Berzelius, *Jahresberichte über die Fortschritte der physischen Wissenschaften* (later *der Chemie*). This serial was the first of its kind, excepting the *Berlinisches Jahrbuch*, and was very valuable for investigators working during the time covered. Where investigations take one back to the literature of that period, it is still of distinct service. In 1849 the material was classified under *Anorganische Chemie, Pflanzen Chemie,* and *Tier Chemie.* The index is not satisfactory.

1847–1910, Liebig and Kopp, *Jahresbericht über die Fortschritte der reinen, pharmaceutischen und technischen Chemie, Physik, Mineralogie und Geologie.* Issued by different editors and varying somewhat in nature, this serial was for years the main source of critical summaries on the important advances in the fields covered. In 1847 the division of material was as follows: physics and physical chemistry; inorganic, organic, analytical, and technical chemistry; mineralogy; and chemical geology. The early indexes are not satisfactory, but this defect was later corrected with the publication of collective indexes.

1855–1937, Wagner, *Jahresbericht über die Leistungen der chemischen Technologie* (issued under different names for some years). The contents of about 200 journals were summarized in this serial. A classified arrangement was used with the material on organic and inorganic chemistry in separate volumes.

1891–1918, Meyer, *Jahrbuch der Chemie* (Bericht über die wichtigsten Fortschritte der reinen und angewandten Chemie). Seventeen divisions are included (1915), with many subdivisions indicated. Original references and subject and author indexes are given.

1892–1941, *Mineral Industry.* The publication known as *Mineral Industry* was an annual review of the mining and metallurgical industry, including statistics, and an account of the year's technical progress.

1904–   , *Annual Reports of the Chemical Society* (London). In 1955 the annual reports on the progress of chemistry were divided into the following classes: general and physical chemistry, inorganic chemistry, organic chemistry, analytical chemistry, biological chemistry, and crystallography.

1906–   , *Science Progress.* This English quarterly is devoted to reviews of various fields of science.

1916–   , *Applied Chemistry Reports* (of the Society of

Chemical Industry). An excellent series of annual reports on the progress of applied chemistry is given. The general scheme of arrangement is the same as that used in the abstracts section of the *Journal of Applied Chemistry.*

Other Sources of Reviews. Like abstracting journals, review serials have long been a recognized type of publication. Thus, the *Berlinisches Jahrbuch für die Pharmacie* began in 1795. Some of these early publications were listed in the previous edition of this book.[1]

The following list includes some of the more important current review serials. The classification follows that used for abstracting journals.

Agricultural and Food Chemistry

Advances in Agronomy
Advances in Carbohydrate Chemistry
Advances in Food Research
Nutrition Reviews

Analytical Chemistry

Analytical Chemistry (section in January and February issues, 1949–1954, and in the April issues, 1955–)

Biological Chemistry

Advances in Biological and Medical Physics
Advances in Enzymology
Advances in Protein Chemistry
Annual Review of Biochemical and Allied Research in India
Annual Review of Biochemistry
Annual Review of Microbiology
Annual Review of Physiology
Bacteriological Reviews
Ergebnisse der Enzymforschung
Ergebnisse der Physiologie
Ergebnisse der Vitamin- und Hormonforschung
Jahresbericht über Gärungs-Organismen
Medicinal Chemistry
Microbiological Reviews
Physiological Reviews
Progress in Biophysics and Biophysical Chemistry
Quarterly Review of Biology

[1] 2d ed., p. 89. For others, see Periodical Bibliographies and Abstracts for the Scientific and Technological Journals of the World, *Bull. Natl. Research Council U.S.*, vol. 1, no. 3, 1920; and Crane, Patterson, and Marr, *op. cit.*, pp. 208–211.

Reviews of Biochemistry
Vitamins and Hormones

General Chemistry

Advances in Chemistry
Annual Review of Nuclear Science
Progress in Nuclear Energy
Quarterly Reviews
Review of Pure and Applied Chemistry (Australia)

Organic Chemistry

Fortschritte der Chemie organischer Naturstoffe
Progress in Organic Chemistry
Progress in Stereochemistry

Pharmaceutical Chemistry

Pharmacological Reviews

Physical Chemistry

Advances in Catalysis and Related Fields
Advances in Colloid Science
Advances in Physics
Annual Review of Physical Chemistry
Jahrbuch der chemisch-technische Reichanstalt
Progress in Metal Physics
Review of Physical Chemistry of Japan
Reviews of Modern Physics

Technological Chemistry

Advances in Chemical Engineering
Annual Review of Petroleum Technology
British Plastics Yearbook
Fats, Oils, and Detergents Yearbook
Fortschritte der chemischen Forschung
Industrial and Engineering Chemistry (part 2 of March and September
   issues)
Natural and Synthetic Fibers Yearbook
Resins, Rubber, and Plastics Yearbook

CHAPTER 7

SECONDARY SOURCES—
BIBLIOGRAPHIES

Before starting an experiment, I always read everything available
on the subject and on related matters.—*Thomas A.Edison*

A résumé of the literature of the problem in which he is interested is the first need of every research worker. To meet this need,
it is necessary either to find or to compile a partial or complete list
of references relating to the subject. Such a list is known as a
"bibliography." Although a completed bibliography may bear a
close resemblance to a page of an index serial, several points in
connection with their compilation, publication, and use seem to
warrant a separate treatment. On the importance of bibliographies in consulting work, the director of one laboratory wrote:

The compilation of bibliographies forms a very important part of
our work. When a new subject comes up for investigation, the library
is requested to compile a list of references to the important literature
on that subject. . . . Experience teaches that the chemist prefers per-
sonally to examine and digest the list on a subject under investigation,
rather than to have someone else do it for him.

A carefully prepared bibiliography aids greatly in enabling
one to determine what has already been done on a given subject
and thus to build on the knowledge already accumulated by
others. Many chemists do not realize how much useful information is practically lost to them owing to the scattered manner
in which it reaches the world. Investigators may spend valuable
time and effort rediscovering facts already published.

Nature and Kinds of Bibliographies

Although a bibliography is essentially a list of references, such
lists differ enough in their characteristics to warrant considering
some of the details involved.

114

Scope. Bibliographies may be either partial or complete (or as nearly so as it is possible to make them). In the latter case, everything found relating to the subject is included, while in the former case some limitation is set in the compilation, such as language, country, journals, books, patents, authors, time covered, uses of material, preparation of substances, or other similar schemes.

Information Included.[1] In the usual bibliography, part or all of the following information is given for each entry: author's name; title of publication; some statement, in addition to the title, indicating the exact location in the publication of the material cited (the last includes for a book the volume, page, and year, or number of the edition; for a patent, the name of the country issuing the patent, the number, and the date; for a public document, the name of the division issuing the document, together with proper designation, number, and date; and for a journal article, the title of the article, series, volume, page, and year); and an annotation indicating the nature of the material to be found in the source to which reference is made. If the bibliography is a separate publication, preferably all the above information should be included. If it is a part of a book, often the author's name, together with some statement regarding the contents, occurs in the body of the discussion. Annotations are the exception except in separately published bibliographies. Regardless of the part of the above data included for a given entry, whatever is given is usually spoken of as a "reference."

Whatever data are given for the reference or citation, they should indicate unmistakably the essential points of those mentioned above, such as volumes and pages; but, at the same time, they should be as brief as possible in the interest of efficiency in reading, proofreading, writing, and preventing error. Unfortunately, the literature of chemistry abounds in annoying examples of digression from this general principle. As instances of this kind, one need mention only such things as the use of Roman numerals, the inclusion of the issue number for a continuously paged chemical journal, the omission of the year, or, more serious yet, the omission of the series. It is a matter not only of confusion in the older literature but also of lack of uniformity in present practice. Many writers disregard the excellent procedure fol-

[1] Mellon, *Proc. Indiana Acad. Sci.*, **37**:83 (1927).

lowed by *Chemical Abstracts*. As an example of what happens in scientific publications, two citations are quoted from an article[1] calling attention to some desirable reforms. These two citations refer to the same article but appeared in different periodicals: "(1) *Ann. Appl. Biol.*, (**24** (1923). No. 2. pp. 151–193, pls. 3, figs. 31); and (2) *Ann. Appl. Biol.* **24**:151–193, 3 pl. 31 fig. 1923." The second contains 16 less characters without sacrificing anything in essential information.

The following examples[2] seem adequate forms, respectively, for (1) periodicals, (2) institutional publications, (3) patents, and (4) books (including manufacturer's technical publications and doctoral dissertations):

1. Smith, *Ann. chim. et phys.* [9], **25**$_{II}$:481 (1912); Brown, *J. Chem. Soc.*, **1930**:450–492.
2. Williams, *U.S. Bur. Mines, Tech. Paper* 135, 40 (1940).
3. Jones, U.S. Patent 1,729,300, Feb. 4, 1929.
4. J. N. Friend, "Textbook of Inorganic Chemistry," **9**$_I$:381–389, Charles Griffin & Co., Ltd., London, 1920.
5. Lange, "Handbook of Chemistry," Handbook Publishers, Sandusky, Ohio, 1956, p. 31.

Arrangement. A bibliography is essentially only a list of references, with no specification regarding the arrangement of the separate entries in the list. Although a list not systematically arranged is to be preferred to none at all, the advantages resulting from the adoption of a definite order are well worth the extra time and effort required to put the references in this form. An examination of the bibliographies published each year reveals a wide variation in their usefulness owing to the kind of data included or to the arrangement used or to both. An outstanding example of a poor publication of this kind may be found in one bibliography of over 400 pages, including many hundreds of entries, published by a national society. Because of its alphabetic arrangement by author, without subject index, very much of its possible usefulness is practically lost, although much time and considerable expense were required for making it.

For most bibliographies, one of the following schemes may be followed in listing references.

1. *Sequential Order*. The simplest arrangement is to list the references in the sequence in which they are mentioned or found.

[1] Merrill, *Science*, **62**:419 (1925).
[2] Mellon, *Proc. Indiana Acad. Sci.*, **40**:57 (1930).

Although this order is rarely, if ever, used in separately published bibliographies, it is fairly common in some important treatises[1] and in many scientific papers and dissertations. One may have to read the accompanying discussion in order to determine the significance of a given citation. In a large bibliography considerable time might be needed to find a given reference in the list.

2. *Chronological Order.* This scheme may be desirable, especially if time of publication of the contributions is an important point, as in patent searches.[2] It serves also to indicate the historical development of a subject. References published in the same year may be given a serial number,[3] or they may be arranged alphabetically by authors.[4] In any chronologically arranged bibliography the subdivision by years should be prominent on the page, as by a center heading. The entries may also be made in reverse chronological order.

A good example of a bibliography of this kind is a manufacturers' technical bulletin issued as "L and N Bibliography of Polarographic Literature." The 2,208 references, for 1903 to 1950, are first arranged in chronological order from 1903 and then alphabetically by authors in each year. Each entry has a number. The author and subject indexes refer to these numbers.[5]

3. *Alphabetical Order.* There are several possibilities for making alphabetical arrangements:

a. One may alphabetize by name or title of the publication containing the contribution. There are few bibliographies of this kind.

b. Items may be alphabetized by the names of the countries issuing the publications listed. Again, such arrangements are rare.[6]

---

[1] J. W. Mellor, "Treatise on Inorganic and Theoretical Chemistry," Longmans, Green & Co., Inc., New York, 1922–1937; R. Abegg et al., "Handbuch der anorganischen Chemie," S. Hirzel Verlag, Leipzig, 1905– .

[2] St. John, *Science*, **70:**217 (1930).

[3] J. L. Howe, Bibliography of the Metals of the Platinum Group, *Smithsonian Inst. Publs.*, no. 1084 (1897).

[4] C. J. West, "Reading List on Vitreous Enameling of Iron and Steel," A. D. Little, Cambridge, Mass., 1921.

[5] "Bibliography E-90," Leeds and Northrup, Philadelphia, 1950.

[6] The patent index of *Chemical Abstracts*, although not a bibliography, is arranged alphabetically by countries.

c. The most common and useful alphabetical arrangement is by authors of the publications listed. Preferably the order should be that followed in the author indexes of *Chemical Abstracts.* For example, names beginning with *Mc* and *Mac* are handled in a particular way in this publication.

A simple unnumbered list is satisfactory for small numbers of references. However, when the number of entries is large, too much time is required to ascertain whether a reference to some specific point is included. For example, one has to read Branner's book[1] to determine whether china-marking ink is mentioned.

To make such an arrangement readily useful, the references should first be assigned successive numbers after alphabetization. Then a comprehensive subject index, based upon the material in each entry, should be prepared. The numbers of all references pertaining to the subject should follow any index heading.[2] The subject indexes of *Chemical Abstracts* are superb examples illustrating the best practice of selecting index headings. It should be emphasized that these indexes are of subjects rather than of words or titles.

4. *Functional Order.* References on many subjects may be arranged in some logical or functional order, which represents a kind of classification of the references in terms of the nature of the material they contain.[3] Thus, the literature for lithium might be arranged as follows: discovery (history), preparation, physical properties, chemical properties, and uses.[4]

During bibliographic work it may be convenient to arrange references according to the nature of the publications in which they occur, e.g., periodicals, public documents, patents (sub-

[1] J. C. Branner, "A Bibliography on Clays and the Ceramic Arts," American Ceramic Society, Columbus, Ohio, 1906.

[2] N. Van Patten, "Bibliography on Corrosion," N. Van Patten, Marblehead, Mass., 1923; C. J. West and H. Gilman, "Organomagnesium Compounds in Synthetic Chemistry," National Research Council, Washington, 1922.

[3] P. Borgstrom et al., "Bibliography of Organic Sulfur Compounds," American Petroleum Institute, Baltimore, Md., 1930; D. E. Cable, "1936 Bibliography of Rubber Literature," Rubber Age, New York, 1937.

[4] For example, the author's card bibliography on colorimetric methods of analysis is first divided into chemistry and instruments. Then each of these subjects is subdivided into some 100 sections. The division tabs serve as a kind of index which enables one to remove very quickly all references on a particular item.

divided by countries), and books. Collections in large libraries are usually arranged in this way in separate quarters.

Some arrangement, such as alphabetical order by authors, is desirable within each subdivision. Each reference may be numbered and a subject index added.

In this kind of arrangement any card containing material belonging to more than one subdivision necessitates either as many cards as there are divisions referred to or cross references to accomplish the same end.

The following classification was used for a bibliography of references on water glass.[1]

Bibliography
Patent literature
History
General
Properties
Manufacture
Applications:
  General and miscellaneous
  Agglutinants:
    General and miscellaneous
    Abrasives
    Cements
  Detergents:
    Analysis
  Egg preservation
  Glass and ceramics
  Medicine and surgery
  Paper
  Structural materials:
    General and miscellaneous
    Artificial stone
    Concrete
    Fireproofing-preservation of wood
    Paints and preservative coatings
    Textiles
  Analysis

An arrangement devised by the author[2] for a bibliography covering methods used in determining the composition of amalgams illustrates the application of a different scheme to a special case.

[1] M. Schrero, "Water Glass," Carnegie Library, Pittsburgh, Pa., 1922.
[2] Mellon, *Proc. Indiana Acad. Sci.*, **34**:157 (1925).

For general, and more or less extensive, bibliographies, the most useful arrangements seem to be alphabetical order by authors and functional order, particularly if there are accompanying annotations—that is, critical statements of the content and value of the material contained in each publication listed. In locating, for example, the references dealing with the corrosion of copper alloys in a general bibliography on corrosion, one would turn in the former case directly to the index and look for the words "alloy" and "copper." In the latter case it would be necessary to locate the division dealing with copper alloys. Probably in most cases an individual using such a bibliography wants information only for special purposes and consequently is not interested in reading through even 50 articles to find that the valuable material is contained in some 3 or 4 which might have been immediately evident in a well-arranged bibliography. If the list has no such arrangement, he must examine all references given in order to select the desired ones or to assure himself that there are none of value included.

Bibliographic Practice[1]

Mention has already been made of the items of information included in a citation to the literature. Preparation of a bibliography on a given subject involves searching for the references (see Chapter 11) and then arranging the information obtained in some usable form (see Problem 18). Although Problem 18 involves the selection of some systematic way of recording each reference, this aspect of the problem is discussed here, along with other aspects of completed bibliographies.

Occasionally someone insists that all details of a reference found should be copied into a bound notebook. For a bibliography of any size this practice is too cumbersome to follow. The alternative is to use a separate card or slip of paper for each reference. The compiler, of course, must guard against loss of individual cards. Two variations of the card technique are of interest.

Plain Cards. Many people use plain cards, convenient sizes being 3 by 5, 4 by 6, and 5 by 7 in. Preferably the larger sizes at least should be ruled. Industrial libraries often use cards with some printing to indicate the space for entering certain parts of

---

[1] See Schrero, *Special Libraries*, **30**:302 (1939), for advice on bibliographic technique.

the bibliographical details. One arrangement is illustrated in Fig. 7. Researchers may prefer to put the different items in some other arrangement. Some searchers use different-colored cards for the different kinds of sources, such as periodicals, public documents, patents, and books. For a working bibliography, all the cards are then arranged in one of the ways described.

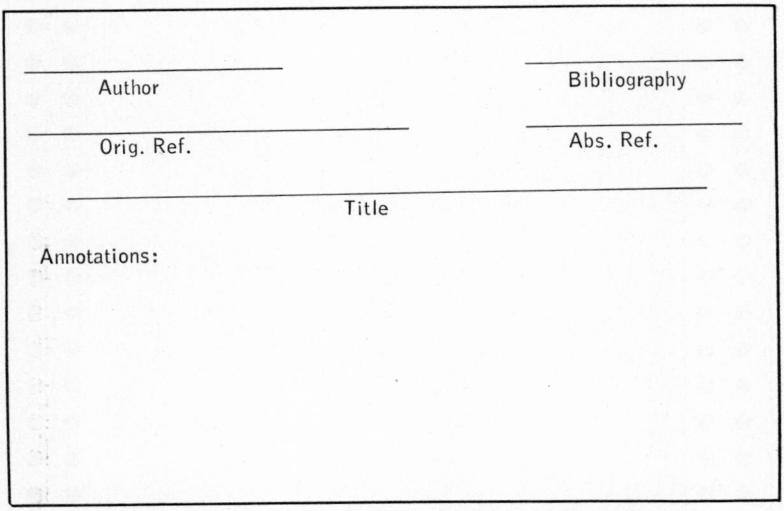

Author	Bibliography
Orig. Ref.	Abs. Ref.

Title

Annotations:

FIG. 7. One arrangement for a bibliography card.

Stiff separator cards with projecting tabs serve to indicate the different sections. This system is very adaptable in that the separator cards may be changed or added to at any time.

Punched Cards. A newer development is the use of punched cards, one for each reference cited. A committee of the American Chemical Society[1] has worked on the problems involved, and the study has progressed to the point that there are books describing the preparation, coding, and use of such cards.[2]

An example of a simple marginally punched card is shown in Fig. 8. There may be one or two rows of the holes. Various

[1] Perry, *Chem. Eng. News*, **27**:754 (1949).

[2] R. S. Casey and J. W. Perry, "Punched Cards: Their Applications to Science and Industry," Reinhold Publishing Corporation, New York, 1951. See also section in R. E. Kirk and D. F. Othmer, "Encyclopedia of Chemical Technology," vol. 8, pp. 449–467, Interscience Publishers, Inc., New York, 1952.

FIG. 8. Keysort Card. (*Reproduced with permission of the McBee Co.*)

sizes of cards are available. The printed numerals and letters may be designed for a variety of specific requirements.[1] The space within the border of holes serves for recording the bibliographic data.

When the bibliography has progressed to the point that no further indexing subdivisions or facets seem likely to be found, a coding system is adopted. This necessitates laying out a classification or code, with each aspect or facet of the subject assigned to a given position or hole on the card. For example, in a bibliography on methods of chemical analysis, hole 1 of the top row of the card shown might be assigned to gravimetric methods of measurement. Then a special hand punch, similar to those used by train conductors, is used to notch away the edge of the card to the inside of this hole for every card involving a gravimetric method. Machine punches are also available. Other holes would be assigned to other aspects of the subject.

In order to select the cards on gravimetric methods from such a set, one first aligns them on edge, all in the same position, so that a long sorting needle resembling an ice pick can be pushed through hole 1 of the cards. Then by holding the needle and shaking the cards apart somewhat, all the cards clipped at hole 1 will drop out. If only gravimetric methods for nickel are wanted, these first fallout cards must be shaken again, this time with the needle in a hole which was clipped out for nickel. If it is to be gravimetric methods for nickel in steel, a third shake is necessary, this time a shake of the nickel cards with the needle pushed through still another hole clipped out for steel. Thus, three clipped-out holes are necessary to sort for (1) method, (2) element, and (3) material. The total number of holes determines the number of possible codable facets or aspects of the subject.

This simple example indicates that the coding system must be elaborately worked out before the holes can be clipped. The coding facets necessary are comparable to the division and subdivision tabs necessary for a classified card file.

There are two chief advantages of punched cards over plain cards: (1) the cards never need to be in any particular order, and (2) no duplicate or cross-reference cards are needed.

[1] For a description of one system, see "Keysort Punching and Sorting Manual," The McBee Company, New York. See also R. H. Parker, "Library Applications of Punched Cards," American Library Association, Chicago, 1952.

For a very large and/or many-faceted file such punched cards are not adequate. Too many cards become inconvenient for hand sorting, and only a limited number of holes are available for coding. Thus, it would be impossible to accommodate a general bibliography on chemical analysis covering all kinds of methods of separation and measurement for all elements, radicals, and compounds in all kinds of materials. Several papers have dealt with alternative systems that seem feasible.[1]

Cards of the type provided for International Business Machines (IBM) seem to be most promising for the more complicated cases. They are designed for machine sorting, of course. With them one may have a problem of providing enough punched holes without severely limiting the space necessary for the bibliographic data. Machine literature searching is being studied intensively.[2] An excellent example of its application is the bibliography on absorption spectra available from the American Society for Testing Materials. A similar bibliography, entitled "Documentation of Molecular Spectroscopy," includes on each card an abstract of the article (if published).[3]

Sources of Bibliographies

Unless one's problem is very specialized or of very recent interest, the chances are that somewhere there are more or less complete lists bearing directly or indirectly upon the subject. Difficulty may be encountered, however, in finding them. They may appear either as separate publications or in connection with some other publication, such as treatises, encyclopedias, monographs, journal articles, or bulletins. Those appearing separately are usually either more or less general in nature or contain many entries, while the shorter ones appear in connection with a chapter in a book or at the end of an article.

[1] Cox, Bailey, and Casey, Punch Cards for a Chemical Bibliography, *Chem. Eng. News*, **23**:1623 (1945); Guy and Geisler, A Punch Card Filing System for Metallurgical Literature, *Metal Progr.*, **52**:993 (1947); and Thiers, A Punch Card System for the Bibliography of Analytical Chemistry, *Virginia J. Sci.*, **2**:28 (1951).

[2] See Perry et al., *Am. Doc.*, **5**:18, 22, 92, 95, 166, 238 (1954); **6**:33, 93, 242 (1955); *College and Research Libraries*, **16**:157 (1955); Staff Report, *Chem. Eng. News*, **32**:866 (1954).

[3] Butterworth's Scientific Publications, London.

Although bibliographies are widely scattered and in many cases can be found only after long searches, there are several publications available which are valuable aids in such work.

H. C. Bolton's "A Select Bibliography of Chemistry"[1] covers the titles of the principal books on chemistry published in America and Europe from the first appearance of chemical literature to the close of the year 1892. The term *chemistry* is taken in its fullest significance, and the bibliography contains books in every department of this early period. The bibliography is confined to independent works and their translations.

To facilitate reference, the work is divided into 8 sections: bibliography; dictionaries; history; biography; chemistry, pure and applied; alchemy; periodicals; and academic dissertations. The first volume covers the field from 1492 to 1892, while the first supplement takes the literature on to 1897 and includes items omitted from the first volume. Out of about 18,000 titles appearing in these volumes, approximately 375 relate to bibliographies. A third volume comprises a list of academic dissertations printed independently between 1492 and 1897. The second supplement continues the work of the other volumes through 1902.

C. J. West and D. D. Berolzheimer's "Bibliography of Bibliographies on Chemistry and Chemical Technology"[2] is the most important bibliographic collection for the chemist and chemical engineer. The main work covers 1900 to 1924, and two supplements go on through 1931. In its compilation about 100 periodicals and treatises were searched for lists of references on special topics. The material was assembled alphabetically by subject and classified as follows: bibliographies, abstract journals and yearbooks, general indexes of serials, bibliographies on special subjects, and personal bibliographies.

Two other works of general bibliographic interest are "A World Bibliography of Bibliographies"[3] and the "Bibliographic Index."[4] A number of bibliographies on specific subjects have

[1] *Smithsonian Inst. Publs. Misc. Collections*, no. 1253 (1893–1904).

[2] National Research Council, Washington, 1925; two supplements, 1924–1931.

[3] T. Besterman, "A World Bibliography of Bibliographies and of Bibliographical Catalogues, Calendars, Abstracts, Digests, Indexes, and the Like," Societas Bibliographica, Geneva, 1955.

[4] The H. W. Wilson Company, New York, cumulative vols., 1937–1955.

already been mentioned as examples of particular kinds of bibliographic practices. The following additional examples may be of interest:

"Bibliography of the Literature of the Minor Elements and Their Relation to Plant and Animal Nutrition," Chilean Nitrate Educational Bureau, New York, 1948–1955.

Dietz, V. R.: "Bibliography of Solid Adsorbents," Government Printing Office, 1944; supplement for 1943–1953, 1956.

"Fiberglas Bibliography," Owens-Corning Fiberglas Corp., Toledo, Ohio, 1950.

Richter, M.: "Internationale Bibliographie der Farbenlehre und ihrer Grenzgebiete," Musterschmidt, Göttingen, Germany, 1952.

Weil, B. H., et al.: "Bibliography on Water and Sewage Analysis," Georgia Institute of Technology, Atlanta, Ga., 1948.

The following papers were presented before the Division of Chemical Literature of the American Chemical Society. In addition to the general background information provided, a very valuable feature for the literature chemist is the bibliography at the end of each article. They all appeared in *Advances in Chemistry Series.*[1]

Carter, P. G.: Sources of Statistics on Chemicals, pp. 47–56.

Ciboch, L.: Literature of Canning and Preserving, pp. 280–285.

Clarke, W. T.: Literature of Cacao, pp. 286–296.

Conrad, C. C., and P. M. Levin: Literature of Man-made Fibers, pp. 191–199.

Crawford, R. W.: Statistics of the Plastics Materials Industry, pp. 90–99.

Crosland, D. M., and W. H. Cady: Literature of Dyes, Mordants, and Bleaches, pp. 200–214.

Davis, S. J.: Literature of Processing and Textile Chemicals, pp. 215–228.

Dyson, G. M.: Nitrogen-containing Compounds from Petroleum and Natural Gas, pp. 395–397.

Egloff, G., M. Alexander, and C. Zimmer: Commerical Development of Hydrocarbons from Petroleum and Natural Gas, pp. 360–369.

Gerlach, A. C.: Marketing Maps, Their Sources and Uses, pp. 100–106.

Goldstein, R. F.: History of the Petroleum Chemical Industry, pp. 321–326.

Hazen, T., and A. J. Weith: Literature on Properties and Applications of Modern Plastics, pp. 139–144.

Hilligan, M. P., and M. J. Krause: Review of Milling and Baking Literature, pp. 247–257.

Honig, P.: Sugar Production, pp. 297–306.

Jacobs, M. B.: Food Industries Literature, pp. 230–246.

Karchmer, J. H.: Sulfur Compounds from Petroleum, pp. 398–425.

Kline, G. M.: Test Methods, Specifications, and Standards for Plastics, pp. 145–150.

[1] *No. 4* (1951), published by the American Chemical Society.

Labov, T. G.: Trade Associations as a Source of Market Data, pp. 22–35.

Lawrence, R. M., J. H. Sprague, Jr., and R. H. Ewell: Sources of Market Information on Petrochemicals, pp. 426–437.

Leidy, W. P.: Literature of Essential Oils, pp. 307–315.

Mark, H. F., and E. S. Proskauer: Basic Science in the Literature of Plastics, pp. 122–128.

Miller, A. E.: Basic Research on Hydrocarbons from Petroleum and Natural Gas, pp. 339–359.

Mohat, H. R.: Information on the Chemical Industry Developed by Antitrust Cases, pp. 114–120.

Nicholson, R.: Technical Literature of the Edible Oil Industry, pp. 274–279.

Nickerson, M. H., and K. T. Barker: Literature Searching for Plastics Engineering, pp. 129–133.

Padwe, M. M.: Oxygen-containing Hydrocarbon Derivatives from Petroleum and Natural Gas, pp. 370–380.

Payne, B. J., and H. R. Kraybill: Literature of Meat and Meat Packing, pp. 263–273.

Pfahler, B.: Halogen-containing Hydrocarbons from Petroleum and Natural Gas, pp. 381–394.

Schaler, C. M.: Chemicals Derived from Petroleum, pp. 316–320.

Seymour-Jones, F. L.: Dairy Industry Literature, pp. 258–262.

Shreve, R. N.: Unit Consumption Factors, pp. 71–78.

Sittig, M.: Raw Materials for Chemicals from Petroleum, pp. 327–338.

Stevens, F. P.: Market Research in Western Europe, pp. 57–70.

Turner, H. Y.: Railroad Transportation Statistics for the Chemical and Allied Products Industry, pp. 36–46.

Warren, R. F.: Sources of Chemical End-use Data, pp. 79–89.

Wehr, H. W., Jr., and G. B. Thayer: Literature Searching for Plastics Fabricating Methods and Machinery, pp. 134–138.

Worner, R. K., and D. B. Skau: Literature of Natural Fibers, pp. 172–190.

CHAPTER 8

SECONDARY SOURCES—WORKS OF REFERENCE

Books are the masters who instruct us without rods and ferules, without hard words and anger, without clothes or money. If you approach them, they are not asleep; if investigating you interrogate them, they conceal nothing; if you mistake them, they never grumble; if you are ignorant, they cannot laugh at you. The library of wisdom, therefore, is more precious than all riches, and nothing that can be wished for is worthy to be compared with it. Whosoever therefore acknowledges himself to be a zealous follower of truth, of happiness, of wisdom, of science, or even of the faith, must of necessity make himself a lover of books.[1]—*Richard de Bury*

The statements of chemical facts and the theories and discussions involving these facts usually are issued first in the publications which have been designated as "primary sources." The first step in the process of bringing the material from an unorganized to an organized state is taken in the index serials and abstract journals. The work of the review serials follows and is closely related to that of the other two. Likewise, bibliographies are more or less related to index serials.

Important as their work is, these organizing agencies do not bring the material into a readily usable form. They are the reaper, which collects the individual stalks of grain and ties them in bundles; but a thrasher or separator is needed to bring out the kernels in a form suitable for ordinary consumption. The separators of chemical literature will now be considered; they constitute the large majority of the so-called "books" on chemistry (not bound periodicals and bulletins).

These works touch practically every phase of chemistry and chemical technology. They vary widely in quality, dependability, usefulness, arrangement, comprehensiveness, and kind of information included. Their quality and dependability depend largely

[1] From "Philobiblon," 1344, the first English book on the joys of reading.

upon the perspective and discernment of the authors. As such works are not published frequently, the information in many cases is not up to date. The arrangement, comprehensiveness, and kind of information included are decided upon by the author; but he is guided in this case by the objective for which the book is produced.

The general value of books has been well summarized by Crane, Patterson, and Marr,[1] who state that such works

introduce the novice to the general field of the science, or some part of it, explain new theories in the light of already known facts, and help to coordinate and systematize knowledge. They furnish information, exhaustive or not, in a form adapted to quick reference, and guide the searcher back to the original sources by means of citations. Historical works record the development of the science, popular books initiate the public into its mysteries and elicit interest and support, and treatises on the chemical arts give the reader the benefit of long experience or of the combined researches of many workers. Who shall say that the chemist can depend on journals alone? The mere fact that over a thousand new books of chemical interest are published annually proves the demand for them.

An attempt has been made to classify the book literature into several more or less distinct groups upon the basis of the general nature of the information included in them. In considering each of these groups, the general plan of this book will be followed—that of describing the nature or characteristics of the group and then giving typical examples or listing the more important or representative contributions. The latter point will be carried a little further in this chapter, since it seems wise to mention some of the works in special fields of chemistry.

The books to be considered include the publications usually spoken of as reference works. They may be specialized and limited presentations related to some narrow phases of work; or the treatment may be sufficiently comprehensive and exhaustive to involve a whole field of chemistry. They are the works to which one turns when in need of either specific facts or comprehensive discussions involving relationships and general significance of facts. Such information is not to be found in the ordinary textbook, except in the case of a few well-known facts.

[1] E. J. Crane, A. M. Patterson, and E. B. Marr, "A Guide to the Literature of Chemistry," p. 11, John Wiley & Sons, Inc., New York, 1957.

A reference book, in the strict sense of the term, is a book to be consulted for information on a definite point rather than to be read through. . . . In a broad sense, any book may be considered a reference book if it contains a great deal of information arranged in an easily accessible form.[1]

Reference books are the clearing houses of knowledge. They are libraries in miniature, focusing into a single book information scattered through a thousand volumes. They are short cuts to learning, pass keys to the accumulated wisdom of the ages.[2]

In the ideal case a work of reference should not only give the authorities for statements of facts, but it should also indicate what knowledge has been gleaned on the particular subject in question. To do this in a practicable manner, attention must be directed to the original publications on the subject. This naturally makes the work of compilation extremely laborious; in some cases, indeed, it happens that scores of independent references are involved in the statement of one particular fact.[3]

These works of reference, depending upon the general arrangement and manner of presenting the material, may be roughly subdivided into five groups: formula indexes, tabular compilations, dictionaries and encyclopedias, formularies, and treatises. Each of these groups will be considered in turn.

Formula Indexes

The amount of information in these works of reference is so large that it has been found desirable to have means by which one may get easily to that part of the stock of facts dealing with a given subject. To meet this need, several different kinds of indexes are used in order to make the contents of publications readily available. Common arrangements are by authors, subjects, patent numbers, empirical formulas, and ring formulas. As an understanding of formula indexes is necessary to use some of the reference works, this arrangement is discussed here. Reference was made to them in connection with abstracting journals.

The location of chemical compounds in an index by name is at times uncertain because names vary and, in the case of complex

[1] M. Hutchins, A. S. Johnson, and M. S. Williams, "Guide to the Use of Libraries," p. 66, The H. W. Wilson Company, New York, 1925.

[2] Jordan, *Literary Era*, **8**:52 (1901).

[3] J. W. Mellor, "Treatise on Inorganic and Theoretical Chemistry," vol. 1, p. viii, Longmans, Green & Co., Inc., New York, 1922.

compounds, may be difficult to ascertain. New compounds are constantly being prepared which, if named at all, may receive more than one name that is justified from one point of view or another, and the possibilities of incorrect naming are considerable. Since the kinds and number of component atoms of a chemical compound are unvarying characteristics, a formula index eliminates this uncertainty in a subject index. The systematic name is given with the empirical formula. Formula indexes usually serve as a means of locating the source of more extensive information, but in indicating known compounds they are sufficient in themselves.

Formula indexes have been compiled in several ways: (1) organic compounds, (2) inorganic compounds, (3) both organic and inorganic compounds, (4) anions, groups, and radicals, and (5) rings. The best-known indexes of each kind will be considered.

Organic Compounds. The best-known system for indexing organic compounds by simple empirical formulas was designed by M. M. Richter. It is used in the two works described hereafter.

M. M. Richter, "Lexikon der Kohlenstoff-Verbindungen," Voss, Leipzig, 1910–1912. This work covered all organic compounds known at the time of its publication, December 31, 1909.[1] It was intended to be an index to the third edition of Beilstein's treatise (discussed later).

The compounds listed are arranged according to their molecular formula, water of crystallization being neglected. The details of arrangement, as described in the work, are as follows:

1. Formulas are divided into groups according to the number of carbon atoms present. All compounds containing one carbon atom are listed first— the "C_1-Gruppe."

2. Formulas of each group are divided into classes on the basis of the number of elements, in addition to carbon, contained in the compound. In the "C_1-Gruppe" are listed first all compounds containing one element other than carbon, the "C_1-Gruppe mit einem Element." Then follows the "C_1-Gruppe mit zwei Elementen," and so on through all compounds containing only one carbon atom.

3. Formulas are arranged in each group in alphabetical order, according to the elements present. The alphabet of the system, or the succession of the elements combined with carbon as determined by the frequency of occurrence, is not the ordinary alphabet, but one worked out by Richter. Its order is $C, H, O, N, Cl, Br, I, F, S, P$, and then the others in ordinary alphabetical order from A to Z, according to symbols.

[1] The Richter system does not provide for inorganic compounds.

4. Formulas are arranged finally according to the number of atoms of each element which, in addition to carbon, are contained in the compound. All compounds containing two carbons and two hydrogens are considered before those containing two carbons and three hydrogens.

Suppose one is looking for information on ethyl cyanide, C_2H_5CN. The formula is arranged in the form C_3H_5N. At the top of the pages are Arabic and Roman numerals, which serve as a guide. The former indicate the number of carbon atoms in the formulas listed on the page, and the latter indicate the number of other elements combined with the carbon. In this case, one would turn to the page with "3 II" upon it and look for the formulas with five hydrogens and one nitrogen.

The percentage composition is given for the more important compounds. All isomers are listed separately, as "1)," "2)," etc. For each there is given the preferred German name, often another recognized name, statement of physical state or M.Pt. or B.Pt., salts formed, reference to original paper or papers, including reference to the *Zentralblatt*[1] in many cases, and for many of the compounds a reference to the third edition of Beilstein's "Handbuch der organischen Chemie." The Roman numeral is for the volume (an asterisk signifies a supplement) and the Arabic numeral for the page. If a reference to Beilstein is not given, the compound is not described in the third edition.

The work contains the references to the papers which describe the methods of preparation of the compounds and their properties, as well as those which deal with the immediate changes which they undergo. No reference is made to purely theoretical papers or to those with analytical, physical, mathematical, crystallographic, and medicophysiological contents. A name index is given in Volume IV. In the second edition there is given, in a separate table, the percentage composition of the compounds listed, about 90,000. This table is now issued as a separate publication. For many years several important foreign periodicals have indexed organic compounds according to the Richter system, and it is used in the first formula index for the fourth edition of the Beilstein treatise (discussed later).

R. Stelzner, "Literatur-Register der organischen Chemie," Vieweg-Verlag, Brunswick, Germany, 1913–1926. The formula index of the third edition of Richter brings the literature of

---

[1] See discussion of *Chemisches Zentralblatt* in Chap. 6.

organic chemistry only to 1910. The fourth edition of Beilstein, discussed in the next section, comes to this point also in the main part. To provide references to the voluminous literature on the subject for the period 1910 to 1921, the Deutsche Chemische Gesellschaft issued the "Literatur-Register der organischen Chemie," under the editorship of Stelzner, in five volumes.[1]

The compounds are listed by formula, as in Richter's "Lexikon," and under each the references are arranged according to the following outline, which serves to classify them on the basis of the material included:

Historical, constitution, configuration
Occurrence, mode of formation, preparation (isolation, purification)
Analytical (methods of estimation, separation, analysis)
Physical properties and reactions (influence on the properties of other bodies)
Chemical behavior (reactions, transformation)
Physiological behavior
Technical use
Salts, esters, compounds with other materials

A statement is given in connection with most of the references indicating the main point of the paper. Certain physical constants are given. In the back of the volumes there is included an index of names, with their Richter formula.

Inorganic Compounds. The formula index of M. K. Hoffmann, "Lexikon der anorganischen Verbindungen," Johann Ambrosius Barth, Verlag, Leipzig, April, 1909, is a list of all analytical and synthetic inorganic compounds known at the time of its publication.[2]

The elements are listed in the order of nonmetals, light metals, heavy metals, and the argon group, each element being given a number, as indicated at the top of page 134. The elements are taken up in their serial order, as given in the table, the element itself being considered first. Then come the compounds between it and the preceding elements, in the reverse order; that is, number 17, for example, is listed, then compounds of number 17 with number 16, followed by those containing numbers 17 and 16 and some preceding element. Others follow in a similar manner.

[1] After 1921 this work was superseded by the formula indexes of *Chemisches Zentralblatt*.

[2] From 1909 to 1920, when the formula index of *Chemical Abstracts* began, there is no systematic compilation of inorganic compounds by formulas.

1. H	17. Li	33. As	49. Tb	65. W
2. O	18. Rb	34. Sb	50. Er	66. V
3. Cl	19. Cs	35. Bi	51. Yb	67. U
4. Br	20. Ca	36. Ti	52. Sc	68. Ta
5. I	21. Sr	37. Ge	53. Tm	69. Nb
6. F	22. Ba	38. Zr	54. Dy	70. Au
7. S	23. Ra	39. Sn	55. B	71. Pt
8. Se	24. Be	40. Th	56. Al	72. Ru
9. Te	25. Mg	41. Ce	57. Ga	73. Rh
10. N	26. Zn	42. La	58. In	74. Pd
11. P	27. Cd	43. Nd	59. Mn	75. Ir
12. C	28. Pb	44. Pr	60. Fe	76. Os
13. Si	29. Tl	45. Sm	61. Co	77. He
14. NH_3	30. Cu	46. Eu	62. Ni	78. Ne
14b NH_4	31. Ag	47. Gd	63. Cr	79. A
15. K	32. Hg	48. Y	64. Mo	80. Kr
16. Na				81. Xe

In using the index one may find a given compound by following the steps indicated: (1) establish a rough formula, omitting the water of crystallization; (2) from the table obtain the number for each element—for sulfuric acid $H = 1$, $S = 7$, and $O = 2$; (3) arrange the formula according to descending order of the numbers —for sulfuric acid it is 7, 2, 1, or SO_4H_2; (4) locate the formula in the index by looking under the element having the highest number—for sulfuric acid look under "sulfur." Also the compound may be found from the alphabetical list of formulas in Volume III, the entry being under the symbol appearing first in the alphabet.

Under each formula the following information is generally given, in the order indicated: the ordinary formula (or optional formula), name of the compound (or element), references to journal articles (author and journal), references to Gmelin-Kraut's "Handbuch" (the symbol "N.:" is followed by the volume, part, and page for the seventh German edition), and a statement of the color, crystalline form, or physical state of the substance.

The volumes are arranged as follows:

Vol. I_I (1917)   Introduction; general remarks; elements 1 to 31 (H to Ag)
Vol. I_{II} (1919)   Elements 32 to 55 (Hg to B)
Vol. II (1912)   Elements 56 to 81 (Al to Xe); list of bibliographies
Vol. III (1919)   General information; periodicals; abbreviations . . .

Both Organic and Inorganic Compounds. In order to answer quickly the question of novelty for patent applications covering new compounds, E. A. Hill[1] devised a combined index for use in the Classification Division of the U.S. Patent Office. The Hill system, with slight modifications,[2] has been used since 1920 in the formula indexes of *Chemical Abstracts*. It applies equally well to both inorganic and organic compounds.

The arrangement of symbols in the formulas is alphabetical except that in carbon compounds C always comes first, followed immediately by H, if hydrogen is present. The arrangement of formulas is also alphabetical except that the number of atoms of any specific kind influences the order of compounds; e.g., all formulas with C (one carbon atom only) come before those with C_2; thus, CCl_2O, CCl_4, $CHCl_3$, CHN, $CHNO$, CH_2Br_2, CH_2O, CH_3Cl, CO, C_2Ca, $C_2H_4O_2$. The arrangement of entries under any heading is alphabetical according to the preferred names of the isomers.[3]

To use the index, first reject any water of crystallization and rewrite the empirical formula in the alphabetical order of the chemical symbols, except that in carbon compounds put carbon first and hydrogen second; then look in the proper alphabetical location in the index, noting the first symbol of the rewritten formula, together with the number of times it occurs. According to this arrangement, one would find the following compounds listed under the respective formulas: rubidium permanganate, MnO_4Rb; ammonium sulfate, $H_8N_2O_4S$; and acetyl bromide, C_2H_3BrO.

The Hill system is used in the latest formula index of the Beilstein treatise (discussed below).

Anions, Groups, Radicals, and Suffixes. For indexing purposes *Chemical Abstracts* has compiled lists of many inorganic and organic anions, groups, and radicals.[4] The arrangement is name-formula and formula-name. Inorganic and organic groups are listed separately, the Hill system being used in the formulas.

[1] *J. Am. Chem. Soc.*, **22**:478 (1900); **29**:936 (1907); **34**:416 (1912).

[2] Crane and Hockett, *Chem. Abstr.*, **14**:4557 (1920).

[3] See Formula Index (*Chem. Abstr.*), p. 1_F (1954).

[4] *Chem. Abstr.*, **39**:5956–5969 (1945). Issued separately, as an appendix, in "The Naming and Indexing of Chemical Compounds by *Chemical Abstracts*."

Ring Indexes. The *Chemical Abstracts* index of ring complexes is arranged by bold-faced figures. The order is one-ring systems, with single figures indicating simple rings of three rings, four rings, etc.; two-ring systems, with two figures denoting double rings, of three and five, four and six, etc., members; then the triple and still more complex forms. Under each combination of figures the kind and number of atoms in the ring(s) are expressed in formulas. Included is the name for the simplest parent compound(s) containing the particular ring(s). To illustrate:

6,6,6 C_5N,—C_6—C_6 Acridan
                        Acridine
                        Benzisoquinoline
                        Benzoquinoline
                        Phenanthridine

This illustration designates a complex ring of three components, each of six members. The first is heterocyclic, containing five carbon atoms and one nitrogen atom, and the other two are carbocyclic rings of six atoms each. Parent compounds of this configuration will be found in the (*Chemical Abstracts*) index under the five names given.[1]

Patterson and Capell's "The Ring Index" consists of some 4,000 parent ring systems serially numbered, with structural formulas, numberings, names, and references (including those to the completed volumes of the Beilstein set). The object is to have the serial number identify the ring system. Adequate explanations are included for the naming and classification used.[2] A supplement is in preparation.

Tabular Compilations

There are enormous numbers of individual facts which, when collected and properly arranged simply as statements of facts, are of frequent and wide use. This material is usually arranged in tabular or graphical form and includes such items as atomic weights, molecular weights, boiling and melting points, solubilities, absorption spectra, and other physical constants.

There seem to be no distinctive points of difference among the various works of this type, except in the amount and kind of

[1] See instructions to subject indexes of *Chemical Abstracts*.
[2] See Taylor, *Ind. Eng. Chem.*, **40**:734 (1948), for a proposed enumerative nomenclature of organic ring systems.

material included, and there is not much tendency to classify the material on the basis of fields of chemistry. The reason, of course, is obvious. The solubility of calcium citrate, for example, may be of just as much importance to the biochemist as to the physical chemist.

Some of the well-known works are described below. Statements are included to indicate the general nature of the contents and to direct attention to any special features.

Handbooks. Various small works of this type contain the information thought to be of most general interest, such as physical constants for a limited number of organic and inorganic substances and other similar data in considerable variety. Some, such as those by Perry and the American Society for Metals, contain much more than physical data. Unfortunately, in those more definitely chemical in nature, different authors have selected different items, so that one may need several such works where a considerable range of facts is necessary. Thus, one book has an extensive classified list of books, another has much on physics and mathematics, another emphasizes metallurgy, and still another includes outlines of analytical methods. In most cases original references are not included. Several of the more common works are listed below:

Atack, F. W.: "Handbook of Chemical Data," Reinhold Publishing Corporation, New York, 1957.

Blanck, F. C. (ed.): "Handbook of Food and Agriculture," Reinhold Publishing Corporation, New York, 1955.

Conway, B. E.: "Electrochemical Data," Elsevier Publishing Company, Amsterdam, 1952.

Dobriner, K., et al.: "Infrared Absorption Spectra of Steroids," Interscience Publishers, Inc., New York, 1953.

Dreisbach, R. R.: "Physical Properties of Chemical Compounds," American Chemical Society, Columbus, Ohio, 1955.

————: "Pressure-Volume-Temperature Relationships of Organic Compounds," Handbook Publishers, Sandusky, Ohio, 1952.

Feather, N., et al.: "Kaye and Laby's Tables of Physical and Chemical Constants," Longmans, Green & Co., Inc., New York, 1956.

Ferris, S. W.: "Handbook of Hydrocarbons," Academic Press, Inc., New York, 1955.

Forsythe, W. E.: "Smithsonian Physical Tables," Smithsonian Institution, Washington, 1954.

Gray, D. E. (ed.): "American Institute of Physics Handbook," McGraw-Hill Book Company, Inc., New York, 1957.

Gysel, H.: "Prozenttabellen organischen Verbindungen," Verlag Birkhäuser, Basel, Switzerland, 1951.

Harrison, G. R.: "Wavelength Tables," John Wiley & Sons, Inc., New York, 1939.

Hatt, H. H., T. Pearcey, and A. Z. Szumer: "Anti-composition Tables for Carbon Compounds," Cambridge University Press, New York, 1955.

Hodgman, C. D. (ed.): "Handbook of Chemistry and Physics," Chemical Rubber Co., Cleveland, Ohio, 1957.

Jousset, J., and P. Pigamiol: "Chimie," Dunod, Paris, 1952.

Lange, N. A.: "Handbook of Chemistry," Handbook Publishers, Sandusky, Ohio, 1956.

Maxwell, J. B.: "Data Book on Hydrocarbons," D. Van Nostrand Company, Inc., Princeton, N.J., 1950.

Rauen, H. M.: "Biochemisches Taschenbuch," Springer-Verlag OHG, Vienna, 1956.

Rossini, F. D., et al.: Selected Values of Chemical Thermodynamic Values, *Natl. Bur. Standards U.S., Circ.* 500 (1952).

Spector, W. S. (ed.): "Handbook of Biological Data," W. B. Saunders Company, Philadelphia, 1957.

Spencer, G. L., and G. P. Meade: "Cane Sugar Handbook," Chapman & Hall, Ltd., London, 1955.

Thon, N. (ed.): Tables of Chemical Kinetics, *Natl. Bur. Standards U.S., Circ.* 510 (1951).

Timmermans, J.: "Physicochemical Constants of Pure Organic Compounds," Elsevier Publishing Company, Amsterdam, 1950.

The chemical technologist may need information in fields closely related to chemistry, such as physics and engineering. Such sources have been listed in several publications.[1] Most likely to be of use are the types of handbooks[2] suggested below.

Chemical Engineering

Johnson, A. J., and G. H. Auth: "Fuels and Combustion Handbook," McGraw-Hill Book Company, Inc., New York, 1951.

Mantell, C. L.: "Engineering Materials Handbook," McGraw-Hill Book Company, Inc., New York, 1958.

Miner, D. F., and J. B. Seastone: "Handbook of Engineering Materials," John Wiley & Sons, Inc., New York, 1955.

[1] Mellon, *J. Chem. Educ.,* **10**:619 (1933); N. G. Parke, III, "Guide to the Literature of Mathematics and Physics" (including related works in engineering), McGraw-Hill Book Company, Inc., New York, 1947; R. M. Pearl, "Guide to Geologic Literature," McGraw-Hill Book Company, Inc., New York, 1951; A. D. Roberts, "Guide to Technical Literature," Grafton & Company, London, 1939; R. H. Whitford, "Physics Literature," Scarecrow Press, Washington, D.C., 1954.

[2] These handbooks vary considerably in nature. Some are almost entirely tabular in nature. Others, such as Perry's, contain much additional material. For example, Perry's handbook has 30 sections covering mathematics, physical and chemical data, materials, processes, and operations. The book duplicates one such as Lange's only to a limited extent.

Perry, J. H. (ed.): "Chemical Engineers' Handbook," McGraw-Hill Book Company, Inc., New York, 1950.

Simonds, H. R., A. J. Weith, and M. H. Bigelow: "Handbook of Plastics," D. Van Nostrand Company, Inc., Princeton, N.J., 1949.

Stannett, V., and L. Mitlin: "Pocket Book of Chemical Technology," Chemical Publishing Company, Inc., New York, 1954.

Civil Engineering

Abbett, R. W.: "American Civil Engineering Practice," John Wiley & Sons, Inc., New York, 1956–1957.

Finnern, R.: "Taschenbuch der Bauwirtschaft," N. Ernst and Sohn, Berlin, 1953.

Pantaleo, M. (ed.): "Manuale dell'ingegnere civile," Perrella, Rome, 1952.

Probst, E. H. (ed.): "Civil Engineering Reference Book," Butterworth & Co. (Publishers) Ltd., London, 1951.

Seelye, E. E.: "Data Book for Civil Engineers," John Wiley & Sons, Inc., New York, 1951–1954.

Electrical Engineering

Knowlton, A. E. (ed.): "Standard Handbook for Electrical Engineers," McGraw-Hill Book Company, Inc., New York, 1949.

Pender, H., and W. A. Del Mar (eds.): "Electrical Engineers' Handbook," John Wiley & Sons, Inc., New York, 1949–1950.

General Engineering and Financial Data

Brady, G. S.: "Materials Handbook," McGraw-Hill Book Company, Inc., New York, 1956.

Eshbach, O. W. (ed.): "Handbook of Engineering Fundamentals," John Wiley & Sons, Inc., New York, 1952.

Ewell, R. H. (ed.): "Chemical Economics Handbook," Stanford Research Institute, Stanford, Calif., 1952–   .

Ireson, W. G., and E. L. Grant: "Handbook of Industrial Engineering and Management," Prentice-Hall, Inc., Englewood Cliffs, N.J., 1955.

Montgomery, R. H.: "Financial Handbook," The Ronald Press Company, New York, 1948.

Paton, W. A.: "Accountant's Handbook," The Ronald Press Company, New York, 1944.

Perry, J. H. (ed.): "Chemical Business Handbook," McGraw-Hill Book Company, Inc., New York, 1954.

Prockter, C. E. (ed.): "Kempe's Engineers' Yearbook for 1956," Morgan Brothers, London, 1956.

Mechanical Engineering

Camm, F. J. (ed.): "Newnes Engineers' Reference Book," Newnes, London, 1954.

Carmichael, C. (ed.): "Kent's Mechanical Engineers' Handbook," John Wiley & Sons, Inc., New York, 1950.

Dubbel, H. (ed.): "Taschenbuch für die Maschinenbau," Springer-Verlag OHG, Vienna, 1953.

Marks, L. S. (ed.): "Mechanical Engineers' Handbook," McGraw-Hill Book Company, Inc., New York, 1951.

Metallurgical Engineering

Hampel, C. A.: "Rare Metals Handbook," Reinhold Publishing Corporation, New York, 1954.

Horger, O. J. (ed.): "ASME Handbook: Metals—Engineering—Design," McGraw-Hill Book Company, Inc., New York, 1953.

Hoyt, S. L.: "Metals and Alloys Data Book," Reinhold Publishing Corporation, New York, 1952.

———— (ed.): "ASME Handbook: Metals Properties," McGraw-Hill Book Company, Inc., New York, 1954.

Huckert, J. (ed.): "ASME Handbook: Engineering Tables," McGraw-Hill Book Company, Inc., New York, 1956.

Lyman, T. (ed.): "Metals Handbook," American Society for Metals, 1948; also 2 supplements.

Smithells, C. J.: "Metals Reference Book," Interscience Publishers, Inc., New York, 1955.

Uhlig, H. H.: "The Corrosion Handbook," John Wiley & Sons, Inc., New York, 1948.

Woldman, N. E.: "Engineering Alloys," American Society for Metals, Cleveland, Ohio, 1954.

Refrigeration Engineering and Air Conditioning

Bolstad, M. M.: "Air Conditioning, Refrigerating Data Book" (design volume), American Society of Refrigerating Engineers, New York, 1955.

Hendrickson, H. H. (ed.): "Air Conditioning, Refrigerating Data Book" (applications volume), American Society of Refrigerating Engineers, New York, 1955.

Comprehensive Works. The large, comprehensive works include, as far as possible, all the known data of this kind. They usually cite references to the original literature so that one may consult details when it is desirable to know the conditions under which the constant was determined.

E. W. Washburn, "International Critical Tables," McGraw-Hill Book Company, Inc., New York, 1926–1930. The publication of "International Critical Tables" marked the appearance of the first comprehensive compilation of tabular data in the English language. The material was collected, critically evaluated, and arranged by some 300 chemists, physicists, and technologists in more than a dozen countries. The data selected came largely from the first seven volumes of the French annual tables (discussed below).

The program covered all available information of value concerning the physical properties and numerical characteristics of (1) pure substances, (2) mixtures of definite composition, (3) the important classes of industrial materials, (4) many natural materials and products, and (5) selected bodies or systems, such as the earth and its main physical subdivisions, the solar and stellar systems, and certain biological organisms, including man. Publications in all languages up to 1924 were examined for data, and much unpublished information was collected. No supplements have been issued. Lists of errata were published with each volume.

Each volume carries a table of contents showing the kind of material included, and many of the sections begin with an outline of their subject matter. An index volume enables one to locate easily the various types of data. Certain peculiarities of the index are explained in the introduction.

Specific data for a given system may or may not be easily found. In some cases a general formula has to be used to calculate the desired data; in other cases the difficulty comes in interpreting the tabular system used. Often it centers in employing the "key-number" formula for compounds. This "standard arrangement" of data in "A," "A-B," "B," and "C" tables, explained in Volume I, page 96, and Volume III, page viii, should be mastered by users of the set.

The principal explanatory text is in four languages: English, French, German, and Italian. Citations to the literature are gathered together at the end of each section, where reference is then made to the list of publications at the end of each volume. An introductory paragraph explains the method of handling references. Volume VII gives a complete list of publications cited. It should be kept in mind that the references included are not likely to be later than 2 to 3 years preceding the date of publication of the individual volume consulted.

After nearly 30 years, the new Office of Critical Tables has been established by the National Research Council. It will coordinate the work of compiling groups. Presumably any publications will supplement "International Critical Tables."

A. Eucken (ed.), "Landolt-Börnstein's Zahlenwerke und Funktionen aus Physik, Chemie, Astronomie, Geophysik, und Technik," Springer-Verlag OHG, Vienna. Until the publication of "International Critical Tables," the Landolt-Börnstein treatise was the preeminent source for physicochemical constants and similar data. To the edition of 1923 three supplements were added by 1936. Much of the work, therefore, is later than "International Critical Tables." The original classification into some 30 divisions, given in detail in the table of contents, is followed in the supplements. In the indexes in the supplements are included the pages in the previous parts of the set for the same entry. References to the literature are at the end of each section.

The proposed coverage of the new edition now appearing follows:

Band I. Atom- und Molekularphysik

　1 Teil (1950)　Atome und Ionen
　2 Teil (1951)　Molekulen I
　3 Teil (1951)　Molekulen II
　4 Teil (1955)　Kristalle
　5 Teil (1952)　Atomkerne und Elementarteilchen

Band II. Makrophysik und Chemie

　1 Teil (　　)
　2 Teil (　　)
　3 Teil (1956)　Schmelzgleichgewichte und Grenzflächenerscheinungen

Band III. Astronomie und Geophysik
Band IV. Technik

　1 Teil (1955)　Stoffwerte und mechanische Verhalten von Nichtmetallen

C. Marie (ed.), "Tables annuelles de constants et donnée numérique," Gauthier-Villars & Cie, Paris. The "Annual Tables" were started to bring together each year all the numerical data published in chemistry, physics, biology, and technology. Although the summaries have not appeared annually or as promptly as desirable, the results achieved by the international commission are probably all that could be done under the circumstances. The indexes and text for each table are given in both French and English. Two cumulative indexes (in French) cover the first 10 volumes. Since 1926 this set supplements "International Critical Tables."

The years covered by each volume follow:

I (1910); II (1911); III (1912); IV (1913–1916); V (1917–1922); VI (1923–1924); VII (1925–1926); VIII (1927–1928); IX (1929); X (1930); XI (1931–1934); XII (1935–1936)

In 1947 publication was resumed, under different auspices, and with the title "Tables de constantes et données numériques.

Constantes sélectionnées." The following numbered monographs have appeared:

1. *Longueurs d'onde des émissions X et des discontinuités d'absorption X* (1926–1946).
2. *Physique nucléaire* (1896–1946).
3. *Pouvoir rotatoire magnétique; Effet magnéto-optique de Kerr* (1876–1947).
4. *Données spectroscopiques concernant les molécules diatomiques* (1894–1951).
5. *Atlas deslongueurs d'onde caractéristiques des bandes d'émission et d'absorption des molécules diatomiques* (1911–1952).
6. *Pouvoir rotatoire naturel. I. Stéroides* (1863–1954).

G. *Egloff, "Physical Constants of Hydrocarbons,"* Reinhold Publishing Corporation, New York, 1939–1947. This set, restricted to pure hydrocarbons, lists what are considered the most reliable values for the melting point, boiling point, specific gravity, and refractive index, together with original references.

A. *Seidell and W. F. Linke, "Solubilities of Inorganic and Organic Compounds"* and supplement, D. Van Nostrand Company, Inc., Princeton, N.J., 1940–1952. Information includes sources of solubility data, methods of calculating them to desired terms, interpretation of their tabular arrangement, and some of the methods used for the accurate determination of solubility. For each table the author and year of publication are given. By referring to the author index, the journal reference may be found.

F. D. *Rossini, "Catalog of Spectral Data,"* American Petroleum Institute Research Project 44, 1953–   .

F. D. *Rossini, "Selected Values of Properties of Hydrocarbons and Related Compounds,"* Carnegie Institute of Technology, Pittsburgh, Pa., 1955–   .

Dictionaries and Encyclopedias

Another class of reference works includes dictionaries and encyclopedias. These publications are grouped together since the words "dictionary" and "encyclopedia" have been used more or less synonymously in connection with chemical publications.

In current dictionaries of the English language a dictionary is defined as a work containing the words belonging to some province of knowledge. It deals primarily with words and is concerned with the word itself. Considered from this standpoint, the true chemical dictionary is one which includes a list of chemical terms with their definitions and usage, rather than one dealing with subjects arranged in alphabetical order.

An encyclopedia is a comprehensive summary of knowledge or of a branch of knowledge, a work in which the various branches of science are discussed separately. It deals primarily with subjects and is concerned with the thing the word represents. Encyclopedias of chemistry, then, are composed of separate discussions or presentations of topics in the form of a comprehensive summary of the whole field of chemistry or a large, representative portion. The usual arrangement is alphabetical by subjects. The general scheme is to give for each topic or subject a summary presenting the information that is considered to be of the most general value. The articles are historical, descriptive, explanatory, and statistical. References may or may not be given to sources where more extensive information is to be found.

With this distinction between dictionaries and encyclopedias in mind, an attempt has been made to separate them into two lists, as shown below. Some mistakes may have been made, since not all the works mentioned were available for examination.

Dictionaries

Bailey, D., and K. C. Bailey: "An Etymological Dictionary of Chemistry and Mineralogy," Edward Arnold & Co., London, 1929.

Beadnell, H.: "Dictionary of Scientific Terms," C. A. Watts & Co., Ltd., London, 1938.

Bennett, H. (ed.): "Concise Chemical and Technical Dictionary," Chemical Publishing Company, Inc., New York, 1947.

Brown, V. J., and D. G. Runner: "Engineering Terminology," Gillette Publishing Co., Chicago, 1939.

Campbell, F. H.: "Chemical Dictionary," Chemical Publishing Company, Inc., New York, 1942.

Dorland, W. A. N.: "The American Illustrated Medical Dictionary," W. B. Saunders Company, Philadelphia, 1954.

Gardner, W.: "Chemical Synonyms and Trade Names," D. Van Nostrand Company, Inc., Princeton, N.J., 1944.

Grant, J. (ed.): "Hackh's Chemical Dictionary," Blakiston Division, McGraw-Hill Book Company, Inc., New York, 1944.

Haynes, W.: "Chemical Trade Names and Synonyms," D. Van Nostrand Company, Inc., Princeton, N.J., 1951.

Henderson, I. F., and W. D. Henderson, "A Dictionary of Scientific Terms," D. Van Nostrand Company, Inc., Princeton, N.J., 1939.

Henderson, J. G.: "Metallurgical Dictionary," Reinhold Publishing Corporation, New York, 1953.

Maerz, A., and M. R. Paul: "A Dictionary of Color," 2d ed., McGraw-Hill Book Company, Inc., New York, 1950.

Malisoff, W. M.: "The Dictionary of Biochemistry and Related Subjects," Philosophical Library, Inc., New York, 1943.

Merlub-Sobel, M.: "Metals and Alloys Dictionary," Chemical Publishing
    Company, Inc., New York, 1944.
Michels, W. C., et al.: "International Dictionary of Physics and Elec-
    tronics," D. Van Nostrand Company, Inc., Princeton, N.J., 1956.
Molina Font, J.: "Diccionario quimico comercial, industrial y farmacéntico,"
    Editorial de Libros Cientificos, Mexico City, 1949.
Stedman, T. L.: "Stedman's Medical Dictionary," Williams & Wilkins
    Company, Baltimore, 1954.
"Van Nostrand's Chemists' Dictionary," D. Van Nostrand Company,
    Inc., Princeton, N.J., 1953.
Zimmerman, O. T., and I. Lavine: "Industrial Research Service's Handbook
    of Material Trade Names," Industrial Research Service, Dover, N.H.,
    1946.
————: "Scientific and Technical Abbreviations, Signs, and Symbols,"
    Industrial Research Service, Dover, N.H., 1949.

Encyclopedias. Encyclopedias are divided here into two groups,
the basis being up-to-dateness and language availability.

In the first group are those which seem of most current use to
Americans. They include both works of single volumes and multivolume sets.

Clark, G. L., and G. G. Hawley (eds.): "The Encyclopedia of Chemistry,"
    Reinhold Publishing Corporation, New York, 1957.
Crouse, W. H. (ed.): "McGraw-Hill Encyclopedia of Science and Tech-
    nology," McGraw-Hill Book Company, Inc., New York, 1957–   .
Foerst, W. (ed.): "Ullmann's Enzyklopädie der technischen Chemie,"
    Urban & Schwarzenberg, Berlin, 1951–   .
Heilbron, I., et al. (eds.): "Thorpe's Dictionary of Applied Chemistry,"
    Longmans, Green & Co., Inc., New York, 1937-1956.
Kirk, R. E., and D. F. Othmer (eds.): "Encyclopedia of Chemical Tech-
    nology," Interscience Publishers, Inc., New York, 1947–1955.
"The Merck Index," Merck and Co., Rahway, N.J., 1952.
Miall, S., and L. M. Miall (eds.): "A New Dictionary of Chemistry,"
    Longmans, Green & Co., Inc., New York, 1949.
Rose, A., and E. Rose (eds.): "Condensed Chemical Dictionary," Reinhold
    Publishing Corporation, New York, 1956.
Stewart, J. R.: "An Encyclopedia of the Chemical Process Industries,"
    Chemical Publishing Company, Inc., New York, 1956.
Strong, R. K. (ed.): "Kingzett's Chemical Encyclopaedia," D. Van
    Nostrand Company, Inc., Princeton, N.J., 1952.
"Van Nostrand's Scientific Encyclopedia," D. Van Nostrand Company,
    Inc., Princeton, N.J., 1947.

In the second group are the less useful foreign sets, along with
those in English and other languages which now are chiefly of
historical interest.

Berliner, A., and K. Scheel: "Physikalisches Handwörterbuch," Springer-Verlag OHG, Vienna, 1932.

Duval, C.: "Dictionnaire de chimie théorique et industrielle," Librairie des sciences et des arts, Paris, 1939.

————, R. Duval, and R. Dolique: "Dictionnaire de la chimie et des applications," Bibliothèque de formation professionelle, Paris, 1935.

Fremy, M. E. (ed.): "Encyclopédie chimique," Dunod, Paris, 1882–1905.

Hunt, R. (ed.): "Ure's Dictionary of Arts, Manufactures, and Mines," Longmans, Green & Co., Ltd., London, 1867–1878.

Ladenburg, A. (ed.): "Handwörterbuch der Chemie," E. Trewendt, Breslau, Germany, 1883–1896.

Liebig, J., J. C. Poggendorff, and F. Wöhler: "Handwörterbuch der reinen und angewandten Chemie," 1842–1940; rev. by H. von Fehling (ed.), as "Neues Handwörterbuch der Chemie," Vieweg-Verlag, Brunswick, Germany, 1871–1930.

Muspratt, J. S.: "Enzyklopädisches Handbuch der technischen Chemie," Vieweg-Verlag, Brunswick, Germany, 1888–1922.

Nicholson, W.: "A Dictionary of Chemistry," Longman, Hurst, Nees, and Orme, London, 1795–1808.

Römpp, H.: "Chemie-Lexikon," Franckh'sche Verlagshandlung, Stuttgart, Germany, 1953.

Schoengold, M. D.: "Encyclopedia of Substances and Synthetics," Philosophical Library, Inc., New York, 1943.

Stewart, J. R.: "National Paint Dictionary," Chemical Publishing Company, Inc., New York, 1940.

Tweney, C. F., and L. E. C. Hughes (eds.): "Chamber's Technical Dictionary," The Macmillan Company, New York, 1949.

————: "Hutchinson's Technical and Scientific Encyclopedia," The Macmillan Company, New York, 1936.

Villavecchia, G. V.: "Dizionario di merceologia e di chimica applicata," U. Hoepli, Milan, Italy, 1942–1943.

Watts, H. A. (ed.): "A Dictionary of Chemistry," 1872–1874; rev. by H. F. Morley and M. M. P. Muir (eds.), Longmans, Green & Co., Ltd., London, 1888–1894.

In addition to these encyclopedias dealing with chemistry, general encyclopedias, such as the "Encyclopaedia Britannica," frequently contain valuable discussions of chemical subjects.

The works known as "almanacs" provide another source of information of possible chemical value. These publications contain a wide variety of facts in tabular and graphic form. Since they often appear annually, they serve as supplements to the large encyclopedias. The following selection is representative. The year appearing at the left indicates the date of the first appearance of the work.

1868 "World Almanac," *New York World Telegram and Sun,* New York.
1869 "Whitaker's Almanack," Whitaker, London.
1908 "New International Yearbook," Dodd, Mead & Company, Inc., New York.
1910 "American Yearbook," Appleton-Century-Crofts, Inc., New York.
1923 "American Annual," Encyclopedia Americana, New York.
1947 "Information Please Almanac," Doubleday & Company, Inc., New York.

Formularies

As a result of the work of practical experimenters and manufacturing chemists, there has been accumulated an extensive collection of formulas and recipes consisting of directions for performing given reactions or making certain products. In general, such information is intended to be distinctly practical in nature, with emphasis upon commercial methods. In the following representative publications may be found a large variety of recipes:

Bennett, H. (ed.): "The Chemical Formulary," Chemical Publishing Company, Inc., New York, 1933–1956.

Blumenthal, S.: "Food Manufacturing," Chemical Publishing Company, Inc., New York, 1947.

Francke, D. E.: "Hospital Formulary of Selected Drugs," Hamilton Press, Hamilton, Ill., 1955.

Freeman, M.: "New Practical Formulary," Chemical Publishing Company, Inc., New York, 1955.

Gattefossé, R. M.: "Formulary of Perfumery," L. Hill, Ltd., London, 1952.

Hiscox, G. D., and T. O. Sloane (eds.): "Henley's Twentieth Century Book of Formulas, Processes, and Trade Secrets," The Norman W. Henley Publishing Company, New York, 1945.

Hopkins, A. A. (ed.): "Standard American Encyclopedia of Formulas," Grosset & Dunlap, Inc., New York, 1953.

Jameson, L.: "Jameson's Manufacturer's Practical Recipes," Earle, London, 1934.

Keithler, W. R.: "The Formulation of Cosmetics and Cosmetic Specialties," Drug and Cosmetic Industry, New York, 1956.

Minrath, W. R. (ed.): "Van Nostrand's Practical Formulary," D. Van Nostrand Company, Inc., Princeton, N.J., 1957.

"National Formulary," American Pharmaceutical Association, Washington, D.C., 1955.

"Pharmaceutical Formulas," Chemist and Druggist, New York, 1953–1956.

"The Pharmaceutical Recipe Book," American Pharmaceutical Association, Washington, D.C., 1943.

Ranshaw, G. S. (ed.): "Manufacturers' Practical Recipes," Shaw Publishing Company, Washington, 1948.

Treatises

In many instances one wants to know merely some physical constant for a given element, compound, or system, and the required information may be found in tabular compilations. In many other instances, it may be necessary to know about the occurrence of an element or compound, the methods of preparation and purification, the chemical properties of systems, the uses of materials, the methods of analysis and testing, general relationships, or other facts.

Information of this kind may be given in an elementary textbook—if it is some simple fact about a common element—in a chemical dictionary, or in a monograph. But the best place, in general, to look for such facts is in the works known as "treatises." Here one finds facts, together with discussions of them. If the discussion is critical, in the sense that an opinion is given regarding the merit of the material presented, we have the highest type of treatise. Whether critical or not, there is always an extensive or complete presentation of the material of a given field, based upon some general outline, such as groups of elements or classes of compounds. The more important original references are given.

In these publications it is the general practice to limit the material to some broad field of chemistry, such as organic, inorganic, or biological. Kayser's treatise on spectroscopy is an example of limiting the material to the application of a single instrument in the whole field of chemistry.

Anyone unfamiliar with a large treatise should examine the introductory section to determine any peculiarities of the set, such as the system of arrangement, abbreviations of periodicals and words, the details of the table of contents, and any limitations regarding the kind of information included.

Time lag is most disconcerting in these large works of reference.[1] Publication of such sets in up-to-date form is probably the most difficult task in the realm of chemical literature. Examination of the dates of publication of the inorganic treatises described in this section will reveal the present situation for any element that may be selected. When such sources are used, their dates of publication must be borne in mind.

Occasionally volumes of a treatise (such as certain German

[1] Mellon, *J. Chem. Educ.*, **10**:284 (1933).

sets) seem to have been merely reprinted but bear the date of reprinting rather than that of the original issue. Unless accompanied by some statement to this effect, such practice may be very misleading to the searcher.

Some of the important treatises will now be considered. First they are divided according to well-recognized fields of chemistry. Then in several of these divisions a distinction is drawn between the multivolume comprehensive sets and those of only two or three volumes.

Organic Chemistry. Attention will be given first to the works which deal with the chemistry of the compounds of carbon. There are several extensive treatises.

F. K. Beilstein, "Handbuch der organischen Chemie," Springer-Verlag OHG, Vienna. The outstanding treatise on organic chemistry[1] was originated by F. K. Beilstein, a Russian chemist. The first edition of two volumes, divided into five parts, was completed in 1882 after 20 years of work. The third edition, consisting of four volumes, four supplements, and an index, was the last by Beilstein. It is to this edition that reference is made so often in the third edition of Richter's "Lexikon." The fourth edition, under the editorship of F. Richter, was issued by the Deutsche Chemische Gesellschaft until after World War II, when it was taken over by the Beilstein Institut.

Exclusive of the naturally occurring compounds of unknown composition (Division IV), 27 volumes were required. These cover the literature only to 1910. Fifteen supplementary volumes bring the literature for the first three divisions to 1920. The second supplement, that is, to 1930, comprises 27 more volumes. The third supplement, to cover the literature to 1950, is under way.

The general arrangement has always been based on kinds of compounds, as hydrocarbons, ketones, and other general types. For the fourth edition the classification was modified so that 4,877 sections (*Systemnummer*) are supposed to meet all requirements. The accompanying outline shows the distribution of the material in the various volumes of the set, together with a general statement of the scheme of classification used.

Indexes, abbreviations of literature sources, other abbreviations, an extensive classified table of contents, and corrections for previous volumes are given in each volume. References to

[1] See Huntress, *J. Chem. Educ.*, **15**:303, 310 (1938).

the literature are given in the body of the text. At the top of each page of the supplements is the page number of the main volume in which the same compounds were discussed.

Divisions. The compounds are first arranged in four main divisions on the basis of whether their structure is known and, if so, how the carbon atoms are bound together.

DIVISION I. ACYCLIC COMPOUNDS (Nos. 1–449)

(Stem nuclei[1] with carbon alone bound in chain form)

   I. Hydrocarbons and —OH, —C=, and =C(OH)—C= derivatives
  II. Carboxylic acids
 III. Carboxylic acid derivatives
 IV. Sulfonic acids, amines, other N compounds, organometallic compounds

DIVISION II. ISOCYCLIC COMPOUNDS (Nos. 450–2,359)

(Compounds with carbon-to-carbon rings)

    V. Hydrocarbons
   VI. Hydroxy compounds, including alcohols, phenols, phenol alcohols
  VII. Carbonyl compounds, including aldehydes, ketones, quinones
 VIII. Hydroxycarbonyl compounds
   IX. Carboxylic acids
    X. Hydroxycarboxylic acids
   XI. Other acids, including S, Se, Te derivatives
  XII. Monoamines
 XIII. Polyamines
 XIV. Carbonyl amines, amino acids
  XV. Hydroxylamines, hydrazines
 XVI. Other nitrogen compounds, organometallic compounds

DIVISION III. HETEROCYCLIC COMPOUNDS (Nos. 2,360–4,720)

(Compounds with other elements besides carbon in the ring)

  XVII. One cyclic oxygen (nuclei, —OH, —C= compounds, S, Se, Te derivatives)
 XVIII. One cyclic oxygen (—C=, acidic, nitrogen, organometallic compounds)
   XIX. Two (or more) cyclic oxygens
   XX. One cyclic nitrogen (nuclei)
  XXI. One cyclic nitrogen (—OH, —C= compounds)

[1] *Stem nuclei* refer to the ultimate groups obtained by substituting hydrogen for all other elements attached to carbon, without disrupting any rings.

XXII. One cyclic nitrogen (other derivatives)
XXIII. Two cyclic nitrogens (nuclei, —OH compounds)
XXIV. Two cyclic nitrogens (—C= compounds)
XXV. Two cyclic nitrogens (other compounds)
XXVI. Three to eight cyclic nitrogens
XXVII. Compounds with both cyclic oxygen and nitrogen atoms
XXVIII. Subject index ⎫
XXIX. Formula index ⎭ Divisions I–III, including first supplement

DIVISION IV. COMPOUNDS OF UNCERTAIN STRUCTURE (Nos. 4,721–4,877)

XXX. Caoutchouc, gutta-percha, balata, carotinoids (literature to 1935)
XXXI. Monosaccharides, oligosaccharides (literature to 1920)
XXXII. Polysaccharides ( )
XXXIII. Alkaloids ( )

The two index volumes (XXVIII and XXIX) cover the main work and the first supplement (to 1920). The formula index to this point uses the Richter system.[1] Volume XXVIII of the second supplement is a collective index of the main work and the first two supplements. Likewise, Volume XXIX of the second supplement is a collective formula index.[2] In contrast to the previous formula index, this one uses the American Hill system.

These index volumes list all organic compounds reported up to 1930. From 1930 on one should understand the set to locate individual compounds.

Generally an inspection of the structural formula will indicate in which of the three divisions a compound of known structure belongs. In the more complicated and uncertain cases the formula may be broken down into the simpler stem nuclei by substituting hydrogen for all the other elements bound to carbon, without disrupting any ring. According to the principle of latest position, the compound will be found in the last division to which any of its nuclei belong.

Subdivisions. Only the heterocyclic division (III) has subdivisions. They are arranged in arbitrary sequence according to the kind and number of hetero atoms, such as oxygen and nitrogen, in the ring. Thus, compounds with oxygen in the ring come before those with nitrogen, and both of these before compounds containing oxygen and nitrogen in the ring.

[1] See Taylor, *Ind. Eng. Chem.*, **40**:470 (1948), for a proposed numerical index key for the Beilstein treatise.

[2] The new formula index is to cover vol. I of the third supplement (i.e., through 1949).

Classes. Divisions I and II and the heterocyclic subdivisions are then arranged in classes on the basis of functioning groups.[1] Class 1 includes only stem-nuclei compounds, such as ethane, benzene, and pyridine. In each of the others the compound contains a group having at least one hydrogen atom replaceable by another substituent. The classes for Volume IV, arranged in the order of discussion, are as follows:

1. Stem nuclei
2. Hydroxy compounds   —OH
3. Carbonyl compounds $=$O or $\left(\begin{smallmatrix} ^{OH} \\ < \\ _{OH} \end{smallmatrix}\right)$
4. Carboxylic acids $=$O(OH) or $\left(\begin{smallmatrix} ^{OH} \\ -OH \\ _{OH} \end{smallmatrix}\right)$
5. Sulfinic acids   —SO(OH)
6. Sulfonic acids   —SO$_2$(OH)
7. Seleninic and selenonic acids   —SeO(OH) and —SeO$_2$(OH)
8. Amines   —NH$_2$
9. Hydroxylamines   —NHOH
10. Hydrazines   —NH·NH$_2$
11. Azo compounds   —N:NH
12–18. Other nitrogen compounds
19–38. Organometallic compounds

Under each class is included certain general information on nomenclature, properties, and derivatives.

Subclasses. In arranging compounds in subclasses the sequence is according (1) to decreasing saturation in stem nuclei, as C_nH_{2n+2}, C_nH_{2n}, etc., compounds; (2) to the number of single characteristic functioning groups, as mono-, di-, tri-, etc., compounds; and (3) to the increasing number of different characteristic groups, as carbonyl, hydroxycarbonyl, aminohydroxycarbonyl, etc., compounds.

Rubrics. Decreasing saturation is also the basis of arrangement within the subclasses, rubric 1 being the most highly saturated type. Each rubric may then be expressed in terms of a general formula, as $C_nH_{2n+2}O$ for monohydroxy alcohols.

[1] In a given division there may be fewer or more than 38 numbered classes. In some cases compounds containing all the functioning groups are not known. Then again a separate class number may be assigned each metallic element, which may make more than 38 actual classes. Since those included are numbered consecutively, a given type of compound cannot be assigned a class number unless the set is consulted. Volume IV has 38 classes, but vol. XVI, supplement 2, has 49.

Series. In each rubric group the compounds of the same degree of saturation are arranged in the order of increasing number of carbon atoms. The series designation, as C_3, shows the number of carbon atoms in the compound. The individual members of the series are the index or parent compounds.

For each index compound the available material is arranged as follows: (1) structure, configuration, historical; (2) occurrence, formation, preparation; (3) properties (color, crystallography, physical constants); (4) chemical properties; (5) physiological action; (6) uses; (7) analytical data (detection, examination, estimation); (8) addition compounds and salts; and (9) derivatives.

Derivatives. The derivatives which each index compound may form require special consideration. There are three types, as follows:

1. FUNCTIONAL DERIVATIVES. These are produced, in effect, by replacing the characteristic hydrogen of the functioning group by an organic or inorganic group (atom). The process involves the reaction of the index compound with some coupling compound, either organic or inorganic, with the elimination of water. Organic coupling compounds contain a hydroxyl group attached to carbon. Inorganic coupling compounds function through a hydroxyl group, as in hydrogen peroxide and oxygenated acids, or a hydrogen directly attached to a halogen, nitrogen, or certain other elements in the periodic system. Such hydrides couple only with hydroxyl in the index compound.

2. NONFUNCTIONAL DERIVATIVES. These are produced by substituting hydrogen of the stem nucleus by one or more of the nonfunctioning groups, —F, —Cl, —Br, —I, —NO, —NO₂, —N₃.

3. REPLACEMENT DERIVATIVES. These are produced by replacing the oxygen of a functioning group by sulfur, selenium, or tellurium.

All these relationships for two index compounds, methyl and ethyl alcohol, are illustrated below.

DIVISION I. ACYCLIC COMPOUNDS

Subdivision
  Class 2   Hydroxy compounds
    Subclass *A*   Monohydroxy compounds
      Rubric 1   Monohydroxy alcohols ($C_nH_{2n+2}O$)
        Series *A* CH_4O—methyl alcohol
                 a. Structure, historical

Subdivision
  Series *A*   *b.* Occurrence, formation, preparation
        c. Physical properties
        d. Chemical properties
        e. Physiological behavior
        f. Uses
        g. Analytical methods
        h. Addition compounds and salts
        i. Derivatives
          a′. Functional
            a″. Organic coupling
            b″. Inorganic
          b′. Substitution
          c′. Replacement
  Series *B* C_2H_6O—ethyl alcohol
  Rubric 2   Monohydroxy alcohols ($C_nH_{2n}O$)
  Subclass *B* Dihydroxy compounds
  Class 3   Carbonyl compounds

Finding a Compound.[1] Ability to locate facts for a given compound is the test of one's knowledge of the set. Finding some compounds is a real puzzle, but familiarity with the set will yield results worth the effort required to master the scheme.

If the compound is listed in the formula index (Volume XXIX), the problem is easy. However, this volume covers the literature only to 1930. Compounds not listed must be located otherwise.

One approach is to find the index compound. As an example of a triple derivative (functional, nonfunctional, and replacement), 4-nitrothioanisole will serve. The formula is

$$O_2N-\bigcirc-S-CH_3$$

[1] Where this brief outline is inadequate, see the following: (1) introduction to the set in vol. I; (2) Hennion, *J. Chem. Educ.*, **21**:34 (1944); (3) E. H. Huntress, "The Use of Beilstein's Handbuch der organischen Chemie," John Wiley & Sons, Inc., New York, 1938; (4) B. Prager, D. Stern, and K. Ilberg, "System der organischen Verbindungen," Springer-Verlag OHG, Vienna, 1929, a 246-page explanation listing the 4,877 types of compounds, common names, and type index; (5) F. Richter, "Kurze Anleitung zur Orientierung in Beilstein's Handbuch der organischen Chemie," Springer-Verlag OHG, Vienna, 1936; (6) B. A. Soule, "Library Guide for the Chemist," McGraw-Hill Book Company, Inc., New York, 1938; and (7) A. I. Vogel, "A Textbook of Practical Organic Chemistry," pp. 1119–1130, Longmans, Green & Co., Inc., New York, 1956.

Sulfur in the position shown indicates a replacement derivative, and the nitro group shows a nonfunctional derivative. Replacing the S with O, and the NO_2 group with H, gives

Reversing the dehydration process producing such an ether,

yields phenol, C_6H_5OH, and methanol, CH_3OH. As phenol is discussed in the treatise after methanol, phenol, a class 2, or hydroxy, compound, is the index compound under which to look.[1]

F. Radt (ed.), "Elsevier's Encyclopaedia of Organic Chemistry," Elsevier Publishing Company, Amsterdam. This treatise is the first work in English designed "to give complete information on all chemical and physical properties and on the most important physiological properties of organic compounds."

The presentation is based on the structure of the compounds, so that those which are most closely related are placed together. Within each of the aliphatic, carbocyclic, and heterocyclic series the structural skeleton determines the arrangement. Then the whole chemistry of a compound, e.g., naphthalene, is in one section, together with its derivatives. Tables and charts summarize data for a series of compounds. References appear at the ends of sections.

Although planned to be a 20-volume set, only the volumes indicated have been issued. Now the work is to be combined with the Beilstein set. The years in parentheses indicate the dates of publication.

SERIES III. CARBOISOCYCLIC CONDENSED COMPOUNDS

12. Bicyclic compounds (nine parts, 1948–1954)

13. Tricyclic compounds (1946)

14. Tetra- and higher cyclic compounds (1940, and four supplements, 1951–1956)

V. Grignard (ed.), "Traité de chimie organique," Masson & Cie, Paris. The first comprehensive treatise in this field in

[1] See Soule, *op. cit.*, for other examples.

French was started under Grignard's direction. This treatise, planned as indicated below, aims to summarize many aspects of organic chemistry rather than to present the details about myriads of compounds.

   I. Analysis; constitution; isomerism; nomenclature (1935)
   II. Optical and electrical properties; mechanism of reactions (1936)
   III. Aliphatic and cyclic hydrocarbons; derivatives (1935)
   IV. Benzene and its derivatives; petroleum (1936)
   V. Alcohols; ethers; organometallic compounds (1937)
   VI. Polyhydroxy alcohols; phenols; thiols (1940)
   VII. Aldehydes; ketones (1950)
   VIII. Quinones and derivatives; cellulose and derivatives (1938)
   IX. Acids; derivatives (1939)
   X. Di- and polyaliphatic acids; S and Se derivatives (1939)
   XI. Hydroxy acids (1945)
   XII. Amines; amino alcohols (1941)
   XIII. Amino acids; amides; nitriles (1941)
   XIV. Nitrogen compounds; As, P, and Si compounds (1939)
   XV. Azo and diazo compounds; triazenes; hydrazines; oximes (1948)
   XVI. Cyclic complexes; oils; resins; sterols (1949)
   XVII. Cyclic complexes; spiranes (1949)
   XVIII. Heterocyclic compounds (1945)
   XIX. Pyrroles; indigo (1942)
   XX. Heterocyclic compounds (1953)
   XXI. Heterocyclic compounds (1953)
   XXII. Industrial organic syntheses; dyes; synthetic high polymers; rubber; perfumes; fermentation; chemotherapy (1953)
   XXIII. Pyrimidines; xanthines; general alphabetical index (1954)

E. Müller (ed.), "Houben-Weyl's Methoden der organischen Chemie," Georg Thieme Verlag, Leipzig. The new fourth edition is projected for 16 volumes (in some 22 parts). It is a monumental set covering the working methods of organic chemistry. As planned, the coverage is as follows.

   I_1. General laboratory methods (   )
   I_2. General laboratory methods (   )
   II. Analytical methods (1953)
   III_1. Physical methods (1955)
   III_2. Physical methods (1955)
   IV_1. General chemical methods (   )
   IV_2. General chemical methods (1955)
   IV_3. General chemical methods (   )
   V_1. Hydrocarbons (   )
   V_2. Halogen compounds (   )
   VI. Oxygen compounds. I (   )

VII₁. Oxygen compounds. II (1954)
VII₂. Oxygen compounds. II (   )
VIII. Oxygen compounds. III (1952)
  IX. Sulfur, selenium, tellurium compounds (1955)
   X. Nitrogen compounds. I (   )
  XI. Nitrogen compounds. II (   )
 XII. Phosphorus, arsenic, antimony, bismuth, silicon, boron, organometallic compounds (   )
XIII. Ring compounds with heteroatoms (   )
 XIV. Synthetic macromolecule substances (   )
  XV. Carbohydrates; proteins; peptides (   )
 XVI. Summary; indexes (   )

E. H. Rodd (ed.), *"Chemistry of Carbon Compounds,"* Elsevier Publishing Company, Amsterdam. In comprehensiveness this new set lies between the great treatises and the introductory textbooks. For many reference purposes the compact coverage is adequate.

 I*a*. Aliphatic compounds (1951)
 I*b*. Aliphatic compounds (1952)
II*a*. Alicyclic compounds (1953)
II*b*. Alicyclic compounds (1953)
III*a*. Aromatic compounds (1954)
III*b*. Aromatic compounds (1956)
  IV. Heterocyclic compounds (   )
   V. Miscellaneous; general index (   )

A. Weissberger (ed.), *"Technique of Organic Chemistry,"* Interscience Publishers, Inc., New York. This is a comprehensive presentation of the techniques used in organic laboratories. Included are the theoretical background, techniques and tools, and merits and limitations of each method. Many contributors have produced the following volumes, several of which are in second editions:

   I. Physical methods of organic chemistry (three parts) (1949–1954)
  II. Catalytic, photochemical, and electrolytic reactions (1956)
 III. Heating; cooling; extraction; crystallization (1956)
  IV. Distillation (1951)
   V. Adsorption and chromatography (1951)
  VI. Micro- and semimicro methods (1954)
 VII. Organic solvents (1955)
VIII. Rates and mechanisms of reactions (1953)
  IX. Chemical applications of spectroscopy (1955)
   X. Chromatography (1957)

Other valuable reference works are the following:

R. *Adams (ed.), "Organic Reactions,"* John Wiley & Sons, Inc., New York, 1942–   . Widely used organic reactions, such as that of Grignard, are critically discussed.

H. *Brederick and E. Müller (eds.), "Organische Chemie in Ein-zeldarstellungen,"* Springer-Verlag OHG, Vienna, 1950–   .

B. *T. Brooks et al. (eds.), "The Chemistry of Petroleum Hydro-carbons,"* Reinhold Publishing Corporation, New York, 1954–1955.

E. *Chargaff and J. N. Davidson, "The Nucleic Acids,"* Academic Press, New York, 1955.

"The Colour Index," Society of Dyers and Colourists, Bradford, England, 1957–   . A vast amount of data deals with homogeneous dyes and pigments in current use.[1]

R. *C. Elderfield (ed.), "Heterocyclic Compounds,"* John Wiley & Sons, Inc., New York, 1950–   . In this new set the subject is treated from the standpoint of modern concepts for the correlation and explanation of observed facts.

J. *E. Faraday, "Encyclopedia of Hydrocarbon Compounds,"* Chemical Publishing Company, Inc., New York, 1946–   . In loose-leaf form the following information is presented: molecular formula, structural formula, occurrence in nature, names of compounds, methods of preparation, physical constants, detection and determination, and properties and reactions. New material and corrections provide for keeping the set up to date. Present coverage is to $C_{14}H_{18}$ compounds.

H. *Gilman (ed.), "Organic Chemistry,"* John Wiley & Sons, Inc., New York, 1943–1953.

I. *M. Heilbron and H. M. Bunbury, "Dictionary of Organic Compounds,"* Oxford University Press, New York, 1953. This compilation includes some 60,000 compounds selected as having the most interest.

H. *Mark et al. (eds.) "High Polymers,"* Interscience Publishers, Inc., New York, 1940–   .

H. *Meyer, "Lebrbuch der organisch-chemischen Methoden,"* Springer-Verlag OHG, Vienna, 1938–1940. Analytical and synthetic methods are the subject of this set.

---

[1] When completed, this set is to replace two earlier works: G. Schultz, "Farbstofftabellen," Akademische Verlagsgesellschaft m.b.H., Leipzig, 1931–1932; and F. M. Rowe (ed.), "Colour Index," Bradford, England, 1924–1928.

"Organic Syntheses," John Wiley & Sons, Inc., New York. Since 1921 American organic chemists have been issuing an annual compilation of tested new laboratory methods for preparing organic compounds. Usually the editorship changes each year. Three cumulative volumes cover the first 29 volumes, 1921–1950.

E. Ott et al. (eds.), *"Cellulose and Cellulose Derivatives,"* Interscience Publishers, Inc., New York, 1954–1955.

J. A. Radley, *"Starch and Its Derivatives,"* Chapman & Hall, Ltd., London, 1953.

W. Theilheimer, *"Synthetic Methods of Organic Chemistry,"* Interscience Publishers, Inc., New York, 1948–   . This set is partly in German and partly in English. Chemical reactions are considered as the breaking of one bond, followed by making of a new bond. Cumulative indexes in Volumes 5 and 8 stress reactions and types of compounds.

H. M. Ulrich (ed.), *"Handbuch der chemischen Untersuchung der Textilfaserstoffe,"* Springer-Verlag OHG, Vienna, 1954–   .

L. Velluz, *"Substances naturelles de synthèse,"* Masson & Cie, Paris, 1951–1954. These preparative methods resemble those of "Organic Syntheses."

A. Weissberger (ed.), *"The Chemistry of Heterocyclic Compounds,"* Interscience Publishers, Inc., New York, 1950–   . The wealth of information on heterocyclic chemistry is further illustrated by this set.

S. T. Yoffe and A. N. Nesmeyanov, *"A Handbook of Magnesium-Organic Compounds,"* Pergamon Press, New York, 1957.

Inorganic Chemistry. The general arrangement of treatises on organic chemistry is according to kinds or classes of compounds. In contrast, the treatises on inorganic chemistry follow more or less closely the order of the family groups in the Mendeleev form of the periodic table. Smaller works show a trend toward a long form of the table, such as that of Bohr (see chart on page 160) or one of its modifications.

R. J. Meyer (ed.), *"Gmelin's Handbuch der anorganischen Chemie,"* Verlag Chemie, G.m.b.H., Berlin. As Beilstein's treatise is the great set for organic chemistry, that of Gmelin is the great set for inorganic chemistry.

Leopold Gmelin issued the first edition of his "Handbuch der theoretischen Chemie" in 1817. The eighth edition was taken

over by the Deutsche Chemische Gesellschaft, under the editorship of R. J. Meyer, with the title "Handbuch der anorganischen
Chemie." In 1935 E. Pietsch became editor, and since 1945 the
set has been issued by the Gmelin Institut. Plans are to complete
the work by 1960, with the literature deadline set at January 1,
1950. Supplementary parts are to be issued for earlier volumes.
Literature after 1950 is being coded for machine searching in the
Gmelin archives.[1]

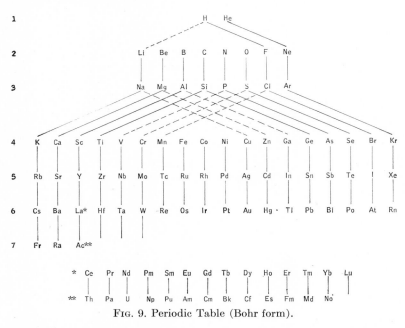

FIG. 9. Periodic Table (Bohr form).

In the eighth edition the presentation covers the history, occurrence, properties, scientific methods of preparation, and commercial processes of manufacture.

The elements are arranged in a list resembling somewhat that
in Hoffman's "Lexikon," except that it begins with the rare gases
and ends with the heavy metals. Separate parts are being issued
for each entry in the list. Binding of the parts in the projected
volumes is not always feasible. Thus, Part 59 for iron now runs to
thousands of pages.

[1] Over 1 million cards are filed at the Gmelin Institut. An information
service is operated to make this information available to subscribers.

The classification system[1] is based on the numerical sequence of elements shown in the accompanying table. In each case the element itself is first discussed. This is followed by its binary compounds, with all the elements above it, in the order shown. More complex compounds follow in the same manner. Supplements for certain metals cover their alloys and patents.

Volume	Number system	Contents and date
I	1, 2	Rare gases, 1926; H, 1927
II	3, 4	O, 1943–1952;* N, 1936
III	5, 6, 7, 8	F, 1926; Cl, 1927; Br, 1931; I, 1931–1933
IV	9, 10, 11, 12	S, 1942–1953; Se, 1949–1953; Te, 1940; Po, 1941
V	13, 14, 15	B, 1926, 1954;† C, ; Si,
VI	16, 17, 18, 19	P, ; As, 1952; Sb, 1949–1950; Bi, 1927
VII	20, 21	Li, 1927; Na, 1928
VIII	22, 23, 24, 25	K, 1938, 1942;† NH₄, 1936; Rb, 1937; Cs, 1938, 1956†
IX	26, 27, 28, 29, 30, 31	Be, 1930; Mg, 1937–1952; Ca, 1950–1957; Sr, 1931; Ba, 1932; Ra, 1928
X	32, 33	Zn, 1924, 1956;† Cd, 1925
XI	34	Hg,
XII	35, 36, 37, 38	Al, 1934–1950; Ga, 1936; In, 1936; Tl, 1940
XIII	39, 40	Rare earths, 1938–1955; Ac, 1942, 1956†
XIV	41, 42, 43, 44	Ti, 1951; Zr, ; Hf, 1941, 1956;† Th, 1955
XV	45, 46, 47	Ge, 1931, 1956;† Sn, ; Pb,
XVI	48, 49, 50, 51	V, ; Nb, ; Ta, ; Pa, 1942–1956†
XVII	52, 53, 54, 55	Cr, ; Mo, 1935; W, 1933; U, 1936
XVIII	56, 57, 58	Mn, ; Ni, ; Co, 1930–1932
XIX	59	Fe, 1929–
XX	60, 61, 62	Cu, 1955– ; Ag, ; Au, 1954
XXI	63, 64, 65, 66, 67	Ru, 1938; Rh, 1938; Pd, 1942; Os, 1939; Ir, 1939
XXII	68, 69, 70, 71	Pt, 1937–1957; Tc, 1941–1955; Re, 1941, 1956;† transurania

* The dash indicates that the volume appeared in parts.
† The second date is the publication date of the supplement.

To locate a compound, keep in mind that the volume for each element contains all combinations with elements whose system numbers are lower than that of the element in question. A desired compound will be found, therefore, in the volume for the element with the highest system number. For example, the com-

[1] A small explanatory volume, published in 1950, lists abbreviations and symbols.

pound K_2PtCl_6 is listed in the volume for platinum as the numbers, in decreasing order, are 68 (Pt), 22 (K), and 6 (Cl). It is in the platinum and potassium section, under compounds with chlorine.

References to the literature are included in parentheses in the body of the discussion, supposedly complete to within 6 months of the date of publication.

Whenever the size of a volume makes it feasible, the material on an element is subdivided into the following sections:

A. History, occurrence, ore dressing, metallurgy, technology, properties of the element, analysis, and alloys
B. Compounds

Each part (or volume) has a table of contents, but there is no index.

J. W. Mellor, "Comprehensive Treatise on Inorganic and Theoretical Chemistry," Longmans, Green & Co., Inc., New York. The arrangement of Mellor's treatise follows somewhat the order of the periodic table. Often general principles or theories are discussed in connection with certain elements. The volumes include the material shown.

    I. General principles, H, O (1922)
   II. F, Cl, Br, I, Li, Na, K, Rb, Cs (1922)
  III. Cu, Ag, Au, Ca, Sr, Ba, radioactivity (1923)
   IV. Ra family, Be, Mg, Zn, Cd, Hg (1923)
    V. B, Al, Ga, In, Tl, Sc, Ce, rare earth metals, C (part 1) (1924)
   VI. C (part 2), Si, silicates (1925)
  VII. Ti, Zr, Hf, Th, Ge, Sn, Pb, inert gases (1927)
 VIII. N, P (1928)
   IX. As, Sb, Bi, V, Nb, Ta (1929)
    X. S, Se (1930)
   XI. Te, Cr, Mo, W (1931)
  XII. U, Mn, Tc, Re, Fe (part 1) (1932)
 XIII. Fe (part 2) (1934)
  XIV. Fe (part 3), Co (1935)
   XV. Ni, Ru, Rh, Pd, Os, Ir (1936)
  XVI. Pt, general index (1937)

The order of presentation under each element is history, preparation, properties, and the hydride, oxide, halide, sulfide, sulfate, carbonate, nitrate, and phosphate compounds. Compounds with elements such as arsenic, carbon, and silicon are described under these elements. Potassium chloride will be found under potassium, but potassium peroxydisulfate is under sulfur. Intermetallic compounds and complex salts discussed under a given element include only compounds with elements already described.

The subject or name of the compound being considered is printed in bold-faced type so that one's eye readily catches it. The original references are grouped at the end of the various sections. The discussion of a given subject usually divides itself into several phases. Suppose it is the first phase being discussed. Mellor has collected all references for this part under "1" at the end of the section, this numeral being mentioned only once—in connection, usually, with the first author named. The numeral is not repeated for the succeeding authors mentioned, but their names will be found by looking through the list under "1."

Supplementary Volume I (1956) covers the halogens, and Volume II (   ) will cover the alkali metals.

M. C. Sneed, J. L. Maynard, and R. C. Brasted (eds.), *"Comprehensive Inorganic Chemistry,"* D. Van Nostrand Company, Inc., Princeton, N.J. For the first time an American comprehensive set of this kind is appearing. The objective is to present the most useful and necessary information for each element and its significant compounds in the light of present concepts of atomic and molecular structures. The published and projected volumes are as follows:

    I. Atomic and molecular structure; nuclear chemistry (1953)
   II. Cu, Ag, Au (1954)
  III. F, Cl, Br, I, At (1954)
  IV. Zn, Cd, Hg, Sc, Y, La series (1955)
   V. N, P, As, Sb, Bi; nonaqueous chemistry (1956)
  VI. H, Li, Na, K, Rb, Cs, Fr (1957)
 VII. Transition elements of groups IV–VII (   )
VIII. Fe, Co, Ni, Pt elements (   )
  IX. Be, Mg, Ca, Sr, Ba, Ra, B, Al, Ga, In, Tl
   X. C, Si, Ge, Sn, Pb (   )
  XI. O, S, Se, Te; inert gases (   )

P. Pascal (ed.), *"Nouveau traité de chimie minérale,"* Masson et Cie, Paris. In the first edition of this set there are good summaries of selected topics, such as complex compounds and the rare earths. The references, collected at the end of sections, are printed in run-in form in groups of 10. The coverage planned for the new edition is as follows:

    I. Introduction; air, water; hydrogen and isotopes; inert gases (1956)
   II. Li, Na, K (   )
  III. Rb, Cs, Fr, Cu, Ag, Au (   )
  IV. Be, Mg, Ca, Sr, Ba, Ra (   )
   V. Zn, Cd, Hg (   )
  VI. B, Al, Ga, In, Tl (   )
 VII. Rare earths, Sc, Y (   )
VIII. C, Si, Ge (   )
  IX. Sn, Pb, Ti, Zr, Hf, Th (   )
   X. N, NH_4, P (1956)
  XI. As, Sb, Bi, V, Nb, T, Pa (   )
 XII. O, S, Se, Te, Po (   )
XIII. Cr, Mo, W (   )
XIV. U, uranides (   )
 XV. F, Cl, Br, I, Tc, Re, Mn (   )
XVI. Fe, Co, Ni (   )
XVII. Complexes of Fe, Co, Ni (   )
XVIII. Ru, Rh, Pd, Os, Ir, Pt (   )
 XIX. Metallic alloys (   )

R. Abegg et al., "*Handbuch der anorganischen Chemie*," S. Hirzel Verlag, Leipzig. This set was started in 1905 and continued for 13 volumes to 1939. It remains incomplete. The presentation was selective, critical, and well organized. For older work, it should be consulted.

G. Brauer (ed.), "*Handbuch der präparativen anorganischen Chemie*," Fred. Enke Verlag, Stuttgart, 1954.

J. N. Friend (ed.), "*Textbook of Inorganic Chemistry*," Charles Griffith & Co., Ltd., London. This set also has been discontinued. From 1914 to 1938 there were 24 volumes published. The material was well selected and presented, and the set has been very useful.

W. Hückel, "*Structural Chemistry of Inorganic Compounds*," Fred. Enke Verlag, Stuttgart, 1950–1951. The general objective in this work is a general structural theory adequate for systematizing the facts of inorganic chemistry. A. F. Wells, "Structural Inorganic Chemistry," 1950, is a related work.

"*Inorganic Syntheses*," John Wiley & Sons, Inc., New York. This set, started in 1938, includes tested methods for the preparation of important inorganic chemicals. It is comparable to "Organic Syntheses." The editorship rotates.

C. A. Jacobson (ed.), "*Encyclopedia of Chemical Reactions*," Reinhold Publishing Corporation, New York, 1946–   . The plan of this treatise comprises the alphabetical listing under each element of all active inorganic substances, together with a limited number of organic compounds, and in a marginal space to the left all substances known to react with the former. The following entry illustrates the plan:

Lithium

No. 46   Lithium dissolves in hydrochloric acid with evolution of gas.
HCl

$$2Li + 2HCl \rightarrow 2LiCl + H_2$$

Bunsen, *Ann.*, **94**, 110 (1855)

J. Kleinberg and J. S. Anderson, "Remy's Treatise on Inorganic Chemistry," Elsevier Publishing Company, Amsterdam, 1956. The chemistry and physics of the elements and their important compounds are described and interpreted in their connection with X-ray and optical spectra, atomic and molecular structure, ionization and electrode potentials, and other modern concepts.

N. V. Sidgwick, "The Chemical Elements and Their Compounds," Oxford University Press, New York, 1950. A descriptive and reasonably critical summary of inorganic chemistry is presented in these two volumes.

J. H. Simon, "Fluorine Chemistry," Academic Press, New York, 1950.

A. Stähler (ed.), "Handbuch der Arbeitsmethoden in der anorganischen Chemie," Veit & Company, Leipzig. Between 1913 and 1926 Stähler issued seven volumes dealing with laboratory operations of inorganic chemistry. The set is somewhat comparable to that of Houben-Weyl for organic chemistry.

Analytical Chemistry. Only in recent times has there been available for analytical chemistry a reference set comparable to the comprehensive works mentioned for organic and inorganic chemistry. Shorter sets have been the general practice. The present situation is summarized here.

W. Fresenius and G. Jander, "Handbuch der analytischen Chemie," Springer-Verlag OHG, Vienna. For analytical chemistry this new treatise is analogous, in a general way, to the Gmelin set for inorganic chemistry. It covers the elements according to families of the periodic table. In giving separate treatment to methods of detection, separation, and determination, the set seems likely to replace the older, and still incomplete, set of Rüdisüle.

The volumes projected are shown below. They are being issued in smaller parts which may be bound separately. Incomplete parts are shown by italicized symbols.

Part I. General Methods

   I. Not announced
  II. Not announced

Part II. Qualitative Analysis

     I. H, Li, Na, K, NH₄, Rb, Cs, Cu, Ag, Au (1944–1955)
    II. Be, Mg, Ca, Sr, Ba, Zn, Cd, Hg (1955)
  III. B, Al, Ga, In, Tl, Sc, Y, rare earths, Ac (1944)
  IV. C, Si, Ge, Sn, Pb, Ti, Zr, Hf, Th (1950–1956)
   V. N, P, As, Sb, Bi, V, Nb, Ta, Pa (1951–1956)
  VI. O, S, Se, Te, Cr, Mo, W, U (1948)
 VII. F, Cl, Br, I, Mn, Tc, Re (1953)
VIII. Fe, Co, Ni, Pt, Pd, Rh, Ir, Ru, Os (1951–1956)
  IX. Vorproben und Trennung der Kationen und Anionen (1956)

Part III. Quantitative Methods of Separation and Determination

     I. Li, Na, K, NH₄, Rb, Cs, Cu, Ag, Au (1940)
    II. Be, Mg, Ca, Sr, Ba, Ra, Zn, Cd, Hg (1940–1945)
  III. B, Al, Ga, In, Tl, Sc, Y, rare earths, Ac (1942–1956)
  IV. *C, Si, Ge, Sn, Pb,* Ti, Zr, Hf, Th (1950–   )
   V. N, P, As, Sb, Bi, *V, Nb, Ta, Pa* (1951–   )
  VI. O, O₃, H₂O₂, S, Se, Te, Po, *Cr, Mo,* W, U (1953–   )
 VII. H, H₂O, F, *Cl, Br, I, Mn, Tc, Re* (1950–   )
VIII. He, Ne, Ar, Kr, Xe, Rn, *Fe, Co, Ni,* Pt, Pd, Ir, Rh, Os, Ru (1949–   )

E. Berl (ed.), "Lunge's Chemische-technische Untersuchungs-methoden," Springer-Verlag OHG, Vienna, 1931–1939. Commercial methods of testing, analyzing, and evaluating industrial materials are covered.

H. Mayer-Kaupp (ed.), "Anleitung für die chemische Laboratoriumspraxis," Springer-Verlag OHG, Vienna. This set emphasizes methods as such, rather than elements and substances. The volumes issued, and their authors, follow.

    I. W. Seith and K. Ruthardt, "Chemische Spektralanalyse," 1949.
   II. G. Kortüm, "Kolorimetrie, Photometrie, und Spektrometrie," 1955.
 III. H. Hohn, "Chemischen Analysen mit den Polarographen," 1948.
 IV. H. M. Rauen, "Gegenstromverteilung," 1953.
  V. W. Otting, "Der Raman-Effekt," 1952.

A. Rüdisüle, "Nachweis, Bestimmung, und Trennung der chemischen Elemente," M. Drechsel, Bern, Switzerland, 1913–1929. Both qualitative and quantitative methods are included for each element covered in the seven volumes published. A supplement to the first four volumes appeared in 1936.

Examples of other valuable reference sets follow.

Berl, W. G. (ed.): "Physical Methods in Chemical Analysis," Academic Press, Inc., New York, 1950–1956.

Böttger, W.: "Physical Methods of Analytical Chemistry," Akademische Verlagsgesellschaft m.b.H., Leipzig, 1939–1943.

Chamot, E. M., and C. W. Mason: "Handbook of Chemical Microscopy," John Wiley & Sons, Inc., New York, 1938–1940.

Duval, C.: "Traité de micro-analyse minérale, qualitative et quantitative," Presses scientifiques internationales, Paris, 1954–1956.

Feigl, F.: "Spot Tests," Elsevier Publishing Company, Amsterdam, 1954.

Furman, N. H. (ed.): "Scott's Standard Methods of Chemical Analysis," D. Van Nostrand Company, Inc., Princeton, N.J., 1939.

Hecht, F., and M. K. Zacherl: "Handbuch der mikrochemischen Methoden," Springer-Verlag OHG, Vienna, 1954–1955.

Huntress, E. H.: "Organic Chlorine Compounds," John Wiley & Sons, Inc., New York, 1948.

——— and S. P. Mulliken: "Identification of Pure Organic Compounds," John Wiley & Sons, Inc., New York, 1941.

Keane, C. A., and P. C. L. Thorne (eds.): "Technical Methods of Chemical Analysis," Gurney & Jackson, London, 1924–1940.

Kolthoff, I. M., and J. J. Lingane: "Polarography," Interscience Publishers, Inc., New York, 1952.

——— and V. A. Stenger: "Volumetric Analysis," Interscience Publishers, Inc., New York, 1942–1957.

Mitchell, J., et al. (eds.): "Organic Analysis," Interscience Publishers, Inc., New York, 1953–   .

Paech, K., and M. V. Tracey: "Moderne Methoden der Pflanzenanalyse," Springer-Verlag OHG, Vienna, 1954–   .

Peters, J. P., and D. D. Van Slyke: "Quantitative Clinical Chemistry," The Williams & Wilkins Company, Baltimore, 1946.

Proske, O., and H. Blumenthal: "Analyse der Metalle," Springer-Verlag OHG, Vienna, 1949–1953.

Snell, F. D., and C. T. Snell: "Colorimetric Methods of Analysis," D. Van Nostrand Company, Inc., Princeton, N.J., 1948–1954.

Strouts, C. R. N., et al.: "Analytical Chemistry," Oxford University Press, New York, 1955.

Treadwell, F. P., and W. T. Hall: "Analytical Chemistry," John Wiley & Sons, Inc., New York, 1931–1942.

Welcher, F. J.: "Organic Analytical Reagents," D. Van Nostrand Company, Inc., Princeton, N.J., 1947–   .

Yaffe, C. D., D. H. Byers, and A. D. Hosey (eds.): "Encyclopedia of Instrumentation for Industrial Hygiene," Speaker-Hines and Thomas, Lansing, Mich., 1956.

Yoe, J. H.: "Photometric Chemical Analysis," John Wiley & Sons, Inc., New York, 1929.

There are many equally valuable single-volume reference books in this field. An outstanding example is the new edition by H. A. Bright and J. I. Hoffman of "Applied Inorganic Analysis," by W. F. Hillebrand and G. E. F. Lundell. When these books become rather specialized, they are hardly distinguishable from monographs (see Chapter 9).

Official methods of testing and analysis for engineering materials, drugs,[1] feeds, fertilizers, foods, and many other commercial products have been issued. They are of great importance in buying, using, and selling products. The following examples are important in the United States.

"ASTM Standards 1955," American Society for Testing Materials, Philadelphia, 1955–1956.
"American Standards" (index and price list), American Standards Association, New York, 1956.
Horwitz, W. (ed.): "Official Methods of Analysis," Association of Official Agricultural Chemists, Washington, D.C., 1955.
Kline, E. K., et al. (eds.): "Standard Methods for the Examination of Water, Sewage and Industrial Wastes," American Public Health Association, New York, 1955.
"Official Methods of Analysis," Society of Leather Trades' Chemists, Croydon, England, 1951.
"Standard Methods for Testing Petroleum and Its Products," Institute of Petroleum, London, 1952.
Wichers, E., et al.: "Reagent Chemicals; American Chemical Society Specifications," American Chemical Society, Washington, D.C., 1955.

Physical Chemistry.[2] For the present purpose physical chemistry may be considered as the branch which deals with the cause and nature of chemical reactions and with the interpretation of specific properties. As organic and inorganic chemistry includes all the chemical elements, and therefore all chemical substances, one would expect to find much discussion belonging to this area in the treatises already considered. Consequently, the tendency has been toward single-volume textbooks and monographs on limited portions of the field, rather than comprehensive treatises. However, several multivolume works are available. Some of those listed are now chiefly of historical interest.

Alexander, J. (ed.): "Colloid Chemistry," Chemical Catalog Company and Reinhold Publishing Corporation, New York, 1926–1950.

[1] See section on pharmaceutical chemistry, p. 172, for pharmacopeias.
[2] As physics and physical chemistry are so closely related, see Whitford, op. cit., and Parke, op. cit.

Bredig, G. (ed.): "Handbuch der angewandten physikalischen Chemie," Johann Ambrosius Barth Verlag, Leipzig, 1905–1931.

Eirich, F. R. (ed.): "Rheology," Academic Press, Inc., New York, 1956–1957.

Emmett, P. H. (ed.): "Catalysis," Reinhold Publishing Corporation, New York, 1954–1957.

Farkas, A.: "Physical Chemistry of the Hydrocarbons," Academic Press, Inc., New York, 1950–1953.

Flügge, S. (ed.): "Handbuch der Physik," Springer-Verlag OHG, Vienna, 1955– .

Jellinek, K.: "Lehrbuch der physikalischen Chemie," Fred. Enke Verlag, Stuttgart, 1928–1937.

Kortüm, G., and J. O'M. Bockris: "Textbook of Electrochemistry," Elsevier Publishing Company, Amsterdam, 1951.

Krczil, F.: "Kurzes Handbuch der Polymerisationstechnik," Akademische Verlagsgesellschaft m.b.H., Leipzig, 1940–1944.

Kruyt, K. R.: "Colloid Science," Elsevier Publishing Company, Amsterdam, 1949–1952.

Ostwald, W., and C. Drucker: "Handbuch der allgemeinen Chemie," Akademische Verlagsgesellschaft m.b.H., Leipzig, 1918–1937.

Partington, J. R.: "An Advanced Treatise on Physical Chemistry," Longmans, Green & Co., Inc., New York, 1949–1954.

Reilly, J., and W. N. Rae: "Physico-Chemical Measurements," D. Van Nostrand Company, Inc., Princeton, N.J., 1948–1954.

Schwab, G. M. (ed.): "Handbuch der Catalyse," Springer-Verlag OHG, Vienna, 1941–1943.

Taylor, H. S., and S. Glasstone: "A Treatise on Physical Chemistry," D. Van Nostrand Company, Inc., Princeton, N.J., 1942–1951.

Weiser, H. B.: "Inorganic Colloid Chemistry," John Wiley & Sons, Inc., New York, 1933–1938.

Wolfe, H. C. (ed.): "Temperature," Reinhold Publishing Corporation, New York, 1941–1955.

Wyckoff, R. W. G.: "Crystal Structures," Interscience Publishers, Inc., New York, 1948–

Many single-volume works have been published on general physical chemistry or on specialized topics. Usually they are textbooks or monographs. Representative titles are listed in Chapter 9.

Industrial Chemistry and Chemical Engineering.[1] In the general area of industrial (applied) chemistry and chemical engineering there is nothing comprehensive comparable to the Beilstein treatise in organic chemistry. It is very difficult, if not

---

[1] Some worthwhile literature is mentioned in Parke, *op. cit.*, as it covers works on engineering related to mathematics and physics.

impossible, to have a compilation of general nature that is reliable very long after the time of publication. Changes in practice are so frequent and advances in technique so steady that new editions could hardly be arranged with sufficient rapidity to keep up with the pace. The works listed here will be found to be of some value.

Baud, P.: "Traité de chimie industrielle," Masson et Cie, Paris, 1951.
Bergmann, M.: "Handbuch der Gerbereichemie und Lederfabrikation," Springer-Verlag OHG, Vienna, 1931–   .
Berl, E.: "Chemische Ingenieur-Technik," Springer-Verlag OHG, Vienna, 1935–   .
Cooke, E. I., and W. Francis: "Martin's Industrial and Manufacturing Chemistry," Philosophical Library, Inc., New York, 1955.
Cremer, H. W. (ed.): "Chemical Engineering Practice," Butterworth & Co. (Publishers), Ltd., London, 1956–   .
Draper, C. S., W. McKay, and S. Lees: "Instrument Engineering," McGraw-Hill Book Company, Inc., New York, 1952–1955.
Engelhardt, V.: "Handbuch der technischen Elektrochemie," Akademische Verlagsgesellschaft m.b.H., Leipzig, 1931–1944.
Eucken, A., and M. Jakob: "Der Chemie-Ingenieur," Akademische Verlagsgesellschaft m.b.H., Leipzig, 1933–1940.
Haynes, W.: "American Chemical Industry," D. Van Nostrand Company, Inc., Princeton, N.J., 1945–1956.
Hougen, O. A., and K. M. Watson: "Chemical Process Principles," John Wiley & Sons, Inc., New York, 1954–   .
Houwink, R.: "Elastomers and Plastomers," Elsevier Publishing Company, Amsterdam, 1948–1950.
"Modern Chemical Processes," Reinhold Publishing Corporation, New York, 1950–1956.
Peters, F., and H. Grossmann (eds.): "Dammar's Chemische Technologie der Neuzeit," Fred. Enke Verlag, Stuttgart, 1925–1932.
Poucher, W. A.: "Perfumes, Cosmetics, and Soaps," Chapman & Hall, Ltd., London, 1936.
Winnacker, K., and E. Weingartner: "Chemische Technologie," Hanser, Munich, 1950–   .

Before World War II there were many specialized treatises on applied chemistry.[1] Thus far, few of them have been revised.

The general practice in works dealing with chemical technology is to limit them to some special field. Many of these, relating to almost every phase of applied chemistry, have been published (see works containing lists of books, mentioned in Chapter 10).

[1] M. G. Mellon, "Chemical Publications: Their Nature and Use," p. 136, McGraw-Hill Book Company, Inc., New York, 1940.

Biological Chemistry. Over a period of several decades a number of outstanding treatises appeared on biological or physiological chemistry (biochemistry). Their present value as reference sources is uncertain. The following sets were probably best known.

Abderhalden, E. (ed.): "Biochemisches Handlexikon," Springer-Verlag OHG, Vienna, 1911–1933.

———: "Handbuch der biologischen Arbeitsmethode," Urban & Schwarzenberg, Berlin, 1920–1939.

Beythien, A., C. Hartwich, and M. Klimmer: "Handbuch der Nahrungsmitteluntersuchung," H. Tauchnitz, Leipzig, 1917–1920.

Bömer, A. W. J. H., A. Juckenack, and J. Tilmans (eds.): "Handbuch der Lebensmittelchemie," Springer-Verlag OHG, Vienna, 1933–1942.

Euler, H.: "Chemie der Enzyme," Bergmann, Munich, 1925–1927.

Oppenheimer, K.: "Die Fermente und ihre Wirkungen," Georg Thieme Verlag, Leipzig, 1924–1925.

———: "Handbuch der Biochemie des Menschen und der Tiere," Gustav Fischer Verlagsbuchhandlung, Jena, Germany, 1924–1936.

New sets are appearing again, but none of them approaches the magnitude of sets such as those of Abderhalden. The following works are of value.

"Biochemical Preparations," John Wiley & Sons, Inc., New York, 1949– .

Chargaff, E., and J. N. Davidson (eds.): "The Nucleic Acids," Academic Press, Inc., New York, 1955.

Colowick, S. P., and N. O. Kaplan (eds.): "Methods in Enzymology," Academic Press, Inc., New York, 1955– .

Deuel, H. J.: "The Lipids," Interscience Publishers, Inc., New York, 1951– .

Flaschentrager, B.: "Physiologischen Chemie," Springer-Verlag OHG, Vienna, 1951– .

Glick, D. (ed.): "Methods of Biochemical Analysis," Interscience Publishers, Inc., New York, 1954–1957.

Lang, K., and E. Lehnartz: "Handbuch der physiologisch- und pathologisch-chemischen Analyse," Springer-Verlag OHG, Vienna, 1953–1955.[1]

Neurath, H., and K. Bailey (eds.): "The Proteins: Chemistry, Biological Activity, and Methods," Academic Press, Inc., New York, 1953–1954.

Pincus, G., and K. V. Thimann (eds.): "The Hormones," Academic Press, Inc., New York, 1948–1955.

Potter, V. R. (ed.): "Methods in Medical Research," Year Book Publishers, Chicago, 1948– .

Rabinowitch, E. I.: "Photosynthesis and Related Processes," Interscience Publishers, Inc., New York, 1945–1955.

Sebrell, W. H., Jr., and R. S. Harris (eds.): "The Vitamins," Academic Press, Inc., New York, 1954.

[1] This is the tenth edition of the famous Hoppe-Seyler–Thierfelder treatise.

Sumner, J. B., and K. Myrbäck (eds.): "The Enzymes," Academic Press, Inc., New York, 1950–1952.

Pharmaceutical Chemistry. As with biochemistry and agricultural chemistry, pharmaceutical chemistry comes ultimately to include the chemistry of certain inorganic and organic materials. In this field these materials are the ones that possess preventive, remedial, or curative physiological properties. The basic chemistry of such substances is covered in treatises already considered. The following treatises are representative of those devoted to the pharmaceutical and pharmacological properties of materials:

Guenther, E.: "The Essential Oils," D. Van Nostrand Company, Inc., Princeton, N.J., 1948–1952.

Heffter, A.: "Handbuch der experimentellen Pharmakologie," Springer-Verlag OHG, Vienna, 1920–1935.

Lebeau, P.: "Traité de pharmacie chimique," Masson et Cie, Paris, 1946–1947.

Manske, R. H. F., and H. L. Holmes: "The Alkaloids: Chemistry and Physiology," Academic Press, Inc., New York, 1950–1954.

Osol, A., and G. E. Farrar (eds.): "The Dispensatory of the United States of America," J. B. Lippincott Company, Philadelphia, 1955.

Wilson, C. O., and T. E. Jones: "The American Drug Index," J. B. Lippincott Company, Philadelphia, 1956.

A rather special type of book is represented by the pharmacopeias of the various countries. They deal with drugs, including their preparation, action, and official methods of testing and analysis. Related to these works are the formularies. The following selections are representative:

"British Pharmaceutical Codex," Pharmaceutical Press, London, 1954.

"British Pharmacopoeia," Pharmaceutical Press, London, 1953.

"The Extra Pharmacopoeia," Pharmaceutical Press, London, 1955.

"International Pharmacopeia," vol. I, Columbia University Press, New York, 1951; vol. II, Pharmaceutical Press, London, 1955.

"National Formulary," J. B. Lippincott Company, Philadelphia, 1955.

"New and Nonofficial Remedies," J. B. Lippincott Company, Philadelphia, 1956.

"The Pharmacopeia of the United States of America," Mack Publishing Co., Easton, Pa., 1955.

Agricultural Chemistry. Agricultural chemistry is largely applied general biological chemistry, which in turn rests upon the general principles of inorganic, organic, physical, and analytical chemistry. Therefore, a number of the treatises already discussed are of value here, especially those dealing with biological chemistry. In addition, a few deal specifically with agricultural materials.

Blanck, E. (ed.): "Handbuch der Bodenlehre," Springer-Verlag OHG, Vienna, 1929–1932.

Frear, D. E. H. (ed.): "Agricultural Chemistry," D. Van Nostrand Company, Inc., Princeton, N.J., 1950–1951.

Honcamp, F.: "Handbuch der Pflanzenernährung und Düngerlehre," Springer-Verlag OHG, Vienna, 1931.

Jacobs, M. B. (ed.): "The Chemistry and Technology of Food and Food Products," Interscience Publishers, Inc., New York, 1951.

Parker, M. E.: "Elements of Food Engineering," Reinhold Publishing Corporation, New York, 1952–1954.

Winton, A. L., and K. B. Winton: "Structure and Composition of Foods," Chapman & Hall, Ltd., London, 1932–1939.

CHAPTER 9

SECONDARY SOURCES—
MONOGRAPHS AND TEXTBOOKS

> Books are faithful repositories, which may be awhile neglected or forgotten; but when they are opened again, will again impart their instruction.—*Johnson*

In the previous chapter several different kinds of secondary sources were considered as works of reference. Two others remain which in a sense might have been included. Because of their nature, however, separate treatment is accorded them. The two sources are monographs and textbooks.

Monographs

> Of making many books, there is no end; and much study is a weariness of the flesh.—*Ecclesiastes 12:12*

A monograph may be defined as a comprehensive survey of contemporary knowledge relating to a given subject. The general nature of these publications is indicated by the following statement of the Board of Editors of the American Chemical Society Series of Scientific and Technologic Monographs.

The development of knowledge in all branches of science, and especially in chemistry, has been so rapid during the last fifty years and the fields covered by this development have been so varied that it is difficult for any individual to keep in touch with the progress in branches of science outside his own specialty. In spite of the facilities for the examination of the literature given by *Chemical Abstracts* and such compendia as Beilstein's "Handbuch der organischen Chemie" and Gmelin's "Handbuch der anorganischen Chemie" and the encyclopedias of chemistry, it often takes a great deal of time to coordinate the knowledge available upon a single topic. Consequently, when men who have spent years in the study of important subjects are willing to coordinate their knowledge and present it in concise, readable form, they perform a service of the highest value to their fellow chemists.

Two rather distinct purposes are to be served by such monographs. The first purpose, whose fulfillment will probably render to chemists in general the most service, is to present the knowledge available upon the chosen topic in a readable form, intelligible to those whose activities may be along a wholly different line. Many chemists fail to realize how closely their investigations may be connected with other work which, on the surface, appears far afield from their own. Monographs enable such men to form closer contact with the work of chemists in other lines of research. The second purpose is to promote research in the branch of science covered by the monograph, by furnishing a well digested survey of the progress already made in that field and by pointing out directions in which investigation needs to be extended. To facilitate the attainment of this purpose, it is intended to include extended references to the literature, which will enable anyone to follow up the subject in more detail. If the literature is so voluminous that a complete bibliography is impracticable, a critical selection is made of those papers which are most important.

According to a statement in an English series, monographs serve another purpose.

It is difficult in the case of large treatises to keep abreast of so rapidly a growing science by means of new editions. Monographs may be issued more frequently upon the various divisions of a general subject, each publication independent of and yet dependent upon the others, so that from time to time as new material and the demand therefore necessitates, a new edition of each monograph can be issued without reissuing the whole series. In this way, both the expenses of publication and the expense to the purchasers are diminished, and by a moderate outlay it is possible to obtain a full account of any particular subject as nearly current as possible.

Monographs are frequently issued as members of a series, written by individual authors under the general direction of an editor or board of editors. Soule[1] has listed more than 30 such series of monographs. New series and new volumes for old series keep appearing.

In addition, many books not belonging to any monograph series obviously meet the specifications for this kind of publication. They may or may not be called monographs. Except for textbooks and periodical sets, it seems likely that most of the

[1] B. A. Soule, "Library Guide for the Chemist," p. 86, McGraw-Hill Book Company, Inc., New York, 1937.

books one sees on library shelves might well be classified as monographs.

When prepared by one who knows his field and who can and will write, monographs are among our most useful and dependable sources. Thus, Vail's monograph "The Soluble Silicates" appeared only after the author had many years of experience with the Philadelphia Quartz Company. Few others could have written out of such a background of practical knowledge.

The narrower the field encompassed by the author, the more intensive the treatment is likely to be. The monograph by Dorsey, "Properties of Ordinary Water-substance," for example, devotes 673 pages to perhaps our best-known chemical.

In the following list are representative selections of monographs.

REPRESENTATIVE MONOGRAPHS

Agricultural Chemistry

Bear, F. E. (ed.): "Chemistry of the Soils," Reinhold Publishing Corporation, New York, 1955.

Eckey, E. W.: "Vegetable Fats and Oils," Reinhold Publishing Corporation, New York, 1954

Kelly, W. P.: "Alkali Soils," Reinhold Publishing Corporation, New York, 1951.

Tressler, D. R., and M. A. Joslyn: "The Chemistry and Technology of Fruit and Vegetable Juice Production," Avi Publishing Company, New York, 1954.

Wise, L. E., and E. C. Jahn: "Wood Chemistry," Reinhold Publishing Corporation, New York, 1952.

Analytical Chemistry

Bates, R. G.: "Electrometric pH Determinations," John Wiley & Sons, Inc., New York, 1954.

Groves, A. W.: "Silicate Analysis," George Allen & Unwin, Ltd., London, 1951.

Mellon, M. G.: "Analytical Absorption Spectroscopy," John Wiley & Sons, Inc., New York, 1950.

Mitchell, J., Jr., and D. M. Smith: "Aquametry," Interscience Publishers, Inc., New York, 1948.

Schoeller, W. R., and A. R. Powell: "Analysis of Minerals and Ores of the Rarer Elements," Hafner Publishing Company, New York, 1953.

Biological Chemistry

Clarke, H. T., J. R. Johnson, and R. Robinson: "The Chemistry of Penicillin," Princeton University Press, Princeton, N.J., 1949.

Fox, D. L.: "Animal Biochromes and Structural Colours," Cambridge University Press, New York, 1953.

Karrer, P., and E. Jucker: "Carotenoids," Elsevier Publishing Company, Amsterdam, 1950.

Tauber, H.: "The Chemistry and Technology of Enzymes," John Wiley & Sons, Inc., New York, 1949.

Williams, R. J., et al.: "The Biochemistry of B Vitamins," Reinhold Publishing Corporation, New York, 1950.

Industrial Chemistry

Bangham, D. H. (ed.): "Progress in Coal Science," Butterworth & Co. (Publishers) Ltd., London, 1950.

Comings, E. W.: "High Pressure Technology," McGraw-Hill Book Company, Inc., New York, 1956.

Morey, G. W.: "The Properties of Glass," Reinhold Publishing Corporation, New York, 1954.

Rossini, F. D., B. J. Mair, and A. J. Streiff: "Hydrocarbons from Petroleum," Reinhold Publishing Corporation, New York, 1953.

Rudolfs, W.: "Industrial Wastes," Reinhold Publishing Corporation, New York, 1953.

Schildknecht, C. E.: "Vinyl and Related Polymers," John Wiley & Sons, Inc., New York, 1953.

Vail, J. G.: "Soluble Silicates, Their Properties and Uses," Reinhold Publishing Corporation, New York, 1952.

Inorganic Chemistry

Audrieth, L. F.: "The Chemistry of Hydrazine," John Wiley & Sons, Inc., New York, 1951.

Dorsey, N. E.: "Properties of Ordinary Water-substance," Reinhold Publishing Corporation, New York, 1940.

Hurd, D. T.: "An Introduction to the Chemistry of the Hydrides," John Wiley & Sons, Inc., New York, 1952.

Schumb, W. C., et al.: "Hydrogen Peroxide," Reinhold Publishing Corporation, New York, 1955.

Vickery, R. C.: "Chemistry of the Lanthanons," Butterworth & Co. (Publishers) Ltd., London, 1953.

Wells, A. F.: "Structural Inorganic Chemistry," Oxford University Press, New York, 1950.

Metallurgy

Gray, A. G.: "Modern Electroplating," John Wiley & Sons, Inc., New York, 1953.

Kubaschewski, O., and E. L. Evans: "Metallurgical Thermochemistry," John Wiley & Sons, Inc., New York, 1956.

Li, K. C., and C. Y. Wang: "Tungsten," Reinhold Publishing Corporation, New York, 1955.

Miller, G. L.: "Zirconium," Butterworth & Co. (Publishers) Ltd., London, 1954.

Monypenny, J. H. G.: "Stainless Iron and Steel," Chapman & Hall, Ltd., London, 1951–1954.

Organic Chemistry

Curme, G. O., Jr. (ed.): "Glycols," Reinhold Publishing Corporation, New York, 1952.

Dunlop, A. P., and F. N. Peters: "The Furans," Reinhold Publishing Corporation, New York, 1953.

Hartough, H. D., et al.: "Thiophene and Its Derivatives," Interscience Publishers, Inc., New York, 1952.

Ingold, C. K.: "Structure and Mechanism in Organic Chemistry," Cornell University Press, Ithaca, N.Y., 1953.

Storch, H. H., et al.: "The Fischer-Tropsch and Related Syntheses," John Wiley & Sons, Inc., New York, 1951.

Wheland, G. W.: "Resonance in Organic Chemistry," John Wiley & Sons, Inc., New York, 1955.

Pharmaceutical Chemistry

Henry, T. A.: "The Plant Alkaloids," 4th ed., The Blakiston Division, McGraw-Hill Book Company, Inc., New York, 1949.

May, P., and G. M. Dyson: "Chemistry of Synthetic Drugs," Longmans, Green & Co., Inc., New York, 1939.

Mellon, R. R., P. Gross, and F. B. Cooper: "Sulfanilamide Therapy of Bacterial Infections," Charles C Thomas, Publisher, Springfield, Ill., 1938.

Northey, E. H.: "The Sulfonamides and Allied Compounds," Reinhold Publishing Corporation, New York, 1948.

Reddish, G. F.: "Antiseptics, Disinfectants, Fungicides, and Chemical and Physical Sterilization," Lea & Febiger, Philadelphia, 1954.

Physical Chemistry

Hildebrand, J. H., and R. L. Scott: "Solubility of Non-electrolytes," Reinhold Publishing Corporation, New York, 1950.

Noyes, W. A., and P. A. Leighton: "The Photochemistry of Gases," Reinhold Publishing Corporation, New York, 1941.

Pauling, L. C.: "The Nature of the Chemical Bond, and the Structure of Molecules and Crystals," Cornell University Press, Ithaca, N.Y., 1940.

Ricci, J. E.: "Hydrogen Ion Concentration," Princeton University Press, Princeton, N.J., 1952.

Weiser, H. B.: "The Hydrous Oxides," McGraw-Hill Book Company, Inc., New York, 1926.

Textbooks

Oh, . . . that mine adversary had written a book.—*Job 31:35*

There remains a large, heterogeneous mass of books which do not come under the headings already discussed. Such books are not bibliographies, indexes, handbooks, treatises, dictionaries, encyclopedias, or monographs, as these terms are used here. To designate the publications constituting this remaining class, the word "textbook" is used. It is employed in the sense of a manual of instruction.

No sharp lines can be drawn, of course, to differentiate all the kinds of publications already discussed. Indexes stand apart rather distinctly; but monographs merge into treatises, treatises into encyclopedias, and textbooks into monographs. As the word "textbook" is used in this country, we usually refer to a single-volume work. In contrast, Friend's "Textbook of Inorganic Chemistry" and Jellinek's "Lehrbuch der physikalischen Chemie" are really treatises of 24 and 5 volumes, respectively.

In general, monographs present a more or less exhaustive survey of contemporary knowledge for special subjects, but they often omit many of the details, especially if mainly of historical interest. Treatises resemble monographs somewhat, but they are much more comprehensive in subject matter and generally include a broad area of chemistry, such as organic. Encyclopedias consist of a collection of short summaries on the more significant topics in the whole field of chemistry, or some large portion of it.

Compared to these other sources, textbooks are more selective and less exhaustive and comprehensive. If one assumes that textbooks are manuals of instruction, the primary aim in producing such works is to have them serve for instructional purposes. Because of this objective, such books should be representative of principles rather than detailed in nature. In addition to stressing general principles for the area covered, textbooks should contain sufficient descriptive and explanatory matter to impress the desired points upon the student. Often numerical problems are included, as in analytical and physical chemistry.

As ordinarily written, textbooks seldom represent the author's own contributions. He searches the field which the book is designed to cover and selects the facts, theories, and principles which it seems desirable from his viewpoint to include. These gleanings are then arranged in the order and way which he deems preferable. Thus, the author's chief function is to select, arrange, and discuss.

Not all textbooks treat a subject in the same way. Three more or less distinct types are recognizable. Some serve simply as a source of directions for working in the laboratory. The nature of their contents is frequently indicated by the title, such as "Laboratory Manual of Colloid Chemistry" or "Experimental Organic Chemistry." Others are devoted entirely to descriptive and/or theoretical matter. An example in physical chemistry is "Chemical Principles." A considerable number represent a combination of the other two types. They contain descriptive and theoretical matter, together with directions for performing exercises relating to or illustrating the other portion of the text. Many texts for elementary quantitative analysis illustrate this type.

Textbooks as a class are probably not as reliable sources as monographs. In general, the broader the field covered by a textbook the more likely is error or lack of balance. The monograph writer is, ideally at least, an authority in the specialty on which he writes. In contrast, the author of a book on elementary general chemistry usually presumes to sample the broad areas of at least inorganic, organic, and physical chemistry, along with some physics. For anyone to write authoritatively, in the sense of personal experience over such a range of subjects, is practically impossible today.

A common practice in such writing is to cull facts and ideas from other texts, monographs, treatises, secondary and primary periodicals, and other sources. All such material, when gathered together, is then arranged on a level and in a way thought by the author to be suitable for the instruction contemplated. If the same error appears in several such texts, it indicates that all the authors used the same inaccurate source.

Usually a textbook is written by one or two authors, although an occasional one has more. Also, the usual practice of publishers is to issue such books as separate publications rather than as members of a publisher's series. An example of a series is the "International Chemical Series," now under the consulting editorship of L. P. Hammett.

As some of the more important periodicals, treatises, and other publications have been mentioned, there is included here a short list of selected textbooks in several fields of chemistry. It should not be assumed that, because certain titles are included, the books are considered the best or latest in their fields. They are intended merely to be illustrative of the class. For the most part the works are in English, since they are the common textbooks in this country.

It should be kept in mind that what would be a satisfactory book for one purpose might well be quite unsuitable for another. Some books are intended to be only elementary and for the use of beginning students. Others are for advanced study and may partake of the nature of a reference work in including material more detailed, more comprehensive, and often more difficult to grasp.

REPRESENTATIVE TEXTBOOKS

Agricultural Chemistry

Dutcher, R. A., C. O. Jensen, and P. M. Althouse: "Introduction to Agricultural Biochemistry," John Wiley & Sons, Inc., New York, 1951.

Maynard, L. A., and John K. Loosli: "Animal Nutrition," 4th ed., McGraw-Hill Book Company, Inc., New York, 1956.

Robbins, W. W., A. S. Crafts, and R. N. Raynor: "Weed Control," 2d ed., McGraw-Hill Book Company, Inc., New York, 1952.

Russell, E. J.: "Soil Conditions and Plant Growth," Longmans, Green & Co., Inc., New York, 1950.

Sherman, H. C.: "Chemistry of Food and Nutrition," The Macmillan Company, New York, 1951.

Whistler, R. L.: "Polysaccharide Chemistry," Academic Press, Inc., New York, 1953.

Analytical Chemistry (Qualitative)

Curtman, L. J.: "Introduction to Semimicro Qualitative Chemical Analysis," The Macmillan Company, New York, 1942.

Hogness, T. R., and W. C. Johnson: "Qualitative Analysis and Chemical Equilibrium," Henry Holt and Company, Inc., New York, 1954.

McAlpine, R. K., and B. A. Soule: "Fundamentals of Qualitative Chemical Analysis," D. Van Nostrand Company, Inc., Princeton, N.J., 1956.

Noyes, A. A., and W. C. Bray: "A System of Qualitative Analysis for the Rarer Elements," The Macmillan Company, New York, 1927.

Shriner, R. L., R. C. Fuson, and D. Y. Curtin: "The Systematic Identification of Organic Compounds," John Wiley & Sons, Inc., New York, 1956.

Analytical Chemistry (Quantitative)

Diehl, H., and G. F. Smith: "Quantitative Analysis," John Wiley & Sons, Inc., New York, 1952.

Kolthoff, I. M., and E. B. Sandell: "Textbook of Quantitative Inorganic Analysis," The Macmillan Company, New York, 1955.

Mellon, M. G.: "Quantitative Analysis; Methods of Separation and Measurement," Thomas Y. Crowell Company, New York, 1955.

Swift, E. H.: "Introductory Quantitative Analysis," Prentice-Hall, Inc., Englewood Cliffs, N.J., 1950.

Willard, H. H., N. H. Furman, and C. E. Bricker: "Elements of Quantitative Analysis," D. Van Nostrand Company, Inc., Princeton, N.J., 1956.

Biological Chemistry

Cantarow, A., and M. Trumper: "Clinical Biochemistry," W. B. Saunders Company, Philadelphia, 1955.

Downes, H.: "The Chemistry of Living Cells," W. B. Saunders Company, Philadelphia, 1955.

Fruton, J. S., and S. Simmonds: "General Biochemistry," John Wiley & Sons, Inc., New York, 1953.

Harrow, B., and A. Mazur: "Textbook of Biochemistry," W. B. Saunders Company, Philadelphia, 1954.

Hawk, P. B., B. L. Oser, and W. H. Summerson: "Practical Physiological Chemistry," 13th ed., The Blakiston Division, McGraw-Hill Book Company, Inc., New York, 1954.

White, A., et al.: "Principles of Biochemistry," McGraw-Hill Book Company, Inc., New York, 1954.

General Chemistry

Brescia, F.: "General College Chemistry," The Blakiston Division, McGraw-Hill Book Company, Inc., New York, 1953.

Frey, P.: "College Chemistry," Prentice-Hall, Inc., Englewood Cliffs, N.J., 1952.

Hildebrand, J.: "Principles of Chemistry," The Macmillan Company, New York, 1952.

Luder, W. F., A. A. Vernon, and S. Zuffanti: "General Chemistry," W. B. Saunders Company, Philadelphia, 1953.

Markham, E. C., and S. Smith: "General Chemistry," Houghton Mifflin Company, Boston, 1954.

Pauling, L.: "College Chemistry," Freeman, San Francisco, 1955.

History of Chemistry

Findlay, A.: "A Hundred Years of Chemistry," Gerald Duckworth & Co., Ltd., London, 1948.

Friend, J. N.: "Man and the Chemical Elements," Charles Griffin & Co., Ltd., London, 1951.

Leicester, H. M.: "The Historical Background of Chemistry," John Wiley & Sons, Inc., New York, 1956.

Moore, F. J.: "A History of Chemistry" (rev. by W. T. Hall), 3d ed., McGraw-Hill Book Company, Inc., New York, 1939.

Partington, J. R.: "Origin and Development of Applied Chemistry," The Macmillan Company, New York, 1948.

Weeks, Mary E.: "Discovery of the Elements," Journal of Chemical Education, Easton, Pa., 1956.

Industrial Chemistry and Chemical Engineering

Brown, G. G.: "Unit Operations," John Wiley & Sons, Inc., New York, 1950.

McAdams, W. H.: "Heat Transmission," 3d ed., McGraw-Hill Book Company, Inc., New York, 1954.

McCabe, W. L., and J. C. Smith: "Unit Operations of Chemical Engineering," McGraw-Hill Book Company, Inc., New York, 1956.

Shreve, R. N.: "The Chemical Process Industries," McGraw-Hill Book Company, Inc., New York, 1956.

Smith, J. M.: "Introduction to Chemical Engineering Thermodynamics," McGraw-Hill Book Company, Inc., New York, 1949.

Inorganic Chemistry

Gould, E. S.: "Inorganic Reactions and Structure," Henry Holt and Company, Inc., New York, 1955.

Latimer, W. M.: "The Oxidation States of the Elements and Their Potentials in Aqueous Solutions," Prentice-Hall, Inc., Englewood Cliffs, N.J., 1952.

Moeller, T.: "Inorganic Chemistry," John Wiley & Sons, Inc., New York, 1952.

Sidgwick, N. V.: "The Chemical Elements and Their Compounds," Oxford University Press, New York, 1950.

Thorne, P. C. L., and E. R. Roberts: "Ephraim's Inorganic Chemistry," Oliver & Boyd, Ltd., Edinburgh, 1954.

Wells, A. F.: "Structural Inorganic Chemistry," Oxford University Press, New York, 1950.

Metallography

Barrett, C. S.: "Structure of Metals," 2d ed., McGraw-Hill Book Company, Inc., New York, 1952.

Cottrell, A. H.: "Theoretical Structural Metallurgy," St. Martin's Press, Inc., New York, 1955.

Cullity, B. D.: "X-ray Diffraction for Metallurgists," Addison-Wesley Publishing Company, Cambridge, Mass., 1956.

Hume-Rothery, W., and G. V. Raynor: "The Structure of Metals and Alloys," The Institute of Metals, London, 1954.

Seybolt, A. U., and J. E. Burke: "Procedures in Experimental Metallurgy," John Wiley & Sons, Inc., New York, 1953.

Metallurgy

Bray, J. L.: "Ferrous Process Metallurgy," John Wiley & Sons, Inc., New York, 1954.

Butts, A.: "Metallurgical Problems," 2d ed., McGraw-Hill Book Company, Inc., New York, 1943.

Hayward, C. R.: "An Outline of Metallurgical Practice," D. Van Nostrand Company, Inc., Princeton, N.J., 1952.

Newton, J.: "An Introduction to Metallurgy," John Wiley & Sons, Inc., New York, 1947.

Schuhmann, R., Jr.: "Metallurgical Engineering," vol. I, Addison-Wesley Publishing Company, Cambridge, Mass., 1952.

Organic Chemistry

Conant, J. B., and A. H. Blatt: "The Chemistry of Organic Compounds," The Macmillan Company, New York, 1952.

Fieser, L. F., and Mary Fieser: "Organic Chemistry," D. C. Heath and Company, Boston, 1956.

Fuson, R. C.: "Advanced Organic Chemistry," John Wiley & Sons, Inc., New York, 1950.

Karrer, P.: "Organic Chemistry" (tr. by H. V. Simon and N. G. Bissett), Elsevier Publishing Company, Amsterdam, 1950.

Wertheim, E.: "Textbook of Organic Chemistry," 2d ed., The Blakiston Division, McGraw-Hill Book Company, Inc., New York, 1947.

Wheland, G. W.: "Advanced Organic Chemistry," John Wiley & Sons, Inc., New York, 1951.

Whitmore, F. C.: "Organic Chemistry," D. Van Nostrand Company, Inc., Princeton, N.J., 1951.

Pharmaceutical Chemistry

Barlow, R. B.: "Introduction to Chemical Pharmacology," Methuen & Co., Ltd., London, 1955.

Bodendorf, K.: "Kurzes Lehrbuch der pharmazeutischen Chemie," Springer-Verlag OHG, Vienna, 1954.

Burger, A.: "Medicinal Chemistry; Chemistry, Biochemistry, Therapeutic and Pharmacological Action of Natural and Synthetic Drugs," Interscience Publishers, Inc., New York, 1951.

Jenkins, G. L., and W. H. Hartung: "The Chemistry of Organic Medicinal Products," John Wiley & Sons, Inc., New York, 1957.

Wilson, C. O., and O. Gisuold: "Textbook of Organic Medicinal and Pharmaceutical Chemistry," J. B. Lippincott Company, Philadelphia, 1954.

Physical Chemistry

Daniels, F., and R. A. Alberty: "Physical Chemistry," John Wiley & Sons, Inc., New York, 1955.

Glasstone, S.: "Textbook of Physical Chemistry," D. Van Nostrand Company, Inc., Princeton, N.J., 1946.

Hammett, L. P.: "Introduction to the Study of Physical Chemistry," McGraw-Hill Book Company, Inc., New York, 1952.

Macdougall, F. H.: "Physical Chemistry," The Macmillan Company, New York, 1952.

Moore, W. J.: "Physical Chemistry," Prentice-Hall, Inc., Englewood Cliffs, N.J., 1955.

CHAPTER 10

TERTIARY SOURCES—GUIDES AND DIRECTORIES

> If we could first know where we are, and whither we are tending, we could then better judge what to do, and how to do it.—*Lincoln.*

There remains a variety of miscellaneous sources which might, perhaps, have been included as a subdivision of Chapter 8, since the publications are, in a sense, works of reference. However, for the most part they seem to be sufficiently different to justify separate consideration.

These works are designated here as "tertiary sources," inasmuch as they serve, in part at least, as guides to the secondary and primary sources. They are aids for searching all literature. Also, they provide facts about chemists and their work. The latter category includes plants, products, societies, and related items.

The publications included here often are of more use to non-chemists than to those actually practicing the profession. Reference librarians, for example, receive many questions for which answers are available in tertiary sources.

General Guides

A number of publications are devoted to the over-all problem of chemical literature as such. From a broad viewpoint, they may be classified as books and periodicals.

Books about Chemical Literature. In recent decades the literature has grown to such an extent that books on its nature and use seem justified. At any rate, they have appeared and have found use both in specific courses devoted to the subject in departments of chemistry and in a more general way in library schools.

The following list is arranged in the order of appearance of the first editions:

1919 Ostwald, W.: "Die Chemische Literatur und die Organisation der Wissenschaft," Akademische Verlagsgesellschaft m.b.H., Leipzig.

185

1921   Sparks, M. E.: "Chemical Literature and Its Use,"[1] privately
       published.
1924   Mason, F. A.: "An Introduction to the Literature of Chemistry,"
       Oxford University Press, New York.
1927   Crane, E. J., and A. M. Patterson: "A Guide to the Literature of
       Chemistry," John Wiley & Sons, Inc., New York.
1928   Mellon, M. G.: "Chemical Publications," McGraw-Hill Book Com-
       pany, Inc., New York.
1938   Soule, B. A.: "Library Guide for the Chemist," McGraw-Hill Book
       Company, Inc., New York.
1946   Serrallach, M.: "Bibliographia Quimica," J. Bosch, Barcelona.
1951   Dyson, G. M.: "A Short Guide to the Literature of Chemistry,"
       Longmans, Green & Co., Inc., New York.
1956   van Luik, J.: "Searching the Chemical and Chemical Engineering
       Literature," Purdue University, Lafayette, Ind.

Closely related books of the same type are the following:

Parke, N. G.: "Guide to the Literature of Mathematics and Physics (Includ-
    ing Related Works on Engineering Science)," McGraw-Hill Book
    Company, Inc., New York, 1947.
Pearl, R. M.: "Guide to Geologic Literature," McGraw-Hill Book Company,
    Inc., New York, 1951.
Whitford, R. H.: "Physics Literature," Scarecrow Press, Washington, D.C.,
    1954.

Periodicals on Documentation. In recent years the word
"documentation" has come into use. One meaning is the production, dissemination, and use of publications.

Probably the most useful periodical of this nature is *Chemical
Literature*, the quarterly publication of the Division of Chemical
Literature of the American Chemical Society. Each issue carries
an annotated bibliography on chemical documentation.

More general periodicals of this kind are *American Documentation* (United States), *Journal of Documentation* (Britain), *Revue
de la documentation* (France), *Dokumentation-Fachbibliothek-
Werksbücherei* and *Nachrichten für Dokumentation* (Germany),
and *Tijdschrift voor Efficientie en Documentatie NIDER* (Netherlands). *Special Libraries* (United States) is also of interest.

Biographical Works

Many times in office, study, or library one wants to know biographical data about chemists and workers in related fields. For

---

[1] This small book seems to be the first one prepared as a text for a course
on chemical literature. Such a course was begun in 1913 at the University of
Illinois.

individuals who are well known, such information generally can be found in works of the "Who's Who" type. Questions such as the following arise: date of birth, education, principal field of chemistry, experience, publications, and address of home or place of business.

The following works include the names of many chemists and chemical engineers:[1]

"American Men of Science," Science Press, Lancaster, Pa., 1955.

"Blue Book of Awards," Marquis, Chicago, 1956.

"Chamber's Dictionary of Scientists," E. P. Dutton & Co., Inc., New York, 1951.

"Chemical Society's Memorial Lectures," The Chemical Society, London, 1951.

"Chemical Who's Who," Lewis Historical Publishing Co., New York, 1956.

"Dictionary of American Biography," Charles Scribner's Sons, New York, 1928–1937.

"Handbook of Scientific and Technical Awards in the United States and Canada, 1900–1952," Special Libraries Association, 1956.

"Index Generalis," Dunod, Paris, 1955.

"International Blue Book," Chancery House, New York, 1951–1952.

"International Who's Who," Europa Publications, Ltd., London, 1956.

"Kürschner's deutscher gelehrten Kalendar," Walter De Gruyter & Co., Berlin, 1954.

"Minerva, Jahrbuch der gelehrten Welt," Walter De Gruyter & Co., Berlin, 1952.

"Neue deutsche Biographie," Duncker & Humblot, Munich, 1953–1955.

"Nobel Prize Winners in Chemistry, 1901–50," Abelard-Schuman, Inc., Publishers, New York, 1953.

"Poggendorff's biographisch-literarisches Handwörterbuch," Verlag Chemie, Leipzig, 1925– .

"Poor's Register of Directors and Executives," Standard and Poor's Corp., New York, 1928– .

"Torchbearers of Chemistry," Academic Press, Inc., New York, 1949.

"Universal Pronouncing Dictionary of Biography and Mythology," J. B. Lippincott Company, Philadelphia, 1930.

"Who Knows—and What," Marquis, Chicago, 1954.

"Who Was Who," A. & C. Black, Ltd., London, annual.

"Who's Who," A. & C. Black, Ltd., London, annual.

"Who's Who in America," Marquis, Chicago, 1956.

"Who's Who in American Education," Who's Who in American Education, Nashville, Tenn., 1956.

"Who's Who in British Science," British Book Center, New York, 1954.

"Who's Who in Commerce and Industry,"[2] Marquis, Chicago, 1955.

[1] No editors are indicated since often there is none given. The dates are for the latest editions.

[2] Contains indexed catalogue of principal companies.

"Who's Who in Engineering," Lewis Historical Publishing Co., New York, 1954.
"World Biography," Institute for Research in Biography, New York, 1948.
"World of Learning," Europa Publications, Ltd., London, 1957.

Scientific and Technical Societies

In this category the information desired concerns the names of organizations that exist or did exist and people who belong to them.

Organizations. Useful directories to societies include the following:

Bolton, H. C.: Chemical Societies of the 19th Century, *Smithsonian Inst. Publs. Misc. Collections,* no. 1314 (1902).
"British Sources of Reference and Information, A Guide to Societies, Works of Reference, and Libraries," Association of Special Libraries and Information Bureau, London, 1947.
Judkins, C. J. (ed.): "National Associations of the United States," Washington, D.C., 1949.
———: "Trade and Professional Associations of the United States," Washington, D.C., 1942.
Scientific and Technical Societies of the United States and Canada, *Bull. Natl. Research Council U.S.,* no. 115 (1955).

Membership Lists. Usually at irregular intervals societies publish lists of their members. Of most interest to chemists are those of the American Chemical Society, the American Institute of Chemical Engineers, the American Institute of Chemists, and the American Society for Testing Materials.

Examples of more specialized organizations are the Optical Society of America, the Society for Applied Spectroscopy, and the Coblentz Society.

Book Lists

As stated in the discussion of bibliographies, a librarian deals broadly with four kinds of publications: periodicals, bulletins, patents, and books. The books appear singly or as parts of sets.

Thousands of new books appear each year. There is a problem of knowing not only what are the new ones but also what ones already exist on a given subject. Perhaps the ideal solution to this problem would be access to a library which has everything. As there are few, if any, such libraries, one must use other means.[1]

New Books. One of the best means of trying to keep up with new books is to have one's name placed on the mailing lists of the chief publishers of technical books. Examples of those publishers follow.

United States

Academic Press, Inc., New York
American Book Company, New York
Chemical Publishing Company, Inc., New York
Thomas Y. Crowell Company, New York
Elsevier Press, Inc., Houston, Tex. (distributor for Elsevier Publishing Company, Amsterdam)
D. C. Heath and Company, Boston
Interscience Publishers, Inc., New York
J. B. Lippincott Company, Philadelphia
Longmans, Green & Co., Inc., New York
McGraw-Hill Book Company, Inc. (including The Blakiston Division), New York
The Macmillan Company, New York
Prentice-Hall, Inc., Englewood Cliffs, N.J.
Reinhold Publishing Company, New York
W. B. Saunders Company, Philadelphia
D. Van Nostrand Company, Inc., Princeton, N.J.
John Wiley & Sons, Inc., New York

Great Britain

Blackie & Son, Ltd., Glasgow
Cambridge University Press, London and New York
Charles Griffin & Co., Ltd., London
W. Heffer & Sons, Ltd., Cambridge, England
Oxford University Press, London and New York

France

Centre nationale de la recherche scientifique, Paris
Dunod, Paris
Gauthier-Villars & Cie, Paris
Hermann & Cie, Paris
Librairie Hachette, Paris
Masson et Cie, Paris
Presses universités, Paris

[1] See E. J. Crane, A. M. Patterson, and E. B. Marr, "A Guide to the Literature of Chemistry," pp. 22–56, John Wiley & Sons, Inc., New York, 1957, for an extensive list of reference books. The classification follows the sectional subdivisions of *Chemical Abstracts*.

Germany

Böhlau, Cologne
Duncker & Humblot, Munich
Mohr, Tübingen
R. Oldenbourg-Verlag, Munich
Springer-Verlag OHG, Vienna

Several publishers' periodicals deal with new books. Important examples are *Book Review Digest, Publishers' Trade List Annual, Publishers' Weekly, Technical Book Review Index,*[1] *New Technical Books,*[2] and the *ASLIB Book List.*

Many technical periodicals carry lists of books received for review. Those considered to be the better books are reviewed. Advertisements of publishers very often announce new books before publication. Many new books are listed in the appropriate sections of *Chemical Abstracts.*

Mention may be made here of dealers in foreign books. The following are examples: Stechert-Haffner, Inc., W. J. Johnson, Inc., Four Continents, and Lange, Maxwell and Springer, all of New York; A. C. McClurg and Co., Chicago; B. H. Blackwell, Ltd., Oxford, England; Librairie Hachette, Paris, France; Ulrico Hoepli, Milan, Italy; N. V. M. Nijhoff, The Hague, Netherlands; and H. Land & Cie, Berne, Switzerland.

Old Books. Important general lists of books follow. The time of cumulation varies, there being monthly, annual, and longer periods.

United States[3]

"Books in Print," R. R. Bowker Company, New York, 1948–   .
"Cumulative Book Index,"[4] The H. W. Wilson Company, New York, 1898–   .
Hawkins, R. R. (ed.): "Scientific, Medical, and Technical Books Published in the United States of America,"[5] National Research Council, Washington, D.C., 1930–   .
"Publishers' Trade List Annual," R. R. Bowker Company, New York, 1873–   .
"Technical Book Review Index," Special Libraries Association, New York, 1935–   .

[1] Issued by the Special Libraries Association, New York.
[2] Issued by the New York Public Library.
[3] See also C. M. Winchell, "Guide to Reference Books," American Library Association, Chicago, 1950–1952.
[4] Formerly "The United States Catalog."
[5] Includes several supplements.

Great Britain

"British National Bibliography," Council of British National Bibliography, British Museum, London, 1950– .

"English Catalogue of Books," Publishers' Circular, London, 1801– .

"Reference Catalogue of Current Literature," J. Whitaker and Sons, London, 1874– .

"Whitaker's Cumulative Book List," J. Whitaker and Sons, London, 1924– .

France

"Biblio," Librairie Hachette, Paris, 1933– .

"Bibliographie de la France,"Au cercle de la librairie, Paris, 1811– .

"La Librairie française," Au cercle de la librairie, Paris, 1930– .

Germany

"Barsortiments-Lagerkatalog,"[1] Koehler und Volckmar, Leipzig, 1904– .

"Deutsche Nationalbibliographie," Buch und Bibliothekswesen, Leipzig, 1931– .

"Deutsches Bücherverzeichnis," Börsenverein der deutschen Buchhändler, Leipzig, 1911– .

"Halbjahrsverzeichnis der Neuererscheinungen des deutschen Buchhandels," Börsenverein der deutschen Buchhändler, Leipzig, 1797–1944.

"Jahresverzeichnis des deutschen Schrifttums," Börsenverein der deutschen Buchhändler, Leipzig, 1948– .

Italy

Gaudenzi, N.: "Guida bibliographica internazionale per il Chimico," Sansoni, Florence, Italy, 1952.

Spain and Portugal

Brode, W. R.: Bibliography of Chemistry and Chemical Technology Textbooks in the Spanish and Portuguese Languages, *J. Chem. Educ.*, **26**:553 (1949).

Language Dictionaries

Useful chemical dictionaries follow.

Callaham, L. I.: "Russian-English Technical and Chemical Dictionary," John Wiley & Sons, Inc., New York, 1953.

DeVries, L.: "French-English Science Dictionary," 2d ed., McGraw-Hill Book Company, Inc., New York, 1951.

———: "German-English Science Dictionary," 2d ed., McGraw-Hill Book Company, Inc., New York, 1946.

Duncan, D. R.: "English-Esperanto Chemical Dictionary," British Esperanto Association, London, 1956.

Fouchier, L., and F. Billet: "Chemical Dictionary in Three Languages: English-French-German," Werveries, G.m.b.H., Baden-Baden, Germany, 1953.

[1] Formerly "Deutscher Literatur-Katalog."

Giua, M.: "Dizionario de chimica generale e industriele," Unione tipo-graphico editrice torinese, Torino, Italy, 1948.

Goldberg, M.: "Spanish-English Chemical and Medical Dictionary," McGraw-Hill Book Company, Inc., New York, 1952.

Leidecker, K. F.: "German-English Technical Dictionary," Vanni, New York, 1950–1951.

Patterson, A. M.: "French-English Dictionary for Chemists," John Wiley & Sons, Inc., New York, 1954.

————: "German-English Dictionary for Chemists," John Wiley & Sons, Inc., New York, 1950.

Webel, A.: "A German-English Dictionary of Technical, Scientific, and General Terms," E. P. Dutton & Co., Inc., New York, 1953.

Directories and Trade Catalogues

Trade catalogues are published for the principal purpose of selling manufacturers' products. To the student and engineer they offer useful information about processes, machines, and materials. Also they show the practical application of theories and principles of engineering. Catalogues of equipment are generally illustrated with photographs, diagrams, and drawings, and frequently there are included detailed specifications of the design or properties of the product offered.

Usually from such sources one wants information about some kind of product, such as molecular stills, or about an organization. In the latter case, annual reports and company histories are of interest, for example, to one making an economic or historical survey of a company or an industry.

Included here also are various kinds of directories. Examples are manufacturers of, or dealers in, a given chemical; testing and consulting laboratories; faculties of technical educational institutions; and sources of raw materials.

Some of these works contain a variety of information. Thus, for a given compound a buyer's guide may contain information on sources, producers, dealers, common properties, shipping containers and hazards, trade names, and related items.

The following unclassified selections are representative of this kind of publication. In many cases the titles indicate the general nature of the contents. The date is for the latest edition available.

"American Druggist Blue Book," American Druggist, New York, 1956.

Bennett, H.: Trade-marks, *Advances in Chem. Ser. No. 4*, p. 75 (1951).

"Blue Book" (soap and sanitary chemicals), MacNair-Dorland Co., New York, 1956.

Bonnitt, T. L. (ed.): "McGraw-Hill Directory of Chemicals and Producers," McGraw-Hill Book Company, Inc., New York, 1952.

"British Chemicals and Their Manufacturers," Association of British Chemical Manufacturers, London, 1957.

"Chemical Directory," Dominion Bureau of Statistics, Ottawa, Canada, 1950.

"Chemical Engineering: 1956 Inventory Issue," McGraw-Hill Book Company, Inc., New York, 1956.

"Chemical Engineering Catalog," Reinhold Publishing Corporation, New York, 1956.

"Chemical Industry Facts Book," Manufacturing Chemists' Association, Washington, D.C., 1955.

"Chemical Manufacturers' Directory of England, Wales, and Scotland," S. Marshall, London, 1954.

"Chemical Materials Catalog and Directory of Producers," Reinhold Publishing Corporation, New York, 1956.

"Chemical Week Buyers' Guide Issue," McGraw-Hill Book Company, Inc., New York, 1956.

"Consulting Services," Association of Consulting Chemists and Chemical Engineers, New York, 1955.

"Directory of Certified Clinical Chemists," American Board of Clinical Chemistry, Detroit, 1954.

"Directory of Commercial and College Testing Laboratories," American Society for Testing Materials, Philadelphia, 1955.

"Directory of Graduate Research, Faculties, Publications, and Doctoral Theses in Chemistry and Chemical Engineering at United States Universities," American Chemical Society, Washington, D.C., 1955.

"Drug and Cosmetic Review," Drug and Cosmetic Industry, New York, 1954.

"Drug Topics Red Book," Druggists' Circular, New York, 1941–

Du Mond, T. C. (ed.): "Engineering Materials Manual," Reinhold Publishing Corporation, New York, 1951.

Ernst, A., and L. Neumann (eds.): "Blücher's Auskunftsbuch für die chemische Industrie," Walter De Gruyter & Co., Berlin, 1954.

"Green Book Buyers' Directory," Oil, Paint, and Drug Reporter, New York, 1957.

Gregory, T. C. (ed.): "Uses and Applications of Chemicals and Related Materials," Reinhold Publishing Corporation, New York, 1939–1944.

Gutman, A. B. (ed.): "Modern Drug Encyclopedia and Therapeutic Index," Drug Publications, New York, 1955.

Hallows, J. S. (ed.): "Finishing Handbook and Directory," Sawell Publications, London, 1956.

Haynes, W.: "Chemical Trade Names and Commercial Synonyms," D. Van Nostrand Company, Inc., Princeton, N.J., 1955.

"Industrial Research Laboratories of the United States," National Research Council, Washington, 1956.

"MacRae's Blue Book and Hendricks' Commercial Register," MacRae's Blue Book Co., Chicago, 1953.

"Market Guide," Editor and Publisher, New York, 1953.

"Merck Index of Chemicals and Drugs," Merck and Co., Rahway, N.J., 1952.

"Modern Plastics Encyclopedia and Engineers' Handbook," Plastics Catalogue Corp., New York, 1955.

"New and Nonofficial Remedies" (of American Medical Association), J. B. Lippincott Company, Philadelphia, 1955.

"Pit and Quarry Handbook and Directory of the Nonmetallic Industries," Pit and Quarry Publications, Chicago, 1955.

"Process Industries Handbook of Corrosion Resistant Materials," Reinhold Publishing Corporation, New York, 1947.

"Rubber Red Book," Rubber Age, New York, 1955.

Sax, N. I.: "Handbook of Dangerous Materials," Reinhold Publishing Corporation, New York, 1951.

Snell, F. D., and C. T. Snell: "Chemicals of Commerce," D. Van Nostrand Company, Inc., Princeton, N.J., 1952.

Stewart, J. R.: "An Encyclopedia of the Chemical Process Industries," Chemical Publishing Company, Inc., New York, 1956.

"Sweet's File, Process Industries," Sweet's Cataloging Service, New York, 1952.

"Thomas' Register of American Manufacturers," Thomas Publishing Company, New York, 1956.

Wagner, K. G.: "Autoren-Namen als chemische Begriffe," Verlag Chemie, Weinheim, Germany, 1951.

Wilson, C. O., and T. E. Jones (eds.): "The American Drug Index," J. B. Lippincott Company, Philadelphia, 1956.

"World Chemical Directory of Importers, Exporters, and Manufacturers of Chemicals, Drugs, Plastics, and Oils," Atlas Publishing Company, Inc., New York, 1949.

Wylie, G. J., and N. F. Lowe (eds.): "Directory of Australian Scientific and Industrial Research Organizations," Commonwealth Scientific and Industrial Research Organization, Melbourne, 1953.

Zimmerman, O. T., and I. Lavine: "Handbook of Material Trade Names," Industrial Research Service, Dover, N.H., 1953–1957.

Most states have industrial directories. Examples are "The Alabama Book," "Arizona Industrial Buyers' Guide," "Industrial Directory of Arkansas," "Directory of Florida Manufacturers," "Idaho Industries," and "Guide Book to Minnesota Industry."

Manufacturers' or distributors' catalogues are useful for information on the availability and comparative prices of many common chemicals. Generally specifications are included for "analytical" or "reagent grade" substances. The following manufacturers are among those having such catalogues:

Allied Chemical and Dye Corp., New York, N.Y.
American Cyanamid Co., New York, N.Y.

Commercial Solvents Corp., New York, N.Y.
Dow Chemical Co., Midland, Mich.
Eastman Chemical Products, Inc., Kingsport, Tenn.
E. I. du Pont de Nemours and Co., Wilmington, Del.
Foote Mineral Co., Philadelphia, Pa.
Hercules Powder Co., Wilmington, Del.
J. T. Baker Chemical Co., Phillipsburg, N.J.
Mallinckrodt Chemical Works, St. Louis, Mo.
Merck and Co., Rahway, N.J.
Monsanto Chemical Co., St. Louis, Mo.
Olin Mathieson Chemical Corp., Baltimore, Md.
Union Carbide Chemicals Co., New York, N.Y.
Wyandotte Chemicals Corp., Wyandotte, Mich.

Miscellaneous Items

There are a few miscellaneous sources of this general nature which do not belong in the previous lists. The following publications are examples:

Feingold, S. N.: "Scholarships, Fellowships, and Loans," Bellman Publishing Company, Boston, 1949.
Ruddy, A. C.: "College Scholarships for the Asking," Key Publications, Washington, D.C., 1953.

CHAPTER 11

MAKING SEARCHES
IN THE CHEMICAL LITERATURE[1]

Knowledge is of two kinds. We know a subject ourselves, or we know
where we can find information upon it.—*Johnson*

In case one desires recorded information on some subject, the
first question arising is where to go to find publications such as
those discussed in the preceding chapters. In general, it may be
assumed that some publications will be found wherever progres-
sive chemists are located or where there is a demand for chemical
facts. But in spite of the present supply of books and periodicals,
it is surprising to find the handicap under which some individuals
work in this respect.

Location of Publications. Disregarding the private collections
of individual chemists, one turns naturally to libraries as the
most probable source of desired material. Although there are
hundreds of libraries, probably the large majority of them are of
relatively little value to one needing much chemical information.
Most of those in the smaller colleges and the smaller cities may
be disregarded. A really good, general chemical library is expensive not only to acquire but also to maintain; consequently, the
situation mentioned is not unexpected, if one keeps in mind the
limited funds available in most cases for the support of the whole
library.

Libraries which have really worthwhile collections of chemical
publications may be classified as public, private, and academic.
There are excellent and mediocre collections in each class.

As a part of the material included in their "List of Periodicals
Abstracted by *Chemical Abstracts*," the editors mention 263
libraries in the United States having the best chemical collections.

[1] See A. Kent and J. W. Perry (eds.), "Documentation in Action," Reinhold Publishing Corporation, New York, 1956.

196

Read[1] estimated that about 80 of these are most important. Crane, Patterson, and Marr[2] included a list of 120 American libraries of interest to chemists. A number of valuable collections, however, were omitted in this work.

Public Libraries. There are few collections of much significance in the public libraries of cities having a population of less than 100,000. Of course, it must not be assumed from this arbitrary limitation that mere numbers in population assure a good library; but, ordinarily, the larger the city the greater the demand for such material and the greater the possibility of finding a well-developed technological department. The superb collection of the Library of Congress at Washington is one of the most nearly complete collections in this class. The various state and Federal libraries would be included here.

Private Libraries. Of the private libraries, two rather distinct types will be recognized, the scientific and the industrial. The former are usually maintained by means of private endowments or through some club or professional organization or society. Examples of such institutions are the libraries of the Chemists' Club[3] and the Franklin Institute in New York and Philadelphia, respectively. Such libraries are usually available to those maintaining membership in the organization or contributing to its support in some way. The courtesy of working in such collections is frequently extended to other persons properly qualified.

Private libraries of the industrial type are maintained in connection with manufacturing, consulting, and research organizations, such as the General Electric Company, the consulting laboratory of A. D. Little, and the Mellon Institute. Admirable collections of publications are available in a number of these organizations. Some of these collections are very specialized, covering only limited areas of applied chemistry, while others cover more or less the whole field of chemistry. Although this

[1] W. T. Read, "Industrial Chemistry," p. 20, John Wiley & Sons, Inc., New York, 1945.

[2] E. J. Crane, A. M. Patterson, and E. B. Marr, "A Guide to the Literature of Chemistry," p. 346, Appendix 3, John Wiley & Sons, Inc., New York, 1957.

[3] This collection, containing over 60,000 volumes, is said to be the largest exclusively chemical library in the Western Hemisphere. It is located at 52 East 41st Street, New York. See Killeffer, *Chem. Eng. News*, **27**:2322 (1949).

material is primarily for the use of individuals connected with the organization maintaining the library, it is frequently possible for outsiders to obtain permission to consult the publications.

Libraries of Academic Institutions. In the hundreds of colleges and universities in this country probably less than 20 per cent have chemical collections of much significance for general work. A few of the smaller institutions are well equipped, and occasionally an unusual collection is found; but for the most part the best libraries are at the larger institutions, and particularly at those where much attention is devoted to graduate work. In general, chemists outside the institution may make arrangements to consult such libraries.

As an indication of the relative distribution of the several types of libraries, the following approximate percentages have been calculated for the list of 263 libraries mentioned previously: governmental, 5; public, 14.5; private, scientific, 10.5; private, industrial, 12; and educational institutions, 57.

Interlibrary Loans and Photographic Service. In doing investigational work many individuals will not have available a good chemical library; or even if they have, certain publications will not be found.[1] Many of the libraries mentioned in the list referred to above have relatively incomplete collections, and it is frequently a problem to obtain some special publication, particularly early volumes of the older periodicals. In such cases it is often possible to take advantage of the interlibrary service maintained in many places. Unless the publication desired forms part of an expensive or rare set or is in frequent demand in the library possessing it, one generally can have a nearby library borrow it for a short time.

In the case of short articles, or when it seems unwise to take the chance of having a valuable book lost or damaged, photographic copies of the desired parts may be made at reasonable cost. This service is especially valuable any time one desires an accurate copy of complicated features, such as formulas, diagrams, and tables. Most large libraries are equipped to make full-size reproductions known as "photostats."

To read a 35-mm film copy some kind of magnifying device is necessary. Several types of readers are available. Some indi-

---

[1] The Midwest Inter-library Center in Chicago is developing a program to make available current subscriptions to all periodicals indexed in *Chemical Abstracts*.

viduals, rather than bothering with photographic reproductions, prefer to go to a library to read the originals.

Translations of material in foreign languages may be obtained from some of the large libraries.[1] Consulting literature chemists, of course, make searches, translations, and prepare reports on given subjects.

In the "List of Periodicals Abstracted by *Chemical Abstracts*" are listed the libraries which have at least a partial file of the periodicals included. In certain cities union lists give similar information for the libraries in the region covered. Still more comprehensive is the "Union List of Serials in Libraries of the United States and Canada" (see page 40).

Finding Publications in a Library

For the efficient use of the chemical literature, it is necessary to have an orderly arrangement of the publications in the library, together with some means for finding them easily. It is insufficient merely to assemble the material by placing separate publications side by side on a shelf. Fortunately, librarians have devised systems of arrangement which are relatively easy to understand and use.

Arrangement of Publications. Publications are arranged in a library according to some definite scheme, so that those possessing more or less common characteristics are grouped together. Although various bases of classification may be used, for general work the material is most satisfactorily arranged according to subjects. In carrying out this scheme the Dewey Decimal Classification is most widely used.[2] In accordance with this system, the works covering all branches of knowledge are divided into 10 main divisions, designated with Arabic numerals, as shown below.

000 General works (bibliography, encyclopedias, general periodicals)
100 Philosophy (psychology, ethics)
200 Religion (Bible, church history)
300 Sociology (economics, education)
400 Philology

[1] See also p. 41.
[2] An elaboration of the Dewey system, known as the "Universal Decimal Classification" (U.D.C.), provides for more detailed classification.

500 Natural science (mathematics, physics, chemistry, biology)
600 Useful arts (architecture, engineering, agriculture)
700 Fine arts
800 Literature
900 History (travel, biography)

For convenience these classes are usually referred to as hundreds rather than as units; e.g., the 500s mean the sciences.

Each of these classes may be divided and subdivided, by the addition of other figures, to an almost unlimited extent. For example, 900 being history, 970 stands for the history of America, 973 for the history of the United States, 977 for the history of the North Central states, 977.2 for the history of Indiana, and 977.295 for the history of Tippecanoe County.

Each book, as it comes to the library, is given a number that corresponds as closely as possible to its subject, and all books having the same number are shelved together.

To distinguish books written on the same subject but by different authors, another symbol is used, called the author number or book number. This consists of a letter followed by one or more figures; e.g., in 977.2 D92, "History of Indiana by J. P. Dunn," and 977.2 M78, "History of Indiana by E. E. Moore," D92 and M78 stand for the surnames Dunn and Moore, respectively. In addition, the book number may contain other entries to indicate title, edition, language, or translator.

Books are arranged on the shelves from left to right, first according to their class numbers, and then books with the same class numbers according to their author numbers.

The classification number 977.2 and the book number D92, taken together, are spoken of as the "call number," since by means of it the book can be located on the shelf. This call number is written on and in each volume on the shelves. It appears also in the upper left-hand corner of the card in the card catalogue, which is discussed later. When the call number is written down for reference or when a book is called for, the number should be copied accurately and completely.

The following abridged classification indicates the chief classes of publications that contain information of chemical interest, the Dewey[1] number being shown on the left.

[1] M. Dewey, "Decimal Classification and Relative Index," Forest Press, Essex County, N.Y., 1942.

ABRIDGED SYSTEMS OF CLASSIFICATION

Dewey		*Library of Congress*
000	General works:	A; Z
016.54	Bibliography of chemistry	Z 5521–5526
300	Sociology:	H
310	Statistics:	HA
317.3	U.S. Bureau of the Census	HA 201
340	Law:	K
340.6	Legal chemistry	RA 1001
370	Education:	L
371.66	Laboratory equipment	Q 183
389	Weights and measures	QC 81–119
500	Natural science:	Q
510	Mathematics:	QA
530	Physics:	QC
530.85	U.S. Bureau of Standards	QC 100
535	Light:	QC 351–495
535.84	Spectroscopy	QC 451–467
536	Heat	QC 251–338
537	Electricity	QC 501–771
537.85	Electrometallurgy	TN 681–687
539	Molecular physics	QC 173
540	Chemistry:	QD
540.92	Biography of chemists	
541	Theoretical and physical	QD 453–655
542	Practical and experimental	QD 43–64
543	Analytical, general	QD 71–80
544	Analytical, qualitative	QD 81–100
545	Analytical, quantitative	QD 101–150
546	Inorganic	QD 151–247
547	Organic	QD 248–449
548	Crystallography	QD 901–999
549	Mineralogy	QE 351–399
550	Geology:	QE
551.94	Geochemistry	QE 515
557.3	U.S. Geological Survey	QE 75–76
570	Biology, general:	QH 301–705
578	Microscopy	QH 201–277
600	Useful arts:	T
608	Patents, inventions	T201–339; TP 210
610	Medicine:	R
612	Physiology	QP
612.015	Physiological chemistry	QP 501–801
614	Public health	RA
614.09	U.S. Public Health Service	RA 11
615	Materia medica, pharmacy	RS
620	Engineering, general:	TA
621.35	Chemical electricity	QC 603–605

Dewey		*Library of Congress*
622	Mining engineering	*TN*
622.09	U.S. Bureau of Mines	*TN* 1
628	Sanitary engineering	*TD*
630	Agriculture:	*S*
630.24	Agricultural chemistry	*S* 583–588
630.72	Work of experiment stations	*S* 31–132
631	Soils and fertilizers	*S* 631–667
637	Dairy and dairy products	*SF* 221–275
640	Domestic economy:	*TX*
641.1	Food, chemically considered	*TX* 501–572
660	Chemical technology:	*TP*
661	Chemicals	*TP* 200–248
662	Explosives	*TP* 268–299
663	Beverages	*TP* 500–618
664	Foods	*TP* 370–465
665	Oils, gas	*TP* 343–360
666	Ceramics, glass	*TP* 785–889
667	Bleaching, dyeing	*TP* 890–932
668	Other organic industries	?
669	Metallurgy, assaying	*TN* 550–799
670	Manufactures, articles made of:	*TS*
671	Metals	*TS* 200–770
672	Iron and steel	*TS* 300–380
673	Brass and bronze	*TS* 564–589
674	Wood	*TS* 800–910
675	Leather	*TS* 940–1047
676	Paper	*TS* 1080–1220
677	Textiles	*TS* 1300–1781
678	Rubber	*TS* 1870–1920
679	Celluloid	*TP* 986. *C5*
690	Building:	*TA; TT*
691	Materials, processes	*TA* 401–492
698	Painting, glazing	*TT* 300–380
700	Fine arts:	*N*
770	Photography	*TR*
900	History:	*D*
920	Biography*	*QD* 21–22

* Chemists only.

Each Dewey class may have subdivisions, as .03 for dictionaries, .05 for serials, and .06 for society publications. For further details concerning this system, the reader is referred to Dewey's "Decimal Classification and Relative Index for Libraries."

Another system of classification particularly suited for large libraries is that used in the Library of Congress, the Mellon Institute for Industrial Research, the Chemists' Club in New

York, and others.[1] "LC" call numbers are shown above. According to this scheme, the general fields of knowledge are designated by letters, class Q being science. A second letter is used to differentiate the divisions of each class, QD being chemistry; QP, physiological chemistry; TP, chemical technology; RS, medical and pharmaceutical chemistry; and S, agricultural chemistry. Details regarding this system may be found in the "Library of Congress Classification," available in libraries or obtainable from the Superintendent of Documents at Washington, D.C.

In addition to the two foregoing systems, some librarians have devised special systems of their own or modified one of the more generally used schemes in order to adapt it to special situations.

The Card Catalogue. The card catalogue serves as an index or guide to the publications contained in a library, just as the index of a book enables one to find what is contained therein. In making such catalogues, the practice of librarians varies somewhat. In many cases the catalogue is a single file consisting of a list of the publications by author, by title, and by subject, all in one alphabetical arrangement. In such a case it is known as a "dictionary card catalogue." Under an individual's name will be found a list of the works he has written or works written about him which the library possesses. Again, for each publication dealing with a specific subject, a card is placed in the catalogue under the name of that subject, thus bringing together in one place all references dealing with that subject. The following example indicates the method of indexing a publication when the headings on the cards are for (1) author, (2) title, and (3) subject:

1.	541.39	Sabatier, P
	Sa1	Catalysis in organic chemistry.
2.	541.39	Catalysis in organic chemistry.
	Sa1	Sabatier, P.
3.	541.39	Organic chemistry, catalysis in.
	Sa1	Sabatier, P.

If no author is given or if the title is a significant one, a card is included for the title. From the card catalogue one can ascertain at once the publications in the library on a given subject with a certain title or by a particular author. By means of the letters on

---

[1] See Mason, *J. Chem. Educ.*, **7**:1887 (1930), for a discussion of the reclassification of a chemistry library according to the Library of Congress system. See also Baer, *Special Libraries*, **36**:150 (1945), on reclassifying and recataloguing the Chemists' Club Library.

the front of the drawers and the guide cards inside, one searches in the proper alphabetical place for the author's name or the title or the subject of the publication desired. Each catalogue card, whether its heading is for author, for title, or for subject, furnishes information such as the following:

> Author's full name (government, society, or institution)
> Title of publication
> Call number (in upper left-hand corner)
> Number of pages, size of book, illustrations
> Publisher, date, and place of publication
> Descriptive and bibliographical notes, table of contents

The accompanying example of a catalogue card was prepared for the second edition of this book by the Library of Congress.[1] The typed notation is the call number for the Dewey system, the card being intended for an "author" entry. Cards which are entirely typed usually contain less information than the Library of Congress cards. On the lower half of the card are shown (1) each of the more important subjects under which the book should be catalogued (*A*); (2) the number which would be assigned to the book in accordance with the Library of Congress classification (*B*); and (3) the order number by which the card is obtained from the Library of Congress (*C*).

016.54
M 48

    Mellon, Melvin Guy, 1893–
        Chemical publications, their nature and use, by Melvin Guy Mellon ... 2d ed. New York [etc.] McGraw-Hill book company, inc., 1940.
        xii, 284 p. incl. illus., forms. 21^{cm}. (*Half-title:* International chemical series)
   A { 1. Chemistry—Bibl.   2. Chemistry—Study and teaching.   3. Bibliography—Best books—Chemistry.   i. Title.
                                        40—10067
                                 B   *C*
        Library of Congress   Z5521.M52
        ——— ——— Copy 2.
        Copyright   016.54

---

[1] In addition to preparing such printed cards for every book receiving a United States copyright, the Card Division of the Library of Congress is prepared to sell collections of cards for special fields.

In contrast to the foregoing scheme, another system consists in maintaining three card files, as follows:

1. Author catalogue—arranged alphabetically, containing names of all authors and societies; also titles of all periodicals, of anonymous works, and of important sets or series of works.
2. Classified catalogue—based on the Dewey, or other, system already described. The arrangement of the cards in the classified catalogue corresponds to the actual arrangement of the publications on the shelves.
3. Index to the classified catalogue—arranged alphabetically. To find all the works on a given subject, one consults this index under the name of the subject. The number at the right-hand corner of the card gives the class number under which the works desired may be found in the classified catalogue. For example, if one is interested in electric lighting, the following will be found in the index:

Electric lighting	621.32
Illumination, electric	621.32
Lighting, electric	621.32

The subject is thus fully indexed, and by consulting the classified catalogue under the number 621.32 all works on the subject of electric lighting will be found.

A subject index similar to the one just mentioned has been devised on a decimal system by the U.S. Office of Experiment Stations for the articles in the reports and bulletins issued by the agricultural experiment stations of the various states.[1] In using this index, it is necessary to locate the desired number for the subject in the key to the index and then turn to the cards with this number. Works on analytical chemistry, for example, bear the number 1.26, 1 being for general science, 0.2 for chemistry, and 0.06 for analytical chemistry.

Working in a Library. Although a knowledge of the actual layout of the library in which one is to work is of value in making efficient use of one's time, no general statement can be made covering what will be found in all libraries. There is more or less variation in practice.

Usually in a general library there will be one or more reading or reference rooms, depending upon the size of the library, in which are shelved the reference works, periodicals, and other publications most often used. Current numbers of periodicals may be segregated in a separate periodical reading room. If the

[1] *States Relations Service Doc.* 37, U.S. Department of Agriculture, States Relations Service.

library is of sufficient size, there seems to be a commendable tendency to make several major divisions. Then the chemical publications will probably be found in a technological division having its own reading room and library equipment. But whether the library is of a general or a specialized nature, the usual practice of librarians, in caring for the publications not found in the reading and reference rooms, is to shelve them in the portion of the building known as the "stacks."

In shelving publications, librarians may differ in making certain special arrangements, even though they use the same system of classification, such as the collection in one place of special types of publications, dissertations, governmental bulletins, and odd sizes of books, for example, regardless of the nature of the subject matter in them.

Although one may obtain a given publication with certainty by looking up its call number in the card catalogue and presenting this to a competent member of the library staff, it is frequently much more advantageous, especially if a considerable number of publications must be consulted, to familiarize oneself with the layout, the system of classification, and the rules of the library and then to obtain permission to go directly to the stacks to use the various works there. In working in a periodical set, for example, one frequently wants to refer to various volumes of the set which were not indicated in connection with the first reference sought.

Locating Desired Information.[1] Having acquainted oneself with the different kinds of chemical publications, with the manner of arranging them in a library, and with the means afforded for finding them, there is the question of what constitutes a reliable and efficient method of ascertaining the specific information available upon a given subject. We must be able not only to find the proper books, bulletins, and other works but also to find specific facts which they contain or to assure ourselves that desired facts are unavailable.

The proper procedure to follow is more or less dependent upon the nature of the information desired. As Barrows stated:[2]

[1] See Egloff et al., *J. Chem. Educ.*, **20**:393 (1943), on some problems of scientific literature surveys. See also Perry, *Chem. Eng. News*, **28**:4530 (1950), on the place and importance of the literature chemist in chemical research.

[2] *Chem. Met. Eng.*, **24**:517 (1921).

Searches or investigations of the chemical literature . . . may be made from various standpoints—for example, by the research chemist, to familiarize himself with the available published information along the lines of his research; by the student, as a part of his studies or research; by the writer or author who, in his articles or publications, desires to give credit to the work of others, or to review the prior literature along the lines of his own publication; by the bibliographer, as the basis of his bibliography; by the manufacturer, to obtain information of interest along the lines of his manufacture or along new lines of development; by the patent investigator, in connection with questions relating to the novelty and patentability of inventions, and the validity and infringement of patents.

The volume of material which has to be consulted will vary widely, depending on the object the searcher has in view. If he wants to know the solubility of sodium chloride in water under ordinary conditions, for example, it is sufficient merely to turn to a simple handbook, such as that by Lange or Hodgman, for the data. If knowledge of the details of the procedure employed by the investigator in determining these data is required, larger works of reference must be consulted where the original reference is given. Again, if a complete summary is required covering all the work that has been done on this determination, one must make a much more extended search of all portions of the chemical literature likely to contain such facts.

It is obvious that one entirely unfamiliar with the chemical literature might experience much difficulty in finding even the solubility of sodium chloride in water.[1] He would lack the general knowledge or perspective which provides one with a sense of direction regarding the proper course to follow. This sense of direction, acquired only by experience with the literature, is of immense value in locating facts. Without it, one is greatly handicapped; with it, not only is much time saved but also the thing desired is much more likely to be found. It is a common experience to have senior students, when given a subject to look up in *Chemical Abstracts*, return shortly with the statement that they looked all around but could find little or nothing on their subject.

[1] The student should not forget that, even though certain facts cannot be found in published works, he ordinarily has two other possible methods of obtaining the desired information: he may inquire of the individual who knows what is desired, or he may resort to experiments in the effort to determine the facts for himself.

Given this sense of direction, or perspective, in handling chemical literature, able searchers will know where to look for certain kinds of information. Journals of physical chemistry will not contain papers on the synthesis of new organic compounds; details for the quantitative determination of lead will be found in works on analytical rather than inorganic chemistry; and commercial statistics relating to the chemical industry are to be found in industrial and trade journals and government publications rather than review serials. Such knowledge helps. But the sense of direction is probably of most value in connection with the use of indexes, such as those of reference works, card catalogues, and abstracting journals. So important is this point that the indexing portion of chemical publications deserves special consideration.

Indexes

In general, an index may be considered as a device which indicates the existence, location, or means of finding definite information. In an ordinary book, for example, the index differs from the table of contents in that the latter indicates, more or less in detail, the main divisions of the material in the order in which they are treated, while the former indicates, in alphabetical order, each significant item in the text. Since indexes of publications should be adequate directories for the purpose intended, it is of the first importance to know something about the nature and use of these facilities for locating information.

E. J. Crane, long-time editor of *Chemical Abstracts*, presented a valuable discussion of this subject from the viewpoint of one who has had long experience in both making and using certain kinds of indexes. The quoted paragraphs in the following portion of this chapter are taken from his paper.[1]

The main problem, of course, in using the journal literature is in finding references, all that are pertinent to the subject in hand, in order that one may learn what the literature contains and all that it contains relating to this subject. This is often difficult. It is doubtful if there is a more important problem for students, in college or out, to learn how to solve. Its solution involves to some extent a familiarity with the more important journals, particularly the abstract journals; but above all it involves a knowledge of indexes and how to use them. References to the

[1] *Ind. Eng. Chem.*, **14**:901 (1922). See also Crane, Patterson, and Marr, *op. cit.*, p. 227.

journal literature are often obtained from books or from one paper to others, but mostly they are obtained from indexes, usually of abstract journals. It is frequently assumed that the use of indexes in making literature searches is a simple matter requiring no special experience or ability. This is a mistake. The making of indexes is an art in itself, involving more than a comprehensive knowledge of the general subject being covered, and the use of indexes is not less an art. This deserves emphasis. It is true, because existing indexes vary greatly in kind, thoroughness, and quality. Even in the use of the best subject indexes the user must meet the indexer part way for good results. Conscious effort to become a good index user will well repay any scientist. Many a day has been spent in the laboratory seeking information by experiment which might have been obtained in a few minutes, or hours at the most, in the library, had the literature search been efficient.

What constitutes a good index? The test is to determine whether or not an index will serve as a reliable means for the location, with a minimum of effort, of every bit of information in the source covered which, according to the indexing basis, that source contains. To meet this test an index must be accurate, complete, sufficiently precise in the information supplied, and so planned and arranged as to be convenient to use. Existing indexes fall far short of this ideal in many cases, and of course somewhat short of it in all cases.

The main purpose in indexing is partially lost sight of through an effort to bring some sort of classification into it. Classification in connection with indexing frequently detracts from, rather than enhances, the efficiency and usefulness of an index, and is beside the main purpose.

Scope. Indexes range from a small number of entries in the back of a small book to sets of large volumes. Each individual reference book, bulletin, or monograph will ordinarily contain its own index. In the case of a set of reference works consisting of a number of volumes, each volume may or may not have its own index. If not, and occasionally even if it does, there will be a general index to the whole set. For periodicals, it is the usual practice to have an annual index in the final volume of the year, in case there are two or more issues during the year. In addition, many periodicals have cumulative or collective indexes covering a period of years, frequently 5, 10, or more. These are very desirable for making searches, as in the case of the decennial indexes of *Chemical Abstracts*. They not only save time but also provide the indexer with an opportunity for correcting and improving the material taken from the annual indexes to make up the cumulative work. Indexes to patents may be annual or cumulative. It has already been mentioned that the index serials are annual publications.

Types. Depending chiefly on the nature of the information to be indexed, one finds in more or less common use at least the four following bases of indexing.

1. *By Patent Number.* This type is considered in the chapter dealing with the literature on patents. In most cases one would not have to rely on patent-number indexes only, since other information, such as title of the patent or the patentee's name, would be available for searching in the other types of indexes. *Chemical Abstracts* contains the best-known patent-number indexes.

2. *By Formula.* Two variations of formula index are in use: one consists of empirical formulas and serves for all types of compounds; the other consists of ring formulas for complex organic compounds. A formula index may be used for any chemical compound whose empirical or ring formula is known. It avoids introducing the uncertainty of name which may exist for some compounds, particularly those with the more complicated structures. The different formula indexes in use are discussed in Chapter 8.

3. *By Author.* In practically every printed article relating to chemistry, whether abstract, book, bulletin, periodical, or patent, the name of the author (or patentee) is mentioned. Also in treatises frequent mention is made of the names of investigators. Whenever the number of these names becomes fairly large and it is of importance to be able to find readily the mention made of them, separate author indexes are often issued. This practice is more or less general for periodicals.

The arrangement used is alphabetical, although some variation is found in handling cases like names beginning with *M'* or *Mc.* In such instances, before giving up a search, one should look in all possible places where the entry might occur.

Some other sources of confusion in this type of index are the following: names in languages using non-Roman characters, names with several parts, and names differently spelled but similarly pronounced.[1]

4. *By Subject.* Although at times patent-number and author indexes, and particularly formula indexes, are very useful, their general value is not comparable to that of an index of subjects

---

[1] See introduction to author sections of decennial indexes of *Chemical Abstracts.*

alphabetically arranged. Subject indexes are not only the most generally useful type but are, undoubtedly for this reason, the most common.

It is comparatively easy to make a complete index of the other types, but a complete subject index is an ideal much more difficult to attain. Those available vary widely in this respect, a state of affairs for which the maker is primarily responsible.

The Use of Indexes. Our chief problem in connection with indexes, after we learn the types available, where they are likely to be found, and the kind of information they contain, is to learn how to use them. For indexes of patent numbers and of authors the procedure is obvious; for formula indexes this matter was presented in connection with the discussion of reference works (see Chapter 8). But subject indexes, owing to their nature, require special attention. The following discussion on this point is from the previously mentioned paper by E. J. Crane:[1]

The first step in learning how to use subject indexes with maximum effectiveness is to become familiar with the characteristics and peculiarities of existing chemical indexes.[2] The most significant point to note is whether or not a so-called subject index is really an index of subjects or an index of words. The tendency to index words instead of thoroughly to enter subjects constitutes the greatest weakness in the literature of chemistry. There is a vast difference. Words are of course necessary in the make-up of a subject index, but it is important for an indexer to remember that the words used in the text of a publication are not necessarily the words suitable for index headings or even modifying phrases. Word indexing leads to omissions, scattering, and unnecessary entries. After the most suitable word or group of words from the indexing point of view has been chosen for a heading, it should of course be used consistently no matter what the wording of the text may be. To illustrate a kind of scattering of entries which may result from word indexing, let us consider such a series of article titles as follows: "An apparatus for the determination of carbon dioxide"; "A new absorption apparatus"; "Apparatus for use in the analysis of baking powder"; "An improved potash bulb"; and "Flue-gas analysis." Word indexes would no doubt contain an entry under the heading "Carbon dioxide" for the first title, one under "Absorption apparatus" for the second, under "Baking

[1] For other advice on the use of indexes, see Smith, *Advances in Chem. Ser. No. 4*, pp. 19–23 (1951), and Singer, *Advances in Chem. Ser. No. 4*, pp. 24–25 (1951).

[2] For example, the key or explanatory matter given in both the author and subject indexes of the decennial indexes of *Chemical Abstracts*.

powder" for the third, under "Potash bulb" for the fourth, and under "Flue gas" for the fifth, and probably no others. These entries seem reasonable enough if the titles are considered separately without thought of the others. And yet the articles may all be descriptive of the same sort of apparatus. As a matter of fact, all these titles might conceivably be used for the same article; if the author happened to be working on baking powder or on flue-gas analysis when he conceived the idea for his novel piece of apparatus, or had it in mind particularly for one purpose or the other, he might choose one of the more specific titles for his article rather than one of the more general ones.

In an index entirely based on subjects rather than words, it would be the task of the indexer to see that all these articles got indexed under one heading, or under each of more than one heading, best with cross references pointing from the other possible headings to the one or more headings used. Or, if there seems to be some justification for scattering owing to differences in point of view (word indexing cannot be gotten away from entirely), he would make sure that the necessary cross references are supplied to lead the index user about from heading to heading so that all entries can be readily located. It is not hard to determine whether or not an index is a word index; when this is suspected or noted, one should look around pretty thoroughly in its use instead of being satisfied that the entries found under the obvious heading are all that the index contains on a subject.

It is important to note the approximate degree of completeness of an index in use. There is perhaps no definite point at which a subject index may be said to be complete. The indexing basis is too indefinite. A great many subject indexes are not as full as they ought to be. Aside from word indexing the indexing merely of titles is the most common reason for incompleteness. Titles cannot be depended upon to furnish the information necessary for adequate subject indexing. An index may be reasonably complete from one point of view and not from others. For example, a publication devoted to bacteriology may not reasonably be expected to be indexed fully from the chemical point of view. Completeness in the information supplied in modifying phrases, as well as completeness in index headings, needs to be taken into consideration. It is necessary, of course, to call forth one's resourcefulness to a special degree if a relatively incomplete index is to be used.

Cross references play an important role in subject indexing and in the use of subject indexes. Word indexing is really hard to avoid and cross references are the great preventive. It is a good sign if a subject index has a plentiful supply of cross references, both of the "See" kind and the "See also" kind.[1] They make for uniformity and proper correlation.

[1] Cross references which refer from a possible heading under which no page references are given to the chosen heading where they may be found are called "See" references, as "Mineral oils. See Petroleum." Those which

"See also" cross references are of just as much importance as the "See" kind, though not as much used. The service which they render in directing the index user to related headings or to headings which, though dissimilar for the most part, have entries under them likely to be of interest to the investigator who refers to the original heading, is often the chief means of making a search complete. It is not reasonable to expect an index user, or an indexer, as a matter of fact, to think of all the headings representing related or significant subjects under which headings he may find valuable references that otherwise might be missed. Nevertheless, in the careful indexing, year after year, of a periodical devoted to a more or less definite field, as an abstract journal for example, subjects are met in such a variety of connections and from so many angles that it is possible for a truly comprehensive list of cross references to be built up. The suitability of a given "See also" cross reference may not be clear, much less suggest itself, until a specific case in which it is helpful is observed. It often pays to follow up such a cross reference even when it does not look as if it applies in a given case. The indexer, in surveying the whole field year after year, is in a position to make valuable suggestions in the form of cross references calculated to lead the index user from place to place in the index, so that the chances that his search will be really exhaustive as far as that particular index is concerned are much increased.

Persistence is a good qualification for index searching. It is desirable to avoid being too soon satisfied. There is no task in which thoroughness is more important. It involves first a knowledge of the index system and of the characteristics of the index. Then one needs to be resourceful, exhausting all possibilities, if he is to avoid some futile searches or incomplete findings. One's fund of general knowledge can usually be brought into service to good advantage.

On account of the necessity of drawing on one's general knowledge in making a literature search in any field, it is in many instances important that one should make his own searches. It is not always safe to let someone less informed in a certain field make an index search when a complete survey is desired, even though his familiarity with indexes and the literature in general may be better than one's own. Just as some tasks in the laboratory can be turned over to another to advantage, but not the more important determinations and experiments, so some tasks in the library can be delegated to an assistant, but not all such tasks. Knowledge, skill, and power of observation are factors fruitful of important results in the library as well as in the laboratory. Literature searching is a dignified pursuit, and it cannot with impunity be assigned to a lower level than that of the laboratory side of the problem, as far as the attention it receives is concerned.

connect headings representing allied subjects or containing related entries are called "See also" references, as "Iron alloys. See also Steel."

With a given problem at hand the first step, of course, is to think out the most likely places to look in the indexes to be used. This may be a simple matter or it may be a very difficult one, depending on the nature of the problem. Difficulty increases with indefiniteness. Experience is necessary. In fact the beginner is often completely at a loss to know what to do at this very first stage of his search. This point is stressed in the Report of the Subcommittee on "Research in Chemical Laboratories" presented to the Committee of One Hundred on Scientific Research in December, 1916.[1] In this report, which commends and recommends courses in chemical literature searching in the universities, it is pointed out that the average graduate "fails to analyze the subject" in which he is interested "into its factors, and, hence, generally looks for topics which are too general. Because he does not find any references to the problem as a whole as he has it in mind, he assumes that nothing has been done upon it and that there is nothing in the literature which will be of aid to him in the investigation. Were he to separate his subject into its essential parts and then to consult the literature on each factor, he would find considerable information which he otherwise would miss." Even though some index headings to which to turn, perhaps the more important ones, may be brought to mind without ingenuity, the completeness of a search may be marred by a failure properly to analyze the problem. Indexes with cross references, particularly "See also" ones, help.

Too much dependence on cross references is not advisable. They may not be available at all and they are never complete. With a given heading in mind it is well to cudgel one's brain for synonymous words or phrases to try, as well as for variously related subjects, and it is advisable to try these even though entries as expected are found in the first place to which one has turned. Words or phrases with an opposite meaning to the one in mind may serve as subject headings under which desired entries may be found. For example, the searcher interested in viscosity may find significant entries under the heading "Fluidity" in addition to those under "Viscosity." Incidentally, it may be noted that the word "consistency" may serve as a heading for still other related entries. Or, some entries under "Electric resistance" may interest the searcher whose thought on turning to an index was of "Electric conductivity." If such related subjects are not suggested by cross references and have not been thought of in advance, they may be suggested by the nature of some entry under the heading first turned to if one is on the lookout for them.

The resourcefulness required in making a thorough search through subject indexes can best be discussed by considering an example. Suppose one were interested in looking up all possible references on vitamins. The first place to which to turn naturally would be "Vitamins" in the

[1] *Science*, **45**:34 (1917).

indexes to the various reference sources to be used. This would rarely, if ever, be far enough to go. If only one of the indexes contained "See also" cross references, these might be helpful in the use of the other indexes. This playing of one index against another, so to speak, is always a possible means of helping out. Cross references should be looked for. Since it is not always possible to find such cross references and it is not safe to depend too much on them, to be complete one might follow out a line of thought as follows: Vitamins are constitutents of foods. It may be worth while to look under "Foods." Entries may be found there with some such modifying phrase as "Accessory constituents of." Vitamins are a factor in health and the effect of foods on health involves the idea of diet or ration. These headings, or this heading if they are combined under "Diet," for example, as would seem best in a true subject index, would no doubt prove fruitful of significant references. Studies of proper diet or of an adequate ration for an army would beyond doubt involve the vitamin theory. Experiments to determine the nutritional value of foods are frequently called feeding experiments, so a heading "Feeding experiments" may be looked for to advantage. Food is taken for the purpose of nutrition and the vitamin problem is a nutrition problem. Therefore, the general subject "Nutrition" needs to be examined in the indexes. There is, of course, such a thing as plant nutrition analogous to the vitamin theory in animal nutrition, so the heading "Plant nutrition" or the heading "Plants" would be suggested. If he did not know it, he would likely learn there are substances supposed to be factors in plant life, called "auximones" by Bottomley, which are analogous to the vitamins in animal nutrition. The heading "Auximones" would, of course, then be suggested for reference. The lack of vitamins in the diet is considered by some to be the cause of certain diseases (beriberi, pellagra, polyneuritis, scurvy, xerophthalmia). These ought, therefore, to be referred to as index headings. The general heading "Diseases" should be tried also, such a modifying phrase as "Deficiency" being looked for. Perhaps the next thing for the index user to do would be to ask himself, or someone else, whether or not there is a definite name for this general type of disease; he would find that there is and that the name is "Avitaminosis," which should then be turned to as a heading. Certain specific foods have been used and studied, particularly with reference to the vitamin theory, as, for example, polished rice, milk, butter, orange juice, yeast, tomatoes, etc. It seems unreasonable to be expected to think of these, or at least all of them, and yet an article entitled, say, "The effect on pigeons of eating polished rice," may be word indexed only in some index, and therefore only get under the headings "Rice" and perhaps "Pigeons." Vitamins have been differentiated as "fat-soluble A," "water-soluble B," etc. and are sometimes spoken of merely in these ways. It is conceivable that some indexes may have these names as headings. In the earlier literature studies resembling the modern vitamin studies are to be found in which other names for the accessory food constituents are used, as nutramines (Abderhalden), bios (Wildiers) and oryzanin (Suzuki). The text referred to from any one of the above-mentioned headings may suggest still other headings, as the names of specific foods supposed to be rich in vitamins.

The principle of referring to the general as well as to the specific subject, as exemplified in the preceding paragraph by the subject "Avita-minosis" for the general and by the individual deficiency diseases (beri-beri, etc.) for the specific, is a good one to keep constantly in mind in using subject indexes. This principle applies aptly in searches for information regarding compounds. Group names for compounds may serve as index headings under which entries of interest to the searcher interested in an individual compound may be found. An example will serve to illustrate.

Supposing one were interested in finding all the information he could with reference to the electrolysis of sodium chloride. In addition to looking up the references under the heading "Sodium chloride" in the indexes to be used, it would be desirable to look also for entries of interest under such headings as the following: "Alkali metal halides," "Chlorides," and "Halides." A process described for the electrolysis of alkali metal halides in general may be of just as much interest and value to the search in hand as one specified to be particularly for sodium chloride, and yet the indexes are not likely to carry entries for each of the members of a group of compounds if a definite group is under discussion. Cross references may be supplied in some cases but it is hardly reasonable to expect an index to go further. A process for electrolyzing chlorides, for instance, could not within reason be entered under headings representing each of the numerous known chlorides. The index user must expect to think of such possibilities and make his search complete accordingly. Another different kind of lead to follow to insure a complete search, particularly when the indexes to be used are word indexes, is to think of the products of the process being studied, in this case, chlorine, sodium hydroxide, and possibly sodium hypochlorite. And in addition to looking up the headings represented by the names of these compounds, completeness is insured only by trying the headings "Halogens," "Alkalies" or "Alkali metal hydroxides," and again possibly "Alkali metal hypohalites" and "Hypohalites." The product of some simple electrolytic process which does not involve the recovery of chloride or alkali may be merely called "Bleaching solution" or be given some like name. And still further it may be worth while to look up such a heading as "Potassium chloride" as a representative of a closely related compound which might be subjected to a similar process, or at least might be studied as to the possibilities. Still other headings worthy to be tried are "Electrolytic cells" and possibly "Electrolysis"; this last heading, however, is too general to be used as an index heading for every process involving electrolysis, and is not likely to be used for studies or discussions of specific resourcefulness and the use of one's general knowledge of chemistry must come prominently into play in the making of index searches.

The resourcefulness necessary in the location of information by means of the great variety of subject indexes in existence may seem to be little more than clever guessing at times. A paper on glass, so-called and indexed only under "Glass," may reveal a principle governing the action of metals or other undercooled melts. Authors fail to see the full significance of their experimental results, and it is not often that the indexer will go further than the author in bringing out this significance for attention. The kind of flexible ingenuity necessary for the location of information in this way is perhaps only to be acquired by experience. It is really more than guessing that results in the location of information in this way, and yet it seems as if a little more than reasoning power, something like intuition, is sometimes necessary.

Chemical publications present a special problem, both to the subject indexer and to the index user, in that many headings must consist of the names of chemical compounds. The difficulties encountered are to be attributed (1) to the fact that many compounds have, or may have, more than one name, (2) the names, or at least the best names, of the more complex compounds may be difficult to ascertain, and (3) new compounds are constantly being prepared, which, if named at all, may receive more than one name which is justified from one point of view or another, and the possibilities of incorrect names are great.

It is not feasible to enter into a detailed discussion of the best procedure in building or using indexes of chemical compounds. The difficulties increase with increasing complexity of compounds. Some indexes are based on systematic nomenclature, irrespective of names used by authors; others are not. Cross references within an index and introductions thereto, and the use by index searchers of dictionaries, chemical encyclopedias, handbooks, and other sources of information, leading to a knowledge of the names, sometimes numerous, of compounds, are helps to be utilized. As mentioned above, a knowledge of what constitutes good nomenclature is a great aid in the location of compounds in name indexes. This is particularly important for the organic chemist. It is on account of the almost insurmountable difficulties due to the complexities of chemical nomenclature and because of language differences, that a basis other than their names—namely, their empirical formulas—has been sought and, to a limited extent, used, in the indexing of compounds. A formula index provides a certain means for the location of individual compounds; it is very doubtful if the average chemist can locate compounds in all cases in name indexes even though systematic nomenclature may have been consistently followed in the indexing. In name indexes it is possible, by appropriate devices, to group related compounds to good advantage.[1]

The subject index searcher is confronted with nomenclature problems relating to fields other than that of chemical compounds. For example, the chemist interested in plants must contend with the fact that some indexes use the scientific names (genus and species) of plants as headings and others use common names, of which there are frequently several for the same plant.

The use of indexes in foreign languages presents obvious difficulties. It is one thing to be able to read a foreign language and another to translate one's thoughts into that language. The use of an English-French, English-German, or other like dictionary, depending on the language involved, is about the only help available. The introductions to Patterson's "German-English Dictionary for Chemists" and "French-English Dictionary for Chemists" contain helpful suggestions for determining German and French names of chemical compounds.[2]

Locating Names of Compounds. The attainment of an efficient working knowledge of chemical nomenclature, as mentioned above, is a formidable task. Yet if one should try to locate in an index the more complex compounds, now comparatively common, especially in organic chemistry, without an idea of the system used in naming them, he would be almost hopelessly lost.

Unfortunately, chemists have not yet agreed upon an international basis of nomenclature, although encouraging progress in that direction has been made.[3] But even if that highly desirable goal were now achieved and everyone used the system, preceding the time of its realization we would have 175 years of literature of modern chemistry more or less confused in this respect. This factor almost necessitates one's learning something about each subject index to be used.

For the purposes of this book, only the practice of *Chemical Abstracts* will be considered; the present indexing of this periodical probably represents the best there is. The procedure now followed in it was adopted only after years of study of the problems involved. The following material is an adaptation of excerpts

[1] Patterson, *Ind. Eng. Chem.*, **11**:989 (1919).

[2] See English–foreign-language dictionaries listed in Chap. **10**.

[3] For an official report of a meeting of the International Nomenclature Committee, see Patterson, *Ind. Eng. Chem.*, **18**:320 (1926).

from (1) the section on nomenclature in "Directions for Abstractors and Section Editors of *Chemical Abstracts*"[1] and (2) the subject index of this periodical for 1954.[2] The first consists of points of advice to those having the problem of naming compounds to appear in the index, while the second is a statement of general principles to be kept in mind as an aid in finding names of compounds in the index.

To Index Makers. If the name selected by the abstractor for a compound differs very greatly from that selected by the author, the latter name should be given and should be followed by the former in brackets.

In naming a compound so as to indicate that oxygen is replaced by sulfur the prefix *thio-* (or *thiol-* or *thiono-*) and not *sulfo-* should be used (*sulfo-* denotes the group SO_3H); thus, HSCN, *thio*cyanic acid; H_3AsS_4, *thio*arsenic acid; $CS(NH_2)_2$, *thio*urea; $Na_2S_2O_3$, sodium *thio*sulfate. *Thio-* is used as a name for sulfur replacing hydrogen in cases in which the sulfur serves as a doubling radical; thus, $H_2NC_6H_4SC_6H_4NH_2$, *thio*dianiline. *Thia-*, *oxa-*, or *aza-* is used when sulfur, oxygen, or nitrogen, respectively, replaces carbon (or CH or CH_2), e.g., *thiaaza*spirodecane, *oxa*diazole. *Dithionous acid*, not *hyposulfurous* nor *hydrosulfurous acid*, should be used to designate $H_2S_2O_4$.

The word *hydroxide* should be used for a compound with OH and *hydrate* for a compound with H_2O. Thus, barium *hydroxide*, $Ba(OH)_2$; chlorine *hydrate*, $Cl_2.10H_2O$.

Salts of chloroplatinic acid are *chloroplatinates* (not *platinichlorides*). Similarly, salts of chloroauric acid are to be called *chloroaurates*, and salts of fluoboric acid, *fluoborates*.

Hydroxyl derivatives of hydrocarbons are to be given names ending in *-ol*, as glycer*ol*, resorcin*ol*, pinac*ol* (not pinac*one*), mannit*ol* (not mann*ite*), pyrocatech*ol* (not pyrocatech*in*).

Compounds which are not alcohols but have received names ending in *-ol*, should be spelled *-ole*, as anis*ole*, ind*ole*. The final *e* of the *-ole* ending should be retained in all combinations. Note that C_6H_6 is preferably called *benzene* (not *benzol*), C_7H_8 *toluene*, etc. *Benzene* rather than *benzol* or *benzole* is also preferred for the mixture of hydrocarbons of the benzene series obtained in the refinement of coal tar. *2-Furaldehyde* (or, less desirably, *furfural*) is preferred to *furfurol* or *furfurole* to indicate that the compound is an aldehyde.

As between the endings *-in* and *-ine*, the latter should always be used for *basic* substances, and for them only; *-in* is used for glycerides, glycosides, bitter principles, proteins, etc. Thus anil*ine*, tyros*ine*, pur*ine*,

---

[1] Issued by the American Chemical Society, 1952.

[2] Introduction to Subject Index, *Chem. Abstr.*, 1954.

morph*ine*; but gelat*in* (not gelat*ine*), palmit*in*, amygdal*in*, album*in*, prote*in* (not prote*id*). In translating, it should be borne in mind that for both basic and neutral substances the Germans use *-in* and the French *-ine*. It is to be noted that this rule does not apply to substances which are not considered to be definite compounds, as *gasoline*.

German words ending in *-an* should be translated *-ane* if they are names of hydrocarbons (or parent compounds of the heterocyclic series) which are fully saturated; otherwise *-an*; as meth*ane*, menth*ane*, diox*ane* (but benzodiox*an*, because one ring is unsaturated), fur*an*, pentos*an*.

German names ending in *-it* should be translated *-ite* rather than *-it*; as chlor*ite*. If it seems desirable to retain the original form of a trade name, its initial letter should be capitalized. Alcohols such as *dulcitol* $C_6H_8(OH)_6$ (German *Dulcit*) are exceptions.

German names of acids should generally be translated by substituting *-ic acid* for *säure*. Some well-established names are exceptions, as *Zuckersäure* (saccharic acid), *Milchsäure* (lactic acid), *Valeriansäure* (valeric acid). Although for a few well-established names it is correct to translate *-insäure* as *-ic acid*, for all others *-inic acid* is the correct translation; e.g., *Acridinsäure* is acridic acid. Names ending in *-carbonsäure* are to be translated *-carboxylic acid* (not *-carbonic acid*), but *-carbonyl chloride* is preferred to *-carboxylyl chloride*. The suffix *-säure* should never be translated *-carboxylic acid*.

The latest-listed names of radicals as given in the introductions to the *Decennial Subject Indexes* should be preferred.

In naming organic compounds, the connective *o* is to be used invariably in such names of substituent radicals as *amino-*, *bromo-*, *chloro-*, *cyano-*, and *iodo-*; thus, bromobenzene, chloroacetic, nitroaniline. This conforms to the demands of euphony and also makes for uniformity in indexing. There are a few apparent exceptions to this rule, as cyanamide, nitramino-. *Benzo-*, *naphtho-* (not *benz-*, *naphth-*) are to be used before consonants.

Halo is preferred over *halogeno*.

The names of the groups NH_2, NHR, NR_2, NH, or NR should end in *-ido* only when they are substituents in an acid group, otherwise in *-ino*; thus, o-$C_6H_4(CO)_2NCH_2CO_2H$, phthalim*ido*acetic acid; $NH_2CH_2CH_2$-CH_2CO_2H, γ-am*ino*butyric acid (not amidobutyric acid); $PhNHCH_2$-$CH_2CH_2CO_2H$, γ-anil*ino*butyric acid; $MeC(:NH)CO_2H$, α-im*ino*propionic acid.

Hydroxy-, not *oxy-*, should be used in designating the hydroxyl group: as α-*hydroxy*butyric acid, $CH_3CH_2CH(OH)CO_2H$, not *oxy*butyric acid. *Oxo-* is to be preferred to *oxy-* to designate oxygen in the group —CO—.

For complex radicals, parentheses and brackets should be freely used in order clearly to fix the relation of modifying substituents; e.g., $ClCH_2CH(CO_2H)_2$ should be written (*chloromethyl*)*malonic acid*, not *chloromethylmalonic acid*, for the latter names $MeCCl(CO_2H)_2$.

The term *ether* is to be used in the usual modern acceptation only, and not as an equivalent of *ester*. Esters and metallic salts should be designated in the form *diethyl phthalate, methyl hydrogen succinate,* and *sodium propionate;* and *not* as *diethyl ester of phthalic acid, succinic acid monomethyl ester,* or *sodium salt of propionic acid,* respectively.

Ethers of hydroxy compounds should not be named as O-derivatives where a better name is possible; thus, *α-ethoxypropionic acid,* MeCH-(OEt)CO₂H (not *ethyllactic acid* or *lactic acid ethyl ether*).

In the naming of cyclic compounds, reference to the ring index in the *Decennial Indexes* (or in the recent annual indexes) will be found helpful.

The names *butane, pentane, butyl, pentyl,* etc., should be used only for the normal hydrocarbons and normal hydrocarbon radicals and, with the prefix *cyclo-,* as *cyclo*hexane, for saturated cyclic hydrocarbons and their radicals. Geneva names for aliphatic hydrocarbons, acids, alcohols, aldehydes, and ketones may be used.

The names *ethylene* and *acetylene* have preference over *ethene* and *ethyne*. The names of triple bond (acetylene) hydrocarbons should end in *-yne* instead of *-ine*.

Salts of organic bases with hydrochloric acid should be called *hydrochlorides* (not *hydrochlorates* nor *chlorohydrates*). Similarly, *hydrobromide, hydroiodide, methiodide* (not *iodomethylate*), *methochloride,* and *methosulfate* should be used.

The system of numbering organic compounds used in the annual indexes to *Chemical Abstracts* starting with that of Volume 31 is preferred.

In naming metallo-organic compounds, the alkyl or other organic groups should precede, and be directly attached to, the name of the metal. Thus, *methylmercury iodide, ethylmagnesium bromide,* and *tetraethyllead*.

To Index Users. The simpler inorganic compounds are entered under the usual names, as "Sodium chloride" and "Ammonia." As the first example indicates, inorganic salts are entered with the more electropositive part of the name first and the more electronegative part second.

Very important criteria in the selection of index headings are the general indexing policies of indexing subjects, not words, of putting first as significant a word as possible, and of grouping related subjects or compounds. To this end specific compounds are usually indexed under the simplest general names, i.e., those based on the constituents of compounds and preferably on the structure, but not always indicating the oxidation state of simple groups or cations and not indicating stoichiometric composition or polymerization. Formulas are used for the individual compounds when indexed separately under these group headings. Thus, the various oxides of nitrogen are grouped under the heading "Nitrogen oxides," with bold-faced formulas to set off the individual oxides, instead of being scattered under "Nitrous oxide" (or "Dinitrogen oxide"), "Nitric oxide" (or "Nitrogen oxide"), etc. Ferrous and ferric compounds are grouped under headings such as "Iron sulfates," and compounds of gold, copper, tin, etc., are similarly grouped under headings beginning with the names of the elements themselves, instead of "aurous," "auric," "cuprous," "cupric," "stannous," "stannic," etc.

For binary compounds the order of decreasing electropositivity for nonmetallic elements is followed: Sb, As, B, Si, C, P, Te, Se, S, I, Br, Cl, N, O, F, except that the headings "Nitrogen chloride," "Nitrogen iodide," etc., are used.

Binary compounds of hydrogen are indexed for the most part under the names most commonly used, e.g., "Arsine," "Hydrochloric acid," and "Hydrogen sulfide."

Oxygen (and thio) acids and their salts are entered for the most part under the simplest, most inclusive names of those conforming best with usage; e.g., with a few exceptions, as the phosphoric acids and phosphates, groupings have been made under such headings as "Silicic acids" or "Sodium periodates," with the avoidance of headings with prefixes such as *meso-*, *meta-*, *ortho-*, *para-*, *pyro-*, *di-*, *tri-*, and *poly-;* the prefixes *hypo-*, *per-*, and *peroxy-*, however, are retained.

Acidic salts and basic salts with a few exceptions, such as uranyl salts, are grouped under the simple names for the neutral or normal salts, e.g., "Calcium phosphates," "Copper chlorides," and "Bismuth chlorides," with the formulas or "acid" or "basic" given in the modifications.

Coordination compounds (often complex) are entered under their own names when definite names could be selected that are suitable for index entries and conform with usage or with the rules of the Commission on the Reform of the Nomenclature of Inorganic Chemistry of the International Union of Pure and Applied Chemistry. In general, names have been favored in which all coordinating groups are named before the central coordinating element; exceptions have still been made for the well-established *ferri-* and *ferrocyanide* and *nitroprusside*. Examples of preferred names are *cyanocobaltate (II), chloroplatinate (IV), fluosilicate,* and *cyanomanganate (I).*

Compounds that cannot be given names suitable for index entries are indexed, in each case, under a heading based on the significant element and also, in the case of coordination compounds, often under headings for the coordinated groups if they are significant, unusual, or specially stressed. Thus, in addition to the significant-element entry, an entry occurs at "Ammines" (for compounds containing coordinated ammonia) or at the heading for a specific organic base that plays a similar role to NH_3.

For organic compounds only the general principles are given here, but in the index itself will be found cross references and also notes under "Alcohols," "Ketones," etc., indicating how compounds of these classes are named.

The "chief function" of a compound is expressed *in the main part of the name* wherever possible, and not as a substituent; thus, *"Pyrrolecarboxylic acid,"* not *"Carboxypyrrole"; "Ethyl alcohol"* or *"Ethanol,"* not *"Hydroxyethane"; "Pentanone,"* not *"Oxopentane."*

In compounds of mixed function, the chief function is determined from the following order of precedence: *"onium" compound, acid* (carboxylic, arsonic, sulfonic, stibonic, others), *acid halide, amide, imide, amidine, aldehyde, nitrile, isocyanide, ketone, alcohol, phenol, thiol, amine, oxyamine* $(RONH_2)$, *imine, ether, sulfide* (and *sulfoxide* and *sulfone*). Thus, *hydroxybenzonitrile,* not *cyanophenol; aminophenol,* not *hydroxyaniline.*

A multiple chief function is expressed where feasible, as *-diol, -dicarboxylic acid,* etc., rather than as *hydroxy-ol, carboxy-acid,* etc. But amino and imino groups attached to cyclic bases are treated as substituents, as *aminopyridine.*

The index compound should be as large, and the substituents as small, as is practicable in conformity with the above rules; as, *ethylbenzene,* not *phenylethane.* But such names as *1,1-diphenylethane* and *triphenylmethanol* are exceptions (on the principle of treating like groups alike). When the chief function is in a side chain attached to a complex nucleus, "additive" names are preferred in order to harmonize this rule with the "chief-function" rule; thus, *naphthaleneacetic acid,* not *naphthylacetic acid.*

The main part of the name with its functional ending, if any, is placed first in the index, the names of the substituents following; thus, chloroacetic acid appears in the index as *"Acetic acid, chloro-,"* and *dihydroxyanthraquinone* as *"Anthraquinone, dihydroxy-."* The part thus placed first is called the "index compound"; it may or may not be the "parent compound" (in the second example the parent compound is anthracene).

Names in which two functions are expressed in the index compounds, as *propanolone* and *cyclopentanonecarboxylic acid,* are avoided, except that a few very common ones, such as *phenolsulfonic acid,* are used.

The names of substituent radicals in the name of a compound are arranged in alphabetic order, as *benzylethylmethylphenylammonium* chloride. The number of radicals of each kind does not affect the order; but the compound name of a substituted radical is treated as a unit with its own alphabetic position; thus, *dimethylamino-,* Me_2N, follows *benzyl* but precedes *ethyl.* When the complete name has been formed, it is alphabetized as any other word.

Parentheses, brackets, and even braces are used where necessary to mark off complex radical names.

Arabic numerals are given preference for numbering, although Greek letters are used for some side chains. When trivial names are used for aliphatic acids, the carbon of the COOH group is numbered 1. Acid derivatives like butyl chloride or propionamide are numbered correspondingly; but in the case of an additive name, like *naphthalene-*

propionic acid, Greek letters are used for the side chain (the carbon atom *next* to the COOH group being labeled α). In mixed aromatic-aliphatic compounds as butyrophenone, plain numbers are used for the aliphatic part and primed numbers for the ring; in compounds like cinnamic acid or phenethyl alcohol, Arabic numerals are used for the ring and Greek letters for the side chain. The numbering of each parent ring system is shown by ring formulas in the index under its name. This numbering conforms to the "Proposed International Rules for Numbering Organic Ring Systems" with the following exceptions: *acridine, anthracene, carbazole* (and *isocarbazole*), *cyclopenta[α]-phenanthrene, phenanthrene, purine* (and *β-purine*), *xanthene* (and *isoxanthene*).

When two or more numbers are equally indicated, that one is chosen which gives the smallest number or numbers for the *chief function, then for double bonds* if these must be regarded, *then for triple bonds, then for point of attachment* (as in doubled molecules), *then for substitutes*.

Numbers and letters enclosed in brackets within the name of the parent ring system are used for distinguishing isomers. They do not refer to the over-all numbering of the system.

Numbers followed by *H* (in italics) are used to indicate the position of hydrogen necessary to the existence of the compound; thus, 2*H*-1,3-Oxazine denotes an oxazine in which there is a CH_2 group instead of CH at position 2 (O at 1, N at 3); 4(3*H*)-Quinoline is equivalent to 3,4-dihydro-4-oxoquinoline.

Doubled molecules or radicals are indicated by names commencing with *bi*- (as, *o,o′-Bi*phenol, *Bi*phenyl, Δ⁴,⁴′-*Bi*piperidine). *Bis-, tris-, tetra-kis-*, etc., are used before complex expressions; as, *bis*(dimethylamino).

In using the cross references, their general nature should be kept in mind; thus, the reference "Benzene, ethoxy-, See Phenetole" is applicable not only to this compound itself but also to derivatives which are indexed under "Phenetole" rather than under "Benzene."

For all compounds of known formula, the *Formula Index* should be consulted.

In using any subject index involving the name of a chemical compound there may be considerable difficulty, especially with foreign languages. Even English indexes may be troublesome if the searcher is not familiar with the system used.

One example is the catalogue of organic chemicals of the Eastman Kodak Company. In it the compounds are listed alphabetically by the name recommended by the International Union of Pure and Applied Chemistry. Unless one knows this system, there is no help in the way of empirical or structural formulas.

The problem is worse in German or French indexes, as even the International Union name varies somewhat because of the peculiarities of the languages.

Making Searches[1]

With these points in mind concerning indexes, we may consider briefly certain procedures to follow in locating given kinds of information. The procedure suggested is not to be taken as covering all kinds of searches but rather as indicating a satisfactory scheme for the cases mentioned. Neither should it be considered as the only way to proceed to find the information desired. Different individuals will attack a given type of problem differently, and the same individual may attack different types of problems differently.

From the standpoint of the literature involved, searches (disregarding patents, which were discussed in Chapter 4) will usually be one of two general kinds: those in which specific facts are to be located, which can be found more or less easily in handbooks or other works of reference; and those in which a more or less comprehensive survey of the entire literature, or a considerable portion of it, must be made.

Short Searches.[2] Suppose, in the first instance, that one wishes to know the physical and chemical properties of butyl alcohol. This compound has been known for many years, and its properties have been determined and recorded in periodicals for a sufficient length of time that one should be able to find the desired information in the general works of reference, excepting the possibility of some fact recently discovered. Accordingly, a search would be made in tables of constants for data such as boiling point and refractive index. One would not expect to find in these tables—"International Critical Tables," for example—the chemical properties; rather, they should be sought in a treatise on organic chemistry, such as Beilstein's "Handbuch der organischen Chemie."

The identification of organic compounds may be taken as another kind of problem. Having determined the empirical

[1] For valuable advice on searching, both in general and in specific directions, see the papers listed at the end of this chapter.

[2] See Lewton, *J. Chem. Educ.*, **28**:487 (1951), for suggestions on searching for on-the-spot information.

formula, the chemist may then turn to the formula indexes of Beilstein's "Handbuch der organischen Chemie" (Volume XXIX) and *Chemisches Zentralblatt* or *Chemical Abstracts* to ascertain what compounds of this formula are known. It then remains for him to compare the properties of his compound with those of any found in this way.

Again, it may be necessary to find a method for preparing some compound, as sodium perchlorate, or to introduce a nitro group, let us say, into some compound containing the benzene ring. In cases such as these, the desired information may generally be found by consulting the large, general works of reference covering the field to which the problem belongs. These works include the treatises and encyclopedias mentioned in Chapter 8. It is important to bear in mind that not all methods of preparation are equally satisfactory for all purposes. One may have to produce a very pure product and not be concerned with obtaining a yield of 95 per cent. On the other hand, a method giving a yield of 95 per cent may be the salvation of an industry if it is competing with another using a method giving a yield of 85 per cent. If it is a problem involving the necessity of finding the best method or of devising a special kind of method, a more detailed search, as described below, is generally required.

What has been stated regarding the above-mentioned specific examples applies, in general, to similar problems, whether the field of chemistry in which the problem lies is general, inorganic, analytical, organic, physical, or some other division of pure or applied chemistry. Use is made primarily, of course, of any reference works dealing especially with the field under consideration, following this, if necessary, with consultation of works on related phases of the subject. If the method desired should be of recent development, the works of reference are usually too old to include it, and one should then go directly to the abstracting journals, as indicated later. However, if the method is not so new, it may not be necessary to go to the original literature unless it seems desirable to compare the statements found in the works of reference with those of the original.

A consideration of sources of information bearing on some of the questions a chemist takes to the library, as outlined in Chapter 1, may be of value as further examples of short searches. For these there is included only a statement of the question and the publications likely to be of value in finding information thereon.[1]

1. *References on the Corrosion of Alloys by Ammonia.* Published bibliographies, such as those of West and Berolzheimer or Van Patten; special works bearing on corrosion; abstracting journals.

2. *Life of Berzelius.* Histories of chemistry; biographical articles in periodicals; and biographical sources such as those listed in Chap. 10.

3. *Fluorine Substitution Products of Methane.* Determine the compounds theoretically possible and consult organic formula indexes of Beilstein and *Chemical Abstracts* (or *Chemisches Zentralblatt*).

4. *Occurrence of Barytes in Canada.* Works on mineralogy and geology; "Minerals Yearbook."

5. *Formula for Automobile Lacquer.* General encyclopedias; cyclopedias of formulas; special treatises or monographs on paint and varnish industry; abstracting journals.

6. *Waterproofing Stone and Brick.* Encyclopedias; special works on building materials and ceramics; chemical patents (see Chap. 4); abstracting journals.

7. *Action of Charcoal as a Purifying Agent.* Treatises on theoretical and physical chemistry; works dealing with the chemistry of colloidal systems, particularly adsorption; such topics as decoloration and clarification in encyclopedias and special industrial works; patents; abstracting journals.

8. *Use of Sawdust.* Special works on the chemistry and technology of wood, especially publications of the U.S. Forest Products Laboratory; encyclopedias; patents; abstracting journals.

9. *Analysis of Flue Gas.* Special works on gas and fuel analysis; general works on technical analysis; publications of the U.S. Bureau of Mines; encyclopedias; abstracting journals.

10. *Statistics on Lampblack Industry.* "Minerals Yearbook"; census reports; circulars from U.S. Bureau of Foreign Commerce; current market reports; abstracting journals.

Comprehensive and Exhaustive Searches. In many instances, having defined the nature, purpose, and scope of a problem, one must gather all the available information relating to the whole subject involved, or to certain phases of it, either for the entire period covered by chemical literature or for some definite part of this period. Searches of this kind will usually involve the use of both primary and secondary sources of information.

Before starting a comprehensive search one should have some idea of the approximate degree of completeness desired. In some

---

[1] Further ideas may be obtained from the problem assignments in Chap. 12 and the sources suggested at the end of the lists.

cases one wants everything known; in others only the significant facts from a given date to the present time are sufficient. As stated by Reid:[1]

> It is well to realize that, at present, few searches of scientific and technical literature are ever complete. The practical question, then, is merely how far one can or ought to go in a particular case. According to the nature of the subject and the object with which the search is undertaken a point will always be reached, eventually, where all competent judges must agree that the probability of finding a reference and its possible value if or when found do not warrant the time, trouble or expense involved in continuing.

It would be a waste of time, for example, to search for the application of the vacuum tube in chemical measurements before the time of the invention of the tube.

Different individuals will begin such a search in different ways, although each seeks all the relevant facts in the case.[2] Whatever the method used, it should meet the tests of accuracy, dependability, and efficiency. Some individuals recommend starting with the earliest publications available relating to the problem in hand. By means of indexes, reviews, and abstracts they work forward to date. Others practically reverse the procedure, beginning with the latest indexes and working backward as far as seems profitable. The procedure described below is essentially the practice followed by the writer.

Assuming that all the pertinent facts on a given subject are to be collected, it is probably a question whether one should start on the works of reference or in the indexes of the abstracting journals. Doubtless the former should be consulted first in many cases. A concise, recent summary of information on the topic under consideration, such as those in *Chemical Reviews*, general review serials, encyclopedias, and monographs, may be of much value in providing a background for beginning the more extended search. More frequently, the writer begins with the last indexes of the abstracting journals. One important advantage is that one is likely to find in recent articles a bibliography bearing directly upon the subject in question. It should be stated that, even before

[1] E. E. Reid, "Introduction to Organic Research," p. 140, D. Van Nostrand Company, Inc., Princeton, N.J., 1924.

[2] See Lewton, *J. Chem. Educ.*, **28**:539 (1951), on the art of searching the literature.

the indexes are searched, all available lists of bibliographies, such as that of West and Berolzheimer, are searched for compilations promising to be of value.

It is desirable at this point, or before the search of the index has progressed far, to make an outline of the possible headings which may furnish information of value. A systematic search under each of these should then be made, and all references which offer any promise of containing desired material should be noted. In general, the only safe way is to include all uncertain references until abstracts, or the original, indicate they are irrelevant. After all references seeming to have any bearing on the subject have been selected from the index, the abstracts are then read. Whenever the abstract indicates that the reference is obviously without value it is discarded. All others are recorded, each on a separate card, as indicated later, and filed.

Usually alphabetical filing by authors will be found most desirable. Often nothing more is needed; but in some cases, especially when many references are involved, it is preferable to adopt some system of subdividing the cards. This may be by years, countries, periodicals, natural divisions of the subject, or other suitable classification. In each of these divisions the filing would then ordinarily be alphabetical by authors.

Although one may expect abstracts to furnish a general statement of the contents of the publication abstracted, it is always well to maintain a skeptical attitude toward them. In many cases —probably most—they do not furnish the desired details. Unless it is reasonably certain from an inspection of the title of the publication, and of abstracts of it, either that nothing of interest is contained therein or that all desired information is provided thereby, the original publication should be consulted if possible. In case the original is unobtainable, several abstracting journals giving abstracts for the same article may help.

In some instances all the indexes of *Chemical Abstracts* and other abstracting journals are examined in this way before one starts to read original articles (collective indexes for periodicals should always be used if available). At other times some of the readily available articles, books, and handbooks are read after the collection of only part of the references in the abstracts. Just as soon as the reading is begun, the references branch out in all directions, since each author will have included those he considered significant. All those of value for the problem being investigated are recorded and put in the same file. Perhaps the better way is to divide the file into two sections, putting all references which have been examined and checked in one list and those to be examined in the other. The advantage of such filing appears soon after the search begins. If a reference is found when an article is being read, no record is made until the alphabetical list is examined to ascertain whether such an entry has not already been included, for one will often find the same reference in a number of different papers. In this way all references are put in the list as found, and duplication of cards is avoided.

The four main abstracting journals for general searches are *Chemical Abstracts, Chemisches Zentralblatt,* the *Journal of the Chemical Society,* and the *Journal of the Society of Chemical Industry.*[1] A number of others, having less significance or covering a more specialized field, are mentioned in Chapter 6.

Whether one begins with the abstracting journals or with other types of publications, ultimately both will be used in making a comprehensive search. Each individual will reach his own decision regarding the most efficient practice for his type of problem. In any case, a systematic handling of notes on the references is desirable.

Although this fairly systematic method of searching is, as a rule, most efficient and should generally be followed, simply looking about, more or less at random, is frequently productive of valuable information. In the case of general books one may look here and there, selecting for examination whatever works offer promise of interest; for periodicals it may be worthwhile, as a last resort, to leaf through the volumes, page by page.[2] This is a tiresome, time-consuming task, but one may find just the formula, equation, or other readily apparent item which is desired, when an examination of the titles of articles and the indexes indicated nothing of value.

As far as possible, one should develop the ability to go through the original publications rapidly, selecting at the same time the significant points for the search in hand. This is not an easy task,

[1] The latter two were combined in 1926 as *British Chemical Abstracts,* and subsequently as *British Abstracts,* which ceased publication in 1953.

[2] See H. S. Booth and D. R. Martin, "Boron Trifluoride and Its Derivatives," Preface, John Wiley & Sons, Inc., New York, 1949.

and the development of efficiency in it requires considerable practice. Since the individual familiar with the problem involved knows better than anyone else what is significant, other things being equal, he is the best fitted to conduct this part of the search. One not thinking along the line of investigation involved can hardly be expected to sense the importance of the various points encountered or to be alert in following what may seem at first only unpromising side issues.

Recording Information. The method to be used in recording the information obtained during a search is of some importance also. A useful scheme is to employ a card file of convenient size, using cards of bond paper, cut to the desired dimensions, from a stock of the desired weight. Sheets of the 3- by 5-in. size may be used, although the 4- by 6-in. size affords more room for writing. Such paper is thinner than the ordinary cards.[1] On each one of them is recorded the required information, as indicated in the form shown on page 121. The reference contains the standard abbreviation, if a periodical, or the title, if a book, including volume, page, and year. In the upper right-hand corner is a word to indicate the nature of the bibliography so that different ones can be easily separated if the references happen to become mixed. The citation to the abstracting journal enables one to return quickly to the periodical if desired. The notes include any facts likely to be of value.

When the reference is first taken down from the abstracting journal, or other source, and filed, only the items at the top are recorded. If, on consulting the original source, nothing of value is found, a check is placed in one corner to indicate such examination, but no further entry is made. Keeping the card in the file saves repeating the examination at some later time, if the reference is not recognized when encountered again. If the material is of value, the title is taken down, along with the notes, and the card is checked.

In some cases a more efficient plan is to have one or more extra subscriptions to *Chemical Abstracts* to provide copies for clipping. Any abstracts of interest may be cut out, pasted on filing cards, and put in the proper place. One needs to add only the abstract reference, if desired, and the bibliographical heading.

[1] Library Bureau cards, no. 1192 (3 by 5 in.), unpunched and without vertical lines, are very satisfactory.

Dependability. Only the completely credulous individual uses the scientific literature without questioning the reliability of the information recorded therein. Undoubtedly not all the material printed is correct or always the best obtainable; but in general the achievement in this respect is believed to be high. Nevertheless, in examining every contribution a critical searcher will maintain a skeptical attitude.

To judge the reliability of another's work may be difficult. Wide experience and knowledge on the part of the critic are of great value in providing perspective. For writers of reputation he will be influenced by the quality of their previous contributions. In experimental work the technique used is an indication of general quality. The conclusions reached by an author should be examined in light of the facts upon which they are based. All references should be verified, as many otherwise careful writers are negligent in checking the accuracy of their citations.

Reports on Information Found. If one merely collects all the references available bearing on a given problem, he has at hand the fundamental material for a bibliography on this problem. To make this material readily usable for selecting and looking up the references desired, there remains only the problem of arranging the references in some one of the ways suggested in Chapter 7. If the various references have been examined sufficiently to provide for the inclusion of carefully prepared annotations for each citation, the bibliography as such may constitute a satisfactory report of the search.

But if the bibliography, when properly prepared, does not in itself constitute a sufficient presentation of the material covered, it becomes necessary to prepare a more general type of report. In such a case it will take one of two forms: noncritical or critical. If it is noncritical, there is included for the work of each investigator a statement of what he did (including how he did it, if important experimentally) and the conclusions reached. A critical report, on the other hand, is distinguished by its emphasis on the relative merit or value of each contribution. In this connection one should keep in mind, of course, that, while one report may be entirely noncritical, the extent to which another is critical is a question of degree. Probably in few cases is the best possible approached.

For instructions regarding the preparation of reports the reader should consult Library Problem 19, page 273, including the references mentioned there.

Selected References on Searching. Many papers on searching have been presented before the Division of Chemical Literature of the American Chemical Society. Of those listed herewith, some are general in nature and some deal with specific problems.

General Papers

Advances in Chem. Ser. No. 4 (1951):[1]

Brown, D. F.: Library Techniques in Searching, pp. 146–157.
Doss, M. P., and G. A. Munafo: Preparation of Literature and Patent Surveys, pp. 140–145.
Dyson, G. M.: Searching the Older Chemical Literature, pp. 96–103.
Fleisher, J.: Exploring United States Chemical Patent Literature, pp. 61–69; Exploring Foreign Chemical Patent Literature, pp. 81–95.
Hoffman, T.: Techniques Employed in Making Literature Searches for a Patent Department, pp. 158–163.
Huntress, E. H.: Influence of Nomenclatural Evolution upon Comprehensive Literature Searches, pp. 10–19.
Lane, J. C., and J. Mitschl: Continuous Collection and Classification of Data as an Aid in Preparing Surveys, pp. 164–171.

Advances in Chem. Ser. No. 10 (1954):

Schaler, C. M., and J. F. Smith: Sound and Unsound Shortcuts in Searching the Literature, pp. 441–448.
Smith, J. F., and C. M. Schaler: Basic Principles of Literature Searching, pp. 438–440.

Other References

Berolzheimer: *Chemist*, **13**:426 (1926).
Smith, J. F.: *J. Chem. Educ.*, **4**:1522 (1927).

Specific Papers

Advances in Chem. Ser. No. 4 (1951):

Addinall, C. R., and P. G. Stecher: Searching Medicinal Chemical Literature, pp. 56–61.
Alexander, M.: Searching for Unpublished Data, pp. 112–117.
Ball, N. T., and C. R. Flagg: Searching United States Government Documents, pp. 70–74.
Mellon, M. G., and R. T. Power: Searching Less Familiar Periodicals, pp. 37–44.

[1] Published by the American Chemical Society.

Skeen, J. R.: Methods and Sources in Chemical Market Research, pp. 117–125.

Spitzer, E. F.: Searching the German Chemical Literature, pp. 30–37.

Advances in Chem. Ser. No. 10 (1954):

Fischbach, H.: Abbreviations in the German, French, and Italian Literature, pp. 510–519; Translating German, French, and Italian Chemical Literature, pp. 520–528.

Flagg, C. R., and R. P. Ware: Standards and Specifications, pp. 449–454.

Hoseh, M.: Pitfalls of Transliteration in Indexing and Searching, pp. 541–547.

Lederman, L. F., J. Green, and D. Graf: Searching the Publication Board Collection for Chemical Information, pp. 477–486.

Oatfield, H., and D. J. Lowe: Domestic Sources of Foreign Information on Trade, Statistics, and Scientific Activities, pp. 455–476.

Spitzer, E. F.: French Chemical Literature and Its Use, pp. 487–493.

Stevens, L. J.: Italian Chemical Literature, pp. 500–504.

—— and S. Fujise: Japanese Chemical Literature, pp. 494–499.

Van Haagen, E.: Foreign Alphabetization Practices, pp. 505–509; Transfer of Language Training from German to Swedish, pp. 529–540.

CHAPTER 12

LIBRARY PROBLEMS

A competent searcher should have at his command a knowledge of libraries, including where they are and what is in them, combined with an ability to find and to use the information sought.—Berolzheimer

It has already been pointed out that lecturing to a class on the contents of a library, and on the method of using the material contained therein, will not leave a very lasting impression upon a student or make him proficient in finding desired information. Lectures and discussions may suffice to give a general idea of the problem in hand, but practical experience in handling the various sources of information is of prime importance in gaining a knowledge of how to find desired material in a library. What is true in this field of endeavor is true in many others. One can hardly expect, for example, to learn how to make precise chemical analyses by attending lectures dealing with this subject. Actual experience in the laboratory is the *sine qua non* in obtaining an intimate acquaintance with the work.

In general, it is desirable to give each student an individual assignment.[1] A proper selection of assignments provides the student with the opportunity not only of gaining some familiarity with the place and the method for finding definite information in chemical publications but also of broadening his general knowledge of chemistry. When the work comes in the third year, it is comparatively easy to have most of the assignments made to material that is quite new to the average individual at this stage of his chemical training.

In this chapter form pages are included for library problems. Also there are lists of representative assignments which may be used with the problem sheets. Not all the various assignments are

---

[1] Mellon, *J. Chem. Educ.*, **2**:196 (1925).

of equal difficulty.[1] Thus, Problems 6 and 8 require more knowledge of chemistry and of foreign languages than Problems 5 and 7. Undergraduates may be excused from those for which their educational preparation is inadequate.

Students who have sufficient interest to try to do something more than just meet the minimum requirements in the course should be encouraged to browse around in the library. Although the acquisition of the information required for a specific assignment should result in some extension of the searcher's experience and knowledge, an alert student will avail himself of this opportunity to leaf through the work consulted in order to gain at least a general idea of the publication and its contents. Preferably several works in the same field should be examined sufficiently to observe the general plan and to note their differences and similarities.

Following many of the lists there is a note to indicate at least one source in which the required information may be found. Often an industrious student will discover other usable sources.

---

[1] *To the instructor.* For a class meeting once a week for a semester the 19 problems will be sufficient for the average student. A maximum of 2 weeks may be allowed for the completion of each problem.

It is desirable for the instructor using any new problems to verify the assignments. A student's interest is not enlivened if he finds, after several hours' search, that his assignment was not properly made or that it cannot be fullfilled.

In the author's experience, it has been found convenient in making the assignments, using lists such as those included in this book, to indicate simply that a given individual is to take, for his problem, a given number throughout the lists. In case additional assignments are to be made, the following procedures are suggested: (1) post similar, numbered lists, each student having been given his number; (2) at the time the book is submitted for the inspection of one problem write in the assignment for another; or (3) distribute to each student at class time a slip of paper containing his name and assignment. This should be returned when the problem is submitted for inspection. Mimeographed copies of the blank pages are convenient for students to use to turn in their assignments.

PROBLEMS
Library Problem 1[1]
Periodicals I

1. Supply, for the abbreviation indicated, the required information concerning the journal.

 a. Abbreviation..

 b. Name...

 ....

 c. Country...................Language...........................

 d. Frequency of appearance.....Present volume....................

 e. Volume...............appeared in the year....................

 f. Nearest library containing journal...............................

2. ....

 is the official abbreviation for the journal.............................

 ....

 This periodical contains the following kinds of information:

[1] For assignments, see p. 276.

3. Supply the information indicated for two important...............

     journals publishing articles on.......................................

     ....

     a.[1] Name...

     ....

         Country...................... Place edited....................

         Frequency of appearance......... Present volume................

     b.[1] Name...

     ....

         Country...................... Place edited....................

         Frequency of appearance......... Present volume................

4. During the year........the following article appeared on.............

     ....

     Title...

     ....

     Author(s)..

     Professional connection(s)...

     Abstract reference...

     ....

     Original reference[2]...

     ....

---

[1] Write in full, underscoring the official abbreviation.

[2] Write in full, underscoring the official abbreviation (include series, volume, page, and year).

Library Problem 2[1]

Periodicals II

1. In[2]..........the price of......................was...............

   Source...

   For the year.........the price range is shown by the following curve.

Price,[3] in ....

Jan.   Apr.   July   Oct.

2. The firm(s) indicated, according to current advertising, can furnish the

   following equipment...

   This equipment was advertised in the journal........................

   ....

3. A book review for...

   ....by..................................

   was written by.................................and published in

   ....

[1] For assignments, see p. 278.
[2] Indicate month and year.
[3] Supply price unit and ordinate markings.

4. The accompanying abstract[1] is from an article[2] by....................

published in..

---

[1] Follow the general form employed in *Chemical Abstracts*.

[2] The article should be too recent to have been abstracted in *Chemical Abstracts*.

Library Problem 3[1]

Institutional Publications

Information regarding the items noted may be found in the sources given.

1. Reports of investigations on.......................................

    a. Title of source...

    b. Author(s)............................Date...................

    c. Department of government.............Bureau................

    d. Designation[2]...

2. *a.* A 10-year United States production curve for...................is

    Source[4]...

    b. The two most important products (value) of.....................

    ....are...

    Source..

    c. A general summary of mineral developments in...................

    for.......................may be found in..................

    ....

[1] For assignments, see p. 279.
[2] Kind of publication—e.g., *Bull.* 20.
[3] Supply production unit and ordinate markings.
[4] Reference for 1 year only.

3. United States tariff data for the year. . . . . .for. . . . .

   Amount produced. . . . . .Amount sold. . . . .

   Unit value. . . . . . . .Name and address of one manufacturer. . . . .

   . . . .

   Source. . . . .

4. United States $\frac{\text{import}}{\text{export}}$ data for the year. . . . . .for. . . . .

   Amount. . . . . .Value. . . . .

   Source. . . . .

5. Financial data for the year. . . . . .for. . . . .

   . . . .

   Net worth. . . . . .Net sales. . . . .

   Net income. . . . . .Dividend yield. . . . .

   Source. . . . .

6. Annual United States census data for the year. . . . . .for. . . . .

   . . . . .Production. . . . .

   Sales. . . . . .Value. . . . .

   Source. . . . .

7. Quinquennial United States census data for the period. . . . .

   for. . . . . .in. . . . .

   Number of establishments. . . . . .Number employed. . . . .

   Value added by manufacturing. . . . . .Capital expenditures. . . . .

   Source. . . . .

Library Problem 4[1]

Literature on Patents

1. Supply the information indicated for a patent issued (abstracted) during

   the year.........relating to......................................

   ....

   Patent title..

   ....

   Abstract reference..

   Patentee(s)...........................Number..............

   Country...............................Date..................

2. The following information is for.............Patent number.........

   Patent title..

   Patentee(s)...........................Date..................

3. According to the classification system of the United States Patent Office,

   a. Examining Division.............includes the classes.............

   ....

   b. The class covering...

   and numbered.........is included in Division...................

   c. Class number...........refers to..............................

   ....

   d. ....is the class number for........................

   ....

[1] For assignments, see p. 282.

4. An equivalent patent for...

   is...

5. For a United States chemical patent[1] supply the information indicated.

   Patent title...

   ....

   Official Gazette reference..

   Chemical Abstracts reference......................................

   Patentee(s)..

   Number........................Date of issue........................

   Description or disclosure[2]

   Claims[2]

---

[1] To be obtained from the U.S. Patent Office.
[2] Brief summary of the most important points.

Library Problem 5[1]

Physical Constants I

In the sources noted (author, title, volume, page, date) one may find, for the designated substance or property, the information indicated.

1. Data on...

    Source...

2. For..

    Molecular weight............... Melting point....................

    Boiling point.................. Specific gravity..................

    Other data given..

    Source...

3.[2] For..

    Specific gravity............... Melting point....................

    Acetyl value................... Acid value.......................

    Iodine value................... Hehner value.....................

    Reichert-Meissl value........... Saponification value.............

    Maumene number............... Refractive index.................

    Other data...

[1] For assignments, see p. 284.
[2] Information for some constants is unavailable.

4.[1] . . . .

Specific heat. . . . . .Heat conductivity. . . . .

Heat of combustion. . . . . .Heat of formation. . . . .

Heat of fusion. . . . . .Heat of solution[2]. . . . .

Heat of vaporization. . . . . .Other thermal data. . . . .

5. Substances possessing the following physical property:

Melting point. . . . . .Boiling point. . . . .

Refractive index (liquid). . . . . .Density (liquid). . . . .

Source. . . . .

6. . . . . .is the specific gravity of a. . . . . .per cent aqueous

solution of. . . . . .The Baumé reading for a 10 per cent

solution of this substance is. . . . .

Source. . . . .

7. The most generally useful chemical engineering data on. . . . .

. . . . .include

Source. . . . .

[1] Information for some constants is unavailable.
[2] The consistent term should be *dissolution*.

Library Problem 6[1]

Physical Constants II[2]

In the sources noted (author, title, volume, part, page, date) one may find the designated information.

1. In "International Critical Tables"

  a. General data on.......................................include

  Compiler........................... Scientific field...........

  Position................................. Age..............

  Source..

  b. The specific value of the...................................

  of.............................is.....................

  Investigator...

  Original reference..

  Source..

2. In the Landolt-Börnstein "Zahlenwerke . . . "

  a. General information on

  Source..

  b. Specific data on the.....................................

  of ....

  Source ....

[1] For assignments, see p. 287.
[2] This problem is more difficult than Prob. 5. In the comprehensive works one gets to the original references, i.e., to answers to the questions: "Who stated this?" and "Where did he state it?"

3. In the French "Tables annuelles . . . "

Specific data on...include

....

Investigator...

Original reference...

Source..

4. Solubility of...

in...................................at.................°C is

....

Investigator...

Original reference...

Source..

5. Nuclear data on..include

Investigator...

Original reference...

Source..

Library Problem 7[1]

Organic Chemistry I

1. The chemistry of the compound named...........................

and having the formulas (empirical)...............................

and (structural)..................................may be found in

a.[2] Whitmore, "Organic Chemistry," p. ... (   ).[3]

b.[2] Rodd, "Chemistry of Carbon Compounds," vol. ..., p. ... (**).**

c.[2] Heilbron and Bunbury, "Dictionary of Organic Compounds," **vol.** ..., p. ... (   ).

d.[2] Grignard, "Traité de chimie organique," vol. ..., p. ... (   ).

[1] For assignments, see p. 290.
[2] Include the references to the original literature as found.
[3] Include year of publication of the book.

2. In the sources noted the following information may be found.

    a. In the year . . . . the following references dealing with the

    compound . . . . were abstracted.

        Source . . . .

    b. The transformation known as . . . .

    reaction (process, synthesis, test) is (with specific example)

        Source . . . .

    c. A general discussion on the subject of . . . .

        . . . .

        Source . . . .

3. In the source noted one may find . . . .

    a. The formula (name) of the organic radical . . . .

    is . . . .

    Source . . . .

    b. The following information on the . . . . ring complex

    Number of component rings . . . . Members . . . .
                                    (Number of elements in rings)

    Heterocyclic rings . . . . Carbocyclic rings . . . .

    Parent compounds of this configuration . . . .

    . . . .

    Source . . . .

Library Problem 8[1]

Organic Chemistry II

1. For the compound...

    having the formulas (empirical)...

    and (structural)...the

    following references, with explanations indicated, may be found in

    a. Richter, "Lexikon der Kohlenstoff-Verbindungen," vol. ..., p. ...

        (   ).

    b. Stelzner, "Literatur-Register der organischen Chemie," vol. ....,
        p. ... (   ).

    c. *Chemisches Zentralblatt* (or *Chemical Abstracts*)[2]

2. a. A critical discussion of the chemistry of this compound, with references
        to the original literature as noted, may be found in
        Beilstein, "Handbuch der organischen Chemie," Hw., vol. ..., p. ...
        (   ); Erg. I, vol. ..., p. ...(   ); Erg. II, vol. ..., p. ... (   ).

---

[1] For assignments, see p. 292.
[2] Formula index only.

2. *b.* According to the Beilstein classification, this compound is in

    Division.................... Subdivision........................
         (Skeleton name)   (Kind and number of heteroatoms)

    Class...
         (Number)   (Name and formula of functioning group)

    Subclass...
         (Letter)   (Name)

    Rubric...
         (Number)   (Name)   (General formula)

    Series.......................... System number..............
        (Number of carbon atoms)

    Index compound..

3. The reference(s) noted contain directions for synthesizing............

    Source...

4. The reference(s) noted contain directions for applying the following

    reaction..

    ....

    Source...

5. The reference(s) noted contain directions for applying the laboratory

    operation...

    ....

    Source...

Library Problem 9[1]

Inorganic Chemistry

1. The compound named...

    has the formula...

    a. The following references, with explanations indicated, are in

    　a'. Hoffmann, "Lexikon der anorganischen Verbindungen," vol. ...,

    　　p. ... (　　).

    　a''. ....

    　　　..

    　b''. ....

    　　　..

    　b'. *Chemical Abstracts* (or *Chemisches Zentralblatt*) Formula Index

    b. A critical discussion of the chemistry of this compound, with references
    to the original literature as noted, may be found in

    　a'. Gmelin, "Handbuch der anorganischen Chemie,"....vol. ...,

    　　p. ... (　　).

    　b'. Mellor, "Treatise on Inorganic and Theoretical Chemistry,"

    　　vol. ..., p. ... (　　).

[1] For assignments, see p. 294.

c'. Pascal, "Traité de chimie minérale," vol. ..., p. ... (   ).

d'. Friend, "Textbook of Inorganic Chemistry," vol. ..., p. ...
   (   ).

e'. Sneed et al., "Comprehensive Inorganic Chemistry," vol. ...,

   p. ... (   ).

2. Known compounds containing all the elements........................

   ....in any proportions, include

   Source...

3. In the source noted one may find

   a. The formula (name) of the radical..............................is

   Source...

   b. The formula (name) of the anion..............................is

   Source...

Library Problem 10[1]

Analytical Chemistry

In the sources noted one may find the following information.

1. Procedures for the qualitative tests for..............................

    a. Characteristic reactions

        a'. ....

        b'. ....

        Source..

    b. Methods of detection

        a'. ....

        b'. ....

        Source..

2. Methods (classified to indicate the methods of separation and measurement,[2] e.g., Ca, precipitation—gravimetric) for the determination of....

    ....

    Source..

[1] For assignments, see p. 295.

[2] Mellon, "Quantitative Analysis; Methods of Separation and Measurement," Thomas Y. Crowell Company, New York, 1955.

3. A...method[1] for determining

.........in...consists in

Source...

4. Directions for the analysis of...................................

Source...

[1] A specific kind of measurement may be assigned.

Library Problem 11[1]

Industrial Chemistry I[2]

In the sources indicated the following information may be found.

1. Two books dealing with...

   a. ....

   b. ....

   Source..

2. The product whose brand (trade) name is.........................

   is manufactured (sold) by.......................................

   located at..

   Source..

3. Two firms which manufacture.........................equipment

   a. ....

   b. ....

   Source..

4. The scientific (trade) name of...................................

   is..

   Source..

5. The cost of.......,..

   is approximately..

   Source..

---

[1] For assignments, see p. 296.

[2] For more extensive industrial problems, see Kobe, *J. Chem. Educ.*, **10**:679, 738 (1933); **11**:40, 108 (1934).

6. Two published bibliographies on.................................

    a. ....

    b. ....

    Source..

7. Two firms that sell the chemical.................................

    a. ....

    b. ....

    Source..

8. Two important chemical manufacturing firms in....................

    a. ....

    b. ....

    Source..

9. A commercial method of making....................................

    is..

    Source..

10. Historical facts concerning......................................

    Source..

Library Problem 12[1]

Industrial Chemistry II

In the sources indicated the following information may be found:

1. A review of developments for the year........for...................

....includes the topics

   Source...

2. Two sources of supply of the raw material (specialty)................

   a. ....

   b. ....

   Source...

3. The composition of...

   Source...

4. The commercial grades of...................................are

   Source...

[1] For assignments, see p. 299.

5. Three commercial uses of...................................are

    a. ....

    b. ....

    c. ....

    Source..

6. A manufacturer's technical publication on............................

    covers

    Source..

7. Miscellaneous information for...............................includes

    Container...

    Shipping regulation...

    Tariff..

    Source..

8. Specifications for...include

    Source..

9. Chemically resistant materials for handling............................

    consist of..

    Source..

Library Problem 13[1]

Dyes[2]

State the information requested for the dye.............................

..............................Color index number................

Manufactured by..

Formula

Scientific name..

Other names...

....

Method of preparation

[1] For assignments, see p. 301.
[2] Suggested by G. H. Richter.

Uses

Fastness

Materials dyed

Absorption spectrum

Other data (statistics, etc.)

Library Problem 14[1]

Metallurgy and Metallography[2]

In the sources indicated the following information may be found.

1. Two common ores of...are

   . . . .

   The most important commercial sources are

   Source. . . . .

2. Two methods of treating. . . . . .ores are
   (with chemical reactions)

   Source. . . . .

3. Important uses for. . . . . .are

   Source. . . . .

4. Two books on. . . . .
   (with author, title, publisher, date)

   Source. . . . .

[1] For assignments, see p. 302.
[2] See Rimbach, "How to Find Metallurgical Information," R. Rimbach, Pittsburgh, Pa., 1936.

5. Chemical composition of the alloy....................................

Source...

6. The equilibrium diagram for an alloy containing.....................

Source...

7. The physical properties of..

Source...

8. The corrosion resistance of.....................,......to...........

Source...

9. The current price of...

Source...

Library Problem 15[1]

Medical and Pharmaceutical Chemistry

In the sources indicated the following information may be found.

1. For the drug...

    a. Two sources of supply

    b. The essential chemical compound(s) in it

    c. Its most important physiological action(s)

    d. The commercial method of treatment or preparation

    e. Its pharmaceutical uses

    Source...

[1] For assignments, see p. 304.

2. The United States Pharmacopeia specifications for....................

Source..

3. Two manufacturers of...

Source..

4. The current price of......................during the year.........

Source..

5. The composition of..

Source..

6. A method of analysis (or testing) for

Source..

Library Problem 16[1]

Economic Survey of a Chemical Commodity[2,3]

Data for the Commodity

Raw materials
  Sources of supply
  Specifications for intended quality
  Tonnage requirements for economic handling
Manufacture
  Methods (with flow sheets for a commercial plant)
  Control tests
  Production costs (itemized statement)
  By-products (including utilization or disposal)
Finished product
  Usual purity
  Grades
  Shipping containers
  Shipping regulations
  Specifications required
  Physical properties
  Chemical properties
Items of commercial importance
  Domestic production
  Domestic consumption
  Imports (amount and sources)
    Tariff
  Exports (amount and destinations)
    Tariff
  Names and locations of 5 manufacturers
  Graphical comparison of monthly selling price with weighted index
      of prices of all commodities

---

[1] For assignments, see p. 306.

[2] In industrial chemistry, instead of confining the problem to collecting individual technical facts, as in Probs. 11 to 15, it is often desirable to make an economic survey in the form of a more general report. To compile the information will require the use of some of the sources recommended for the preceding specialized problems, but certain others will be necessary for financial facts. If this problem is to be a finished term report rather than merely a compilation of facts, it might well be combined with Prob. 19. The outline followed is based on a paper by Kobe, *J. Chem. Educ.*, **10**:738 (1933).

[3] Rather than blank pages here, only an outline is suggested to follow in presenting the data.

Financial Data for One Manufacturer

Firm name
  Subsidiary companies
Rating
  Dun and Bradstreet[1]
  Moody[2]
Stocks and bonds outstanding
Stocks listed on exchange at. . . .
Graph of earnings and dividends per share (5-year period)
Graph of stock activity (10-year period)
Important items in last financial report (date)
Research activity
  Size of laboratory (including number of personnel)
  Location
  Program
Conclusions (evaluation of the company)

[1] "The Mercantile Agency Reference Book," Dun and Bradstreet, New York, 1957.

[2] "Moody's Manual of Investments," volume on industrial securities, Moody's Investors Service, New York, 1957.

Library Problem 17[1]

Miscellaneous Information

In the sources indicated the following information may be found.

1. Biographical facts concerning......................................,..........

    Dates of life.......................Nationality....................

    Field of chemistry...

    Important contributions

    Source...

2. The significance in chemistry of the two abbreviations...............

    a. ....

    b. ....

    Source...

3. A summarized discussion of our present knowledge of.................

    ....

    Source...

4. The occurrence (or sources) of....................................

    Source...

[1] For assignments, see p. 306.

5. A popular publication on...

Source...

6. A recipe for...

Source...

7. The reaction of...

Source...

8. Experimental methods for..

Source...

9. A laboratory method for preparing................................

Source...

Library Problem 18[1]

Preparation of a Bibliography

The previous problems are designed to familiarize the student, to some extent at least, with the general nature of the different kinds of publications and with their use in finding information relating to the various questions which a chemist takes to the library. An individual should be able not only to locate special facts and data which he desires but also to make a general survey of the recorded available information on a given subject and to prepare an acceptable report containing a statement of the important points revealed by the survey.

In general, the first step in making such a survey is the compilation of a partial bibliography. As mentioned in Chapter 7, occasionally good lists of references are already available as a starting point; but for this problem it will be assumed that such is not the case. For the preparation of a bibliography as an exercise for a library problem, several points should be considered, such as the following.

Selection of the Subject. The student should select his own subject, as it is then more likely to have a personal interest for him. For those who have no subjects of their own, a list of suitable subjects should be available from which to make selections.

Determination of the Scope of the Subject. Many subjects are either too limited or too broad in their range; that is, too many references will be found for the student to handle in the time available, or too few can be located to give any opportunity for working out a classified bibliography. Although a complete bibliography, even on a comparatively little used element, such as selenium, is rather extensive, the list is much less imposing when the subject is confined to the organic compounds of selenium.

Determination of the Scope of the Bibliography. If a bibliography is not to be complete, one must decide which portion of the whole field of the literature is to be covered. When the compilation of a bibliography is merely a part of a course on chemical literature, a large amount of time is not available. The location of approximately 100 references will give sufficient experience in this type of work.

[1] For assignments, see p. 309.

Determination of the Bibliographical Details to Include. Ordinarily the following items should be recorded for each entry: author (or patentee); original reference, including, if a periodical, its official abbreviation, series, volume, page, and year; or, if some other kind of publication, such information as will indicate unmistakably the source of the material; abstract reference, the abbreviation, volume, and page being sufficient; title of article (or other publication); and annotations if the title does not give a sufficient clue to the nature of the contents.

Method of Searching. General directions for searching are included in Chapter 11. It is valuable experience for a student to be turned loose at this point, with an occasional guiding suggestion, in order to determine what he can find on a given topic. The report should contain a list of the index headings examined during the search for references.

Arrangement of Material. The usual forms of arrangement used in bibliographies are discussed in Chapter 7. Here again the student should probably be left to his own devices not only in the arrangement of the details on the page for each entry but also in the classification or listing of the references as a whole. If the various bibliographies mentioned in Chapter 7 are available for examination, the merits of the different schemes can be ascertained.

The report submitted should be a readily usable bibliography. If it is arranged alphabetically by authors, there should be a subject index. If it is classified, the divisions and subdivisions should be clearly indicated. In card form this means the use of appropriately marked index or separator cards.

Library Problem 19[1]

Preparation of a Critical Report

The previous assignments have dealt primarily with the problem of locating required information in the various sources available. Very often one needs not only to find specific facts but also to make effective use of them in a report.

Let us assume that an ordinary problem of chemical research is undertaken. The general scope of the problem is first determined. Then one usually wants to ascertain what is already known concerning it so that he may begin somewhere near the point where others quit. This involves searching chemical publications and the collection of material. On the basis of this knowledge, experiments are planned, if necessary, and executed, resulting in the accumulation of more data. A final report of the work will frequently include the following points: a statement of the problem; a review of others' work bearing upon it; new experimental work performed, including the data secured; a general discussion of the results, including their connection with previous work; and the general conclusions.

In preparing the review of others' work, the compilation of a bibliography, as given in Library Problem 18, is only a part of the whole task. True, it may require much time and considerable ingenuity in searching; but something more is required if one is to avoid being submerged in the waves of facts and is to get his bearings by gaining a perspective of a considerable portion of the sea around him. The references must be examined; and the material in them must be sifted, classified, correlated, and evaluated. With respect to the facts involved, we must, in the words of Glenn Frank, find them, filter them, focus them, face them, and follow them.

The preparation of a concise review of the information available on some simple problem is suggested as the logical assignment to follow the preparation of a bibliography. The field of the bibliography submitted for Library Problem 18, if not too extensive, or some definite portion of it, may well be taken.

The problem and the technique of preparing the manuscript for such reports have been considered in detail in several other

[1] For assignments, see p. 309.

publications. For general information of this kind the student is referred to the sources listed below. They deal not only with the type of report just discussed but also with the preparation of articles or books, including the final process of printing.

REFERENCES

English

Bell, L.: "A Handbook of Essentials in English," Henry Holt and Company, Inc., New York, 1939.

General Technical Writing

Allen, E. M.: "The Author's Handbook," International Textbook Company, Scranton, Pa., 1938.
"Author's Guide," John Wiley & Sons, Inc., New York, 1950.
Baker, C.: "Technical Publications; Their Purpose, Preparation, and Production," John Wiley & Sons, Inc., New York, 1955.
Crouch, W. G., and R. L. Zetler: "A Guide to Technical Writing," The Ronald Press Company, New York, 1954.
Emberger, M. R., and M. R. Hall: "Scientific Writing," Harcourt, Brace, and Company, Inc., New York, 1955.
Fishbein, M.: "Medical Writing: The Technique and the Art," The Blakiston Division, McGraw-Hill Book Company, Inc., New York, 1948.
Flesch, R.: "The Art of Plain Talk," Harper & Brothers, New York, 1946.
Fulton, M. G.: "Expository Writing," The Macmillan Company, New York, 1939.
Mills, G. H., and J. A. Walter: "Technical Writing," Rinehart & Company, Inc., New York, 1954.
Rickard, T. A.: "Technical Writing," John Wiley & Sons, Inc., New York, 1931.
Sherman, T. A.: "Modern Technical Writing," Prentice-Hall, Inc., Englewood Cliffs, N.J., 1955.
Shidle, N. G.: "Clear Writing for Easy Reading," McGraw-Hill Book Company, Inc., New York, 1951.
Skillin, M. E., R. M. Gay, et al.: "Words into Type," Appleton-Century-Crofts, Inc., New York, 1948.
"Style Manual," Government Printing Office, 1953.

Graphs

Arkin, H., and R. R. Colton: "Graphs," Harper & Brothers, New York, 1940.
Schmidt, C. F.: "Handbook of Graphic Presentation," The Ronald Press Company, New York, 1954.
Worthing, A. G., and J. Geffner: "Treatment of Experimental Data," John Wiley & Sons, Inc., New York, 1943.

Reports and Research Papers

Agg, T. R., and W. L. Foster: "Preparation of Engineering Reports," McGraw-Hill Book Company, Inc., New York, 1935.

Kerekes, F., and R. Winfrey: "Report Preparation," Iowa State College Press, Ames, Iowa, 1951.

Kobe, K. A.: "Chemical Engineering Reports," Interscience Publishers, Inc., New York, 1957.

Nelson, J. R.: "Writing the Technical Report," 3d ed., McGraw-Hill Book Company, Inc., New York, 1952.

Rautenstrauch, W.: "Industrial Surveys and Reports," John Wiley & Sons, Inc., New York, 1940.

Rhodes, F. H.: "Technical Report Writing," McGraw-Hill Book Company, Inc., New York, 1941.

Trelease, S. F.: "The Scientific Paper," The Williams & Wilkins Company, Baltimore, 1947.

Tuttle, R. E., and C. A. Brown: "Writing Useful Reports," Appleton-Century-Crofts, Inc., New York, 1956.

Ulman, J. N.: "Technical Reporting," Henry Holt and Company, Inc., New York, 1952.

Weil, B. H.: "The Technical Report," Reinhold Publishing Corporation, New York, 1954.

Williams, C. B., and J. Ball: "Report Writing," The Ronald Press Company, New York, 1955.

ASSIGNMENTS FOR PROBLEMS

Assignments for Library Problem 1

Part 1. Standard abbreviations for periodicals.

1. *Österr. Chemiker-Ztg.*
2. *Khim. Prom.*
3. *Roczniki Chem.*
4. *Bull. intern. acad. polon. sci.*
5. *Rev. mét.*
6. *Med. lavoro*
7. *Ann. pharm. franç.*
8. *Boll. chim. farm.*
9. *Z. Naturforsch.*
10. *Ukrain. Khim. Zhur.*
11. *Zhur. Priklad. Khim.*
12. *Acta Chem. Scand.*
13. *Vida nueva*
14. *Minerva med.*
15. *Tekstil. Prom.*
16. *Chim. anal.*
17. *Mineral. Mag.*
18. *Zhur. Tekh. Fiz.*
19. *Ricerca sci.*
20. *Saatgut-Wirtsch.*

(Consult "List of Periodicals Abstracted by *Chemical Abstracts*.")

Part 2. Names of journals.[1]

1. *Chemical and Engineering News*
2. *Journal of Chemical Education*
3. *Chemical Literature*
4. *Analytical Chemistry*
5. *Journal of Applied Chemistry (London)*
6. *Industrial and Engineering Chemistry*
7. *Chemical Engineering*
8. *The Journal of Chemical Physics*
9. *Chemische Berichte*
10. *Nucleonics*
11. *Journal of the Electrochemical Society*
12. *Journal of Inorganic and Nuclear Chemistry*
13. *The Journal of Organic Chemistry*
14. *The Journal of Biological Chemistry*
15. *Journal of Agricultural and Food Chemistry*
16. *Chemical Engineering Progress*
17. *Materials & Methods*
18. *Chemical Engineering Science*
19. *American Journal of Public Health*
20. *Gazzetta chimica italiana*

(Consult "List of Periodicals Abstracted by *Chemical Abstracts*.")

---

[1] Only journals available to the student should be assigned.

Part 3.[1] In this part the periodicals required are first limited to some more or less specialized field of chemistry, such as organic. Then, if desired, they may be further limited by designating some country or language.

1. Photography—Germany
2. Spectroscopy—United States
3. Dyes—Great Britain
4. Petroleum—Russia
5. Physical chemistry—India
6. Organic chemistry—Italy
7. Textiles—Japan
8. Analytical chemistry—France
9. Biological chemistry—Netherlands
10. Inorganic chemistry—Sweden
11. General chemistry—Spain
12. Industrial chemistry—Canada
13. Pharmaceutical chemistry—United States
14. Metallurgical chemistry—Germany
15. Glass—Great Britain
16. Foods—Spain
17. Cement—Russia
18. Rubber—France
19. Detergents—United States
20. Water—Germany

Part 4. Articles in periodicals.

1. Triarylboron anions
2. Cyclopentadiene
3. Condensed pyrimidine
4. Schönberg rearrangement
5. Antigen-antibody complexes
6. Polyurethane coatings
7. Melamine plastics
8. Extender oils
9. Zone electrophoresis
10. Rotational viscometer
11. Hydrogen-deuterium exchange
12. Formation of carene
13. Formation of acytals
14. Biosynthesis of isoleucine
15. Ipecac alkaloids
16. Thermosetting resins
17. Radioactive fallout
18. Assay of tritium
19. Chronopotentiometry
20. Vacuum-fusion analysis

(Consult the subject indexes of *Chemical Abstracts*.)

[1] In order to decide on two important journals, the student may consult current issues of *Chemical Abstracts* and turn to the division indicated by the subject of his assignment. From several issues of the abstracting journal a list may be made of the various journals abstracted and the number of abstracts from each noted. The two journals having the largest number of abstracts may be taken for this report. Although this is a superficial procedure, it is sufficiently satisfactory for the requirements of the problem.

Assignments for Library Problem 2

Part 1. Part 1 gives the name (or formula) for some chemical listed in the market reports. Either a date (year and month) may be specified, or the student may be permitted to select his own.

1. Acetanilide	11. Cacodylic acid
2. Albumin, egg	12. *n*-Butyl alcohol
3. Brucine	13. Caffeine
4. Carotene	14. Chloropicrin
5. Dipentene	15. Ethyl iodide
6. Fluorspar	16. Geraniol
7. Heliotropin	17. Iodoform
8. Lithium	18. Milk powder
9. Nitromethane	19. Tung oil
10. Phenobarbital	20. Riboflavin

(Consult market reports in *Chemical and Engineering News* and *Oil, Paint, and Drug Reporter*.)

Part 2. Advertised equipment.

1. Pigment grinder	11. Acid pumps
2. Polyethylene ware	12. Filter aids
3. Heat exchangers	13. Refractories
4. Air compressors	14. Control valves
5. Filter presses	15. Infrared analyzers
6. Pulverizers	16. Deionizers
7. Air classifiers	17. Blenders
8. Thermometers	18. Duriron equipment
9. Air preheaters	19. Gas chromatographs
10. Rotary kilns	20. High-pressure equipment

(Consult current advertising in journals on applied chemistry; see also Advertised Products Directory in *Industrial and Engineering Chemistry*.)

Part 3. Reviews of books in periodicals.

1. Chargaff, E.: "The Nucleic Acids."
2. Friedlander, G.: "Nuclear and Radiochemistry."
3. Garner, W. E.: "Chemistry of the Solid State."
4. Gould, E. S.: "Inorganic Reactions and Structure."
5. Guggenheim, E. A.: "Boltzmann's Distribution Law."
6. Harris, R. S.: "Vitamins and Hormones."
7. Hauser, E. A.: "Silicic Science."
8. Hutchinson, E.: "Physical Chemistry."

9. Libby, W. F.: "Radiocarbon Dating."
10. McDonald, H. J.: "Ionography."
11. Meites, L.: "Polarographic Techniques."
12. Murphy, G. M.: "Production of Heavy Water."
13. Prigogine, I.: "Chemical Thermodynamics."
14. Robinson, R. A.: "Electrolyte Solutions."
15. Schumb, W. C.: "Hydrogen Peroxide."
16. Strouts, O. R. N.: "Analytical Chemistry."
17. Trotman-Dickenson, A. F.: "Gas Kinetics."
18. Wheland, G. W.: "Resonance in Organic Chemistry."
19. Wilson, E. B., Jr.: "Molecular Vibrations."
20. Yarwood, J.: "High Vacuum Technique."

(Consult author indexes of *Technical Book Review Index, New Technical Books,* or of other periodicals likely to contain such reviews.)

Part 4. In this part the student may be permitted to find an article of personal interest, or assignments may be used, such as those given in Problem 1, Part 4.[1]

(To find a specific assignment, consult the author or subject indexes of *Chemical Abstracts* or those of appropriate original-source periodicals.)

Assignments for Library Problem 3

Part 1. Government bulletins.

Assignments of this type may be made from one or more of the lists of publications issued by the various departments of the government. The following list is representative for publications from several of the bureaus.

1. Boiler water	9. Air pollution
2. Chromium	10. Detergents
3. Erosion by the soil	11. Aviation gasoline
4. Schrödinger's equation	12. Tar acids
5. Osmometers	13. Volume dilatometry
6. Cinchona	14. Platinum annealing
7. Mixing fertilizers	15. Molecular stills
8. Trace elements	16. Wood preservation

[1] For the abstract the general form followed in *Chemical Abstracts* is desirable, but a beginning student can hardly be expected to conform closely to all the rules and regulations given in the pamphlet "Directions for Abstractors and Section Editors of *Chemical Abstracts.*" Only an experienced abstractor can meet these requirements of content, style, and form.

17. Green manure
18. Clays

19. Chemotherapy
20. Gamma globulin

(Consult list of publications of appropriate bureaus; or see *Document Index* of government publications.)

Part 2a. Data on mineral production.

1. Asbestos
2. Cement
3. Magnesite
4. Garnet
5. Olivine
6. Lime
7. Salt

8. Barite
9. Emery
10. Marl
11. Mica
12. Gypsum
13. Pyrites
14. Sulfur

15. Bromine
16. Feldspar
17. Fluorspar
18. Graphite
19. Phosphate rock
20. Potassium salts

(Consult *Minerals Yearbook.*[1])

Part 2b. Mineral products of states.

1. Florida
2. New Jersey
3. Pennsylvania
4. Indiana
5. California

6. Georgia
7. New York
8. Ohio
9. Illinois
10. Minnesota

11. North Carolina
12. Massachusetts
13. Alabama
14. Texas
15. Washington

16. Virginia
17. Maine
18. Tennessee
19. Colorado
20. Montana

(Consult *Minerals Yearbook.*)

Part 2c. General information on mineral products.

1. Al
2. Be
3. Ni
4. Mn
5. W

6. Cd
7. B
8. Mg
9. Zn
10. Mo

11. As
12. Cu
13. Zr
14. Hg
15. Ti

16. Cr
17. Pb
18. S
19. V
20. I

(Consult *Minerals Yearbook.*)

Part 3. Tariff report data.

1. Benzene
2. Nitrobenzene
3. Phthalic anhydride
4. Salicylic acid
5. Acetanilide
6. Aniline
7. Anisaldehyde
8. Eugenol
9. 1,4-Dichlorobenzene
10. Isoeugenol

11. Naphthol
12. Phenol, natural
13. Pyridine
14. Styrene
15. p-Xylene
16. Anethole
17. Benzophenone
18. Cineole
19. Menthol
20. Chlorobenzene (mono)

[1] Published by U.S. Bureau of Mines.

(Consult "Synthetic Organic Chemicals."[1])

Part 4. Import-export data.

1. Acetylene black (I)[2]
2. Acetone (E)
3. Cerium compounds (I)
4. Castor oil (E)
5. Ergot derivatives (I)
6. Diphenylamine (E)
7. Kieserite (I)
8. Menthol (E)
9. Pyridine (I)
10. Phthalic anhydride (E)
11. Benzene (I)
12. Antipyretics (E)
13. Chloral hydrate (I)
14. Chlorine (E)
15. Smokeless powder (I)
16. Ethyl ether (E)
17. Litharge (I)
18. Narcotics (E)
19. Quinine sulfate (I)
20. Printing ink (E)

(Consult "Chemical Statistics Handbook.")

Part 5. Financial data.

1. Abbott Laboratories
2. American Viscose Corp.
3. Bristol-Myers Co.
4. Dow Chemical Co.
5. Foote Mineral Co.
6. Hercules Powder Co.
7. Koppers Co.
8. Merck and Co.
9. Phillips Petroleum Co.
10. Victor Chemical Works
11. American Cyanamid Co.
12. Atlas Powder Co.
13. Diamond Alkali Co.
14. Eastman Kodak Co.
15. Glidden Co.
16. Interchemical Corp.
17. Eli Lilly and Co.
18. National Lead Co.
19. Rohm and Haas Co.
20. United Carbon Co.

(Consult "Chemical Statistics Handbook.")

Part 6. National census data.

1. Ammonia
2. Water glass
3. NH_4Cl
4. $CaCO_3$
5. $NiSO_4$
6. Na
7. SO_2
8. Nitric acid
9. H_3BO_3
10. HF
11. $FeCl_3$
12. $POCl_3$
13. $Na_2S_2O_4$
14. Na_2WO_4
15. Iodine
16. $CaOCl_2$
17. $AlCl_3$
18. Hg
19. KI
20. Na_2SiF_6

(Consult "Annual Survey of Manufactures.")

[1] Published by U.S. Tariff Commission.
[2] I = import; E = export.

Part 7. State census data.

1. Food products, in Florida
2. Chemical products, in New Jersey
3. Ceramic products, in Illinois
4. Food products, in California
5. Chemical products, in Texas
6. Ceramic products, in Ohio
7. Food products, in New York
8. Chemical products, in Michigan
9. Ceramic products, in Indiana
10. Food products, in Iowa
11. Pulp and paper, in Maine
12. Petroleum and coal, in Ohio
13. Primary metals, in Utah
14. Pulp and paper, in Wisconsin
15. Petroleum and coal, in Wyoming
16. Primary metals, in Nevada
17. Pulp and paper, in Oregon
18. Petroleum and coal, in Pennsylvania
19. Primary metals, in Montana
20. Pulp and paper, in Vermont

(Consult state census reports.)

Assignments for Library Problem 4

Part 1. Part 1 is designed to acquaint the student with the information relating to patents which is contained in abstracting journals. The date of issue has been omitted in order to give the student more experience in finding the abstract. The patents listed were issued fairly recently.

1. Merocyanine dyes
2. Chitin sulfate
3. Cellulose sponges
4. Beer substitute
5. Recovery of selenium
6. Low-sodium milk
7. Defoliation
8. Dicyanostilbenes
9. Mica pulp
10. Crease-resistant resin
11. Welded molybdenum
12. Coal devolatilization
13. Pimelic acid
14. Dyeing vinylon yarn
15. Dihydropyran
16. Antimist product
17. Dehydrating peat
18. Sulfamerazine
19. Factice
20. Pantetheine

(Consult subject indexes of *Chemical Abstracts*. See Chapter 11 for advice on using subject indexes.)

Part 2. Patent numbers.[1]

1. Australia: 137,130
2. Austria: 177,627
3. Belgium: 513,299
4. Canada: 452,990
5. Denmark: 74,203
6. France: 866,120
7. Germany: 806,006
8. Great Britain: 655,003
9. Hungary: 138,450
10. India: 44,860
11. Italy: 464,210
12. Japan: 3,771 (1952)
13. Netherlands: 72,774
14. Norway: 80,204

[1] Unless the year is indicated, more than one answer may be found for countries not using a continuous numbering system.

15. Russia: 69,000
16. Spain: 203,923
17. Sweden: 133,001

18. Switzerland: 265,710
19. United States: 2,116,000
20. United States: 2,322,001

(Consult patent-number indexes of *Chemical Abstracts*.)

Part 3a. Division-class information.

1. 4	6. 19	11. 25	16. 35
2. 41	7. 44	12. 51	17. 56
3. 60	8. 65	13. 14	18. 46
4. 9	9. 22	14. 24	19. 15
5. 54	10. 59	15. 20	20. 11

(Consult "Manual of Classification."[1])

Part 3b. Class-division information.

1. Acoustics
2. Fermentation
3. Thermostats
4. Ammunition
5. Refrigeration
6. Tobacco
7. Coatings
8. Foods
9. Glass
10. Heat exchange
11. Plastic metalworking
12. Multiple valves
13. Pumps
14. Textiles
15. Electric heating
16. Furnaces
17. Ventilation
18. Metal rolling
19. Abrading
20. Mineral oils

(Consult "Manual of Classification.")

Part 3c. Classification number-item.

1. Diazines
2. Ammonia derivatives
3. Thioureas
4. Baking powders
5. Calorimeters
6. Thermometers
7. Dry cleaning
8. Uranium recovery
9. Crystal detectors
10. Dentures
11. Gas separation
12. Acids and acid anhydrides
13. Autoclaves
14. Cryogenic compositions
15. Photometers
16. Actinometers
17. Azeotropic mixtures
18. Precious-stone working
19. Treatment of hides
20. Hygrometers

(Consult "Manual of Classification.")

[1] Published by U.S. Patent Office.

Part 3d. Item-classification number.

1. 8-15	8. 13-9	15. 19-39
2. 23-2	9. 44-42	16. 49-45
3. 60-50	10. 75-10	17. 83–91
4. 88-107	11. 91-2	18. 95-73
5. 99-22	12. 102–20	19. 110-31
6. 116-101	13. 131-5	20. 134-28
7. 71-55	14. 86–10	

(Consult "Manual of Classification.")

Part 4. Equivalent patents.

1. Switzerland: 139,793	11. Russia: 21,900
2. Germany: 550,474	12. Germany: 544,031
3. France: 722,566	13. France: 646,214
4. Netherlands: 26,264	14. Austria: 125,171
5. Belgium: 360,003	15. United States: 1,838,633
6. Great Britain: 369,082	16. Canada: 280,228
7. United States: 1,831,715	17. United States: 1,842,843
8. Austria: 127,867	18. Netherlands: 25,767
9. Canada: 282,409	19. Belgium: 365,259
10. United States: 1,856,796	20. Great Britain: 362,102

(Consult Patentrückzitate of *Chemisches Zentralblatt.*)

Part 5. For this part the student should select from an abstracting journal, or other suitable source, the subject or title of a United States chemical patent in which he is interested. Having obtained the necessary information, he should then write to the U.S. Patent Office for a copy of the patent specifications (see page 76 for procedure). From this document and from the abstracts found in *Chemical Abstracts* and the *Official Gazette* of the U.S. Patent Office the information required for the problem may be found.

Assignments for Library Problem 5

The assignments for this problem are designed to give experience in the use of several of the smaller collections of physical constants, such as Lange's "Handbook of Chemistry," Hodgman's "Handbook of Chemistry and Physics," and Perry's "Chemical Engineers' Handbook." In Parts 3 to 5 a check mark may be placed at the value that is to be found, in case not all those included in the blank page apply to the assignment made.

Although only names of substances have been given in the lists, in making assignments one might equally well give either names or formulas, provided the student has had sufficient training to enable him to determine the name for a given formula.

Part 1. Physical data.

1. Properties of commercial plastics
2. Chemical properties of commercial woods
3. Efficiency of drying agents
4. Clark and Lubs indicator solutions
5. Standard oxidation-reduction potentials
6. Properties of amino acids
7. Chemical thermodynamic properties
8. Elastic constants for solids
9. Tensile strength of metals
10. Hardness
11. Surface tension of fused salts
12. Antifreeze solutions
13. Velocity of sound in solids
14. Dielectric constants
15. Electrical resistance of electrolytes
16. Calibration tables for thermocouples
17. Fluorescent substances
18. Persistent lines of the elements
19. Transmittance of colored glasses
20. Compressibility of liquids

(Consult the type of small handbook mentioned.)

Part 2. Constants for organic compounds.

1. Acetaldehyde
2. Capric nitrile
3. Decane (*n*)
4. Hydrindone
5. Lauric acid
6. Nitroanisole (*o*)
7. Pelargonic acid
8. Retene
9. Terpinyl acetate
10. Vanillin
11. Benzophenone
12. Elaidic acid
13. Glycol diacetate
14. Indene
15. Menthone
16. Octyl acetate
17. Quinoline
18. Stearone
19. Urethane
20. Xylidine (*p*)

(Consult compilations such as those mentioned.)

Part 3. Constants for oils, fats, and waxes.

1. Acorn oil
2. Beechnut oil
3. Indian beeswax
4. Castor oil

5. Chicken fat
6. Cod-liver oil
7. Croton oil
8. Esparto oil
9. Grape-seed oil
10. Human fat
11. Almond oil
12. Beef tallow

13. Bone fat
14. Chaulmoogra oil
15. Coconut oil
16. Corn oil
17. Deer fat
18. Goose fat
19. Herring oil
20. Seal oil

(Consult small handbooks of physical constants.)

Part 4. Thermal data.

1. Acetylene
2. Asbestos
3. Sawdust
4. Chloroform
5. Cobalt
6. Phosphine
7. Freon

8. Constantin
9. Sulfur dioxide
10. Barium carbonate
11. Furfural
12. Boric oxide
13. Zinc sulfate
14. Bromobenzene

15. Helium
16. Cornstalk
17. Guncotton
18. Formic acid
19. Silver fluoride
20. Lithium chloride

(Consult small handbooks of physical constants.)

Part 5. Property-substance data.

Melting point, °C	Boiling point, °C	Refractive index[1]	Density[1]
1. −100	6. −80	11. 1.355	16. 0.740
2. −13	7. −10	12. 1.387	17. 0.805
3. 14	8. 50	13. 1.402	18. 0.880
4. 190	9. 227	14. 1.415	19. 1.100
5. 350	10. 400	15. 1.426	20. 1.500

(Consult property-substance tables in "International Critical Tables" and Hodgman, "Handbook of Chemistry and Physics.")

Part 6. Specific gravity–Baumé data for aqueous solutions.

Specific gravity	Composition	Tempera-ture, °C	Specific gravity	Composition	Tempera-ture, °C
1. 1.0111	$HC_2H_3O_2$	20/4	7. 1.1328	KCl	20/4
2. 1.1005	NH_4NO_3	20/4	8. 1.1745	NaBr	20/4
3. 1.181	H_2CrO_4	15/4	9. 1.2085	$NaNO_3$	20/4
4. 1.160	$CuCl_2$	20/4	10. 1.1394	H_2SO_4	20/4
5. 0.993	HCN	15/4	11. 0.9575	NH_3	20/4
6. 1.191	$NiCl_2$	20/4	12. 1.1904	$Cd(NO_3)_2$	18/4

[1] Liquids.

13.	1.206	$CuSO_4$	20/4	17.	1.1660	KI	20/4
14.	1.1220	$FeSO_4$	18/4	18.	1.1009	NaCl	20/4
15.	1.2701	$MgSO_4$	20/4	19.	1.212	$SnCl_4$	15/4
16.	1.0175	$H_2C_2O_4$	17.5	20.	1.4890	$ZnCl_2$	20/4

For these assignments one goes from specific gravity to percentage composition, and from percentage to degrees Baumé. (Consult small handbooks of physical constants.)

Part 7. Chemical-engineering data.

1. Flow of fluids
2. Evaporation
3. Gas absorption
4. Drying
5. Adsorption
6. Size reduction
7. High-pressure technique
8. Movement of materials
9. Furnaces
10. Electrochemistry
11. Heat transmission
12. Distillation
13. Solvent extraction
14. Humidification
15. Mechanical separation
16. Mixing materials
17. Process control
18. Fuels
19. Refrigeration
20. Materials of construction

(Consult "Chemical Engineers' Handbook.")

Assignments for Library Problem 6

In contrast to Problem 5, which dealt with the data to be found in the smaller collections of physical constants, this problem is designed for the use of the comprehensive compilations of such information. The most generally useful sources are the American "International Critical Tables," the German "Landolt-Börnstein's Zahlenwerke und Funktionen . . . ," the French "Tables annuelles . . . ," and works limited to some specific kind of data.

Part 1a. General data in "International Critical Tables."

1. Oceanic deposits
2. Mortars
3. Refractory materials
4. Sunlight
5. Hydraulic cements
6. Photometry
7. Laboratory porcelain
8. Barometry
9. Age of rocks
10. Electrolytic cells
11. Saccharimetry
12. Refrigerating brines
13. Clays
14. Resistance thermometers
15. Inks
16. Osmotic pressure
17. Primary cells
18. Thermal radiation
19. Dielectric properties
20. Vitreous enamels

(Consult "International Critical Tables."[1])

Part 1b. Specific data in "International Critical Tables."

1. Osmotic pressure: dextrin
2. Permeability: He in rubber
3. Surface tension: diisoamyl
4. Heat capacity: SO_2
5. Heat of wetting: CS_2 on starch
6. Dielectric constant: He
7. Electrical conductivity: glycol
8. Overvoltage: O_2 on gold
9. Verdet constant: $CHCl_3$
10. Optical rotation: 1-glyceric acid (H_2O)
11. Viscosity: acetylene
12. Fluidity: KI in ammonia
13. Diffusion: urea in CH_3OH
14. Heat of fusion: RbOH
15. Absorption spectrum: $CoBr_2$ in H_2O
16. Electrical resistivity: Mo at 50°
17. Pb-Hg standard cell
18. Magnetic susceptibility: Se at 18°
19. Refractivity: p-xylidine
20. Ferromagnetism: Si steel

(Consult index of "International Critical Tables" for kind of data sought, and then search the appropriate section.)

Part 2a. General data in German tables.

1. Zeeman effect
2. Magnetic moments of atoms
3. Microwave spectra
4. Magnetic moments of molecules
5. Electron spectra of crystals
6. Adsorption
7. Electron emission of metals
8. Oceanography
9. Triclinic crystal systems
10. Flotation
11. Absorption of X rays
12. Dissociation energy of two-atom molecules
13. Raman spectra
14. Naturally radioactive atoms
15. Ionic and atomic radii
16. Cubic crystal systems
17. The solar system
18. Paper chromatography
19. Electrical moments of molecules
20. Viscosity

(Consult "Landolt-Börnstein's Zahlenwerke und Funktionen. . . ."[2])

Part 2b. Specific data in German tables.

1. Velocity of light
2. Verdet constant: H_2O
3. Radioactivity: Po
4. Phase diagram: Cd-Cu
5. Dissociation energy: KI
6. Properties of lime
7. Phase diagram: $MgO-Al_2O_3-SiO_2$
8. Electrical moment: H_2S
9. Crystal structure: benzene
10. Infrared spectrum: heptane
11. Stark effect: Cs
12. Hyperfine structure: Li
13. Crystal structure: BeSe
14. Density: water
15. Curie point: minerals

[1] Vols. I–VII.
[2] Vols. I–IV.

16. Rotation spectrum: PF_3
17. Viscosity: borate glasses
18. Raman spectra: chlorates
19. Thermal properties: Saran
20. Phase diagram: C-Fe-P

(Consult "Landolt-Börnstein's Zahlenwerke und Funktionen. . . ."[1])

Part 3. Specific data in French tables.

1. Elasticity: NaCl
2. Thermal expansion: TlBr
3. Viscosity: Sn at 250°C
4. Thermal conductivity: SiO_2
5. Free energy: S
6. Thermal energy: C—O linkage
7. Equation of state: CH_2Cl_2
8. Diffusion: $H_2 \rightarrow$ Ni
9. Electrical conductivity: Nb
10. Dipole moment: D_2O
11. Compressibility: D_2O
12. Density: $C_2N_2F_8$
13. Surface tension: N_2H_4
14. Specific heat: AlN
15. Activity: AgCl in NH_3
16. Vapor pressure: AsH_3
17. Absorption of sound: CS_2
18. Thermoelectricity: Cu_2O/Cu
19. Magnetic susceptibility: V_2O_5
20. Raman effect: NO_2

(Consult "Tables annuelles. . . . "[2])

Part 4. Solubility data.

1. Methyl chloride in water at 20°
2. K_3AlF_6 in water at 25°
3. Ascorbic acid in C_2H_5OH at 30°
4. H_3BO_3 in 50 per cent H_2SO_4 at 45°
5. Caprylic acid in toluene at 10°
6. BaS_2O_3 in water at 60°
7. Palmitonitrile in acetone at 20°
8. HSO_3NH_2 in water at 20°
9. Morphine in water at 50°
10. KI in D_2O at 15°
11. Water in isopentane at 6°
12. $AsBr_3$ in nitrobenzene at 5°
13. Caproic acid in water at 30°
14. BaS in water at 50°
15. Antipyrine in C_2H_5OH at 30°
16. $CdSeO_4$ in water at 30°
17. Hexadecanol in benzene at 40°
18. $InBr_3$ in water at 40°
19. Palmitanilide in acetone at 10°
20. $LaCl_3$ in water at 10°

(Consult Seidell and Linke, "Solubilities of Inorganic and Organic Compounds," or other similar works.)

Part 5. Nuclear data.

1. Li^6
2. K^{41}
3. Sr^{90}
4. In^{110}
5. Ta^{180}
6. C^{13}
7. Ti^{45}
8. Mo^{101}
9. Te^{130}
10. W^{185}
11. Na^{25}
12. Co^{59}
13. Rh^{105}
14. Ba^{140}
15. Au^{195}
16. P^{30}
17. Zn^{65}
18. Sn^{118}
19. Ho^{165}
20. Hg^{200}

[1] Vols. I–IV.
[2] Vol. 12.

(Consult *National Bureau of Standards Circular* 499.)

Assignments for Library Problem 7

Problem 7, devoted to more or less general information in organic chemistry, is designed to bring the student into contact with various comprehensive reference works in the field (except Beilstein's, for which see Problem 8).

Part 1. Treatment of organic compounds.

1. Acetic anhydride
2. Caprinitrile
3. Ethoxytriglycol
4. Glyceryl laurate
5. Isopropyl ether
6. Mesityl oxide
7. Oleic acid
8. Resorcinol
9. Tributylamine
10. Vinyl acetate
11. Butadiene
12. Decylamine
13. Furan
14. Hydroxyacetic acid
15. Lauric acid
16. Nonyl acetate
17. Phenothioxin
18. Sorbic acid
19. Urethan
20. Amyl phthalate

This part illustrates the different treatment of a compound in a single-volume work (Whitmore) and in more comprehensive works.

(Consult the works specified.)

Part 2a. Unusual or new compounds[1] (empirical formulas).

1. $C_{38}H_{66}NO_4PS_2$
2. $C_{42}H_{24}N_6Na_2O_6S_6$
3. $C_{44}H_{60}Br_2N_2O_2$
4. $C_{49}H_{40}IN_3OS_5$
5. $C_{55}H_{60}Cl_3N_7O_2S_3$
6. $C_{69}H_{68}N_6O_{15}S$
7. $C_{72}H_{156}BCl_3N_4$
8. $C_{80}H_{41}Cl_2N_9O_{11}$
9. $C_{84}H_{76}As_4Cl_4O_2Pd_2$
10. $C_{88}H_{64}CuN_8S_8$
11. $C_{40}H_{24}CoFeN_9O$
12. $C_{43}H_{31}ClCuN_{10}O_{13}S_3$
13. $C_{48}H_{48}FeN_{15}O_{21}$
14. $C_{54}H_{49}Cl_2N_5O_2S_2$
15. $C_{56}H_{32}F_{24}O_2Si_3$
16. $C_{72}H_{147}N_7O_{24}S_3$
17. $C_{77}H_{49}CuN_{11}O_{33}S_{10}$
18. $C_{80}H_{70}Co_2Hg_2I_2N_{10}$
19. $C_{101}H_{119}N_{11}O_{26}P_2$
20. $C_{108}H_{112}N_{18}O_{29}S_6$

(Consult formula indexes of *Chemical Abstracts.*)

Part 2b. Named processes.

1. Wurtz-Fittig reaction
2. Kekulé synthesis
3. Carius determination
4. Liebig combustion
5. Diels-Alder reaction
6. Perkin method

[1] The assignments are all for 1954.

7. Meyer reaction
8. Haworth methylation
9. Phthalic anhydride test
10. Kiliani synthesis
11. Acyloin condensation
12. Bergius process
13. Krafft method

14. Fischer-Tropsch synthesis
15. Wohl-Schweitzer electrolysis
16. Von Baeyer synthesis
17. Dow process
18. Kolbe synthesis
19. Mayer reagent
20. Van Slyke method

(Consult works on organic chemistry.)

Part 2c. General summaries on specific subjects.

1. Oxidation processes
2. Heterocyclic chemistry
3. Antibiotics
4. Chemotherapy
5. Lipids
6. Alkaloids
7. The steroids
8. Redistribution reaction
9. Molecular rearrangements
10. Free radicals

11. Chemistry of explosives
12. The terpenes
13. Organometallic compounds
14. Organic dyes
15. Reaction mechanisms
16. Chlorophyll
17. Cellulose
18. Resonance
19. Synthetic polymers
20. Stereoisomerism

(Consult comprehensive works on organic chemistry.)

Part 3a. Organic groups and radicals.

1. Acetoxy
2. $AsHO_2$
3. Benzimido
4. CNSe
5. Carbyl
6. C_5H_3OS
7. Cymyl
8. $C_6H_3O_2$
9. Glycoyl
10. C_8H_7N

11. Arsinico
12. CH_3N_2O
13. Carbamyl
14. C_3H_2NS
15. Cumidino
16. C_5H_8NO
17. Ethynyl
18. C_7H_4NO
19. Picryl
20. $C_8H_8O_2$

(Consult "The Naming and Indexing of Chemical Compounds by *Chemical Abstracts*"; see also decennial indexes of *Chemical Abstracts*.)

Part 3b. Organic ring complexes.

1. Anthranil
2. Benzofuran
3. Cinnoline
4. Benzopyran
5. Benzobisimidazole

6. Dibenzofuran
7. Benzocinnoline
8. Acephenanthrylene
9. Aromoline
10. Dibenzacridine

11. Indan
12. Pteridine
13. Bispidine
14. 4,7-Methanoindan
15. Benzopyrrocoline

16. Acenaphthene
17. Anthroxazole
18. Benzacridan
19. Benzaceanthrylene
20. *i*-Cholestane

(Consult *Fourth Decennial Index* or annual subject indexes of *Chemical Abstracts*.)

Assignments for Library Problem 8

Parts 1 and 2. Data in the Beilstein set.

1. Ethyl-[4-nitrophenyl]-sulfid*
2. 4-Bromothiobenzoesäure amid
3. Monothiobenzoesäure-S-[4-chloronaphthyl-(1)-ester]
4. Thiozimtsäure amid
5. Monothiokohlensäure-S-[2-nitrobenzyl]-ester amid
6. [4-Nitrophenyl]-benzyl sulfid
7. Methyl-[5-bromo-3-nitro-4-oxy-phenyl]-sulfid
8. 2-Äthylmercapto-4-[3-nitro-phenyl-imino]-dihydropyrimi-dine
9. 2-Bromo-3-oxythionaphthen
10. 4-Chloro-2-oxy-1-methyl-mer-capto-benzol

11. Bis[4-chlorophenyl]-selenid
12. Phenyl-[4-bromophenyl]-sulfid
13. Bis-[3-nitrobenzyl]-diselenid
14. 5-Bromo-3-methyl-2-acetyl thio-phen
15. Chlorthioessigsäureäthylester
16. Äthylthioameisensäure-amid-bromid
17. [2,2′, 2″-Trichloro-α-oxyäthyl]-phenyl-sulfid
18. 4-Methoxy-thiobenzoesäure-[4-chloro-analid]
19. Methyl-[2-nitrobenzyl]-sulfon
20. 1-Phenyl-4-bromo-3-methyl-selen-5-methyl-pyrozol

The aim in these parts is to use the sources which lead one to a complete survey of the chemistry of a compound. The references should be copied as found, those in the formula indexes being accompanied by an indication of the meaning of the various items. Uncommon compounds are preferable as assignments because of the smaller number of references. The examples listed are triple-derivative compounds.

(Consult the works specified.)

Part 3. Procedures for laboratory syntheses.

1. *n*-Butyl glyoxalate
2. Guanylthiourea

3. 2-Chloropyrimidine
4. Azelanitrile

* The German names as used in the Beilstein set are given, although prefer-able English names may be evident.

5. Dimethylfurazan
6. Atrolactic acid
7. Itaconyl chloride
8. Cyanogen iodide
9. Flavone
10. 10-Undecynoic acid
11. Thiobenzophenone
12. Ethyl isocyanide
13. 1-Phenylpiperidine
14. Cycloheptanone
15. Hemimellitene
16. Dimethylketene
17. Pyridine-N-oxide
18. Cyclohexene sulfide
19. Phenylacetamide
20. Stearone

(Consult treatises on synthesis, such as the Theilheimer set
or "Organic Syntheses.")

Part 4. Application of organic reactions.

1. Beckman reaction
2. Stobbe condensation
3. Claisen rearrangement
4. Cyanoethylation
5. von Braun cyanogen bromide reaction
6. Sulfonation of aromatic hydrocarbons
7. Catalytic hydrogenation
8. Sommelet reaction
9. Curtius reaction
10. Resolution of alcohols
11. Wolff-Kishner reduction
12. Cyclic ketones
13. Selenium dioxide oxidation
14. Clemmensen reduction
15. Nitrosation of aliphatic carbon atoms
16. Metalation with organolithium compounds
17. Mannich reaction
18. Oppenauer oxidation
19. β-Lactones
20. Periodic acid oxidation

(Consult "Organic Reactions.")

Part 5. Laboratory operations.

1. Preparation of optically active compounds
2. Electrochemical reactions
3. Preparation of catalysts
4. Kinetic researches
5. Mass spectrometric measurements
6. Fluorescence
7. Decarboxylation
8. Chromatographic separations
9. Elemental analysis
10. X-ray methods
11. Molecular weight of macromolecules
12. Pyrochemical reactions
13. Biochemical reactions
14. Calorimetric measurements
15. Microwave spectroscopy
16. Dielectric methods
17. Functional group analysis
18. Gas analysis
19. Polarography
20. Densimetric methods

(Consult treatises of Müller and of Weissberger.)

Assignments for Library Problem 9

Part 1. Reference in treatises.

1. Perchloric acid
2. Cadmium sulfate
3. Gold bromide
4. Antimony (III) sulfide
5. Chlorine dioxide
6. Sodium bismuthate
7. Cadmium cyanide
8. Mercury iodide
9. Bismuth oxide
10. Copper (I) chloride
11. Zinc carbonate
12. Bismuth hydride
13. Copper fluoride
14. Mercury carbonate
15. Silver bromide
16. Cadmium fluoride
17. Hydrazine chloride
18. Arsenic (III) chloride
19. Gold sulfate
20. Zinc fluoride

(Consult treatises on inorganic chemistry.)

Part 2. Known inorganic compounds.

1. Mg, O, Si, F, Li, K
2. O, Mn, H, Mo, N
3. N, K, I, H, Pt, Cl
4. S, H, Li, O, N
5. N, Cl, Re, O, H
6. S, N, Cr, H, O
7. W, O, K, Si, H
8. Cr, Cl, Na, O, H
9. N, O, Pt, H, Cl
10. S, Na, O, N, Cu, H
11. Na, S, O, P, H, N
12. P, H, Ge, O, I
13. O, Co, N, H, Cl, I
14. P, H, Hg, N, O
15. Cl, N, Co, H, O
16. O, Mo, H, K, Si
17. S, Fe, O, H, N
18. S, K, Cl, Na, O
19. O, W, P, H, V, N
20. N, K, H, O, U

(Consult formula indexes of *Chemical Abstracts.*)

Part 3a. Inorganic groups and radicals.

1. Amido
2. BO_2
3. Fluo
4. CrO_2
5. Thionyl
6. Azido
7. CHO_3
8. Hydrosulfide
9. HN
10. O_3S
11. Carbonato
12. CNSe
13. Imido
14. H_2NO_2S
15. Sulfuryl
16. Chromyl
17. CS
18. Nitrido
19. OP
20. P_2S_3

(Consult reference listed in Problem 8, Part 3.)

Part 3b. Inorganic anions.

1. Azide
2. AlH_4O_4
3. Chloroaurate (I)
4. CNTe
5. Dithionate
6. H_4O_6Te
7. Nitratocerate
8. Beryllate
9. $AsOS_3$
10. Cobalticyanide
11. $CrFO_3$
12. Fluoarsenate
13. I_6Re
14. P_2S_6
15. Bromoaurate (III)
16. BF_2O_2
17. Cyanoiridate (III)
18. F_3O_3W
19. Germanite
20. NO_6S_2

(Consult reference listed in Problem 8, Part 3.)

Assignments for Library Problem 10

Part 1. Qualitative tests.

1. $CO_3{}^{2-}$	6. $CrO_4{}^{2-}$	11. $ClO_4{}^{2-}$	16. $MnO_4{}^{2-}$
2. Be^{2+}	7. Ti^{4+}	12. V^{5+}	17. Ga^{3+}
3. $SeO_4{}^{2-}$	8. O_3	13. H_2O_2	18. $S_2O_3{}^{2-}$
4. $MoO_4{}^{2-}$	9. Sc^{3+}	14. Ce^{4+}	19. Tl^{3+}
5. SO_2	10. CO	15. $SiO_3{}^{2-}$	20. $WO_4{}^{2-}$

(Consult comprehensive works on qualitative analysis.)

Part 2. General quantitative methods.

1. As	6. La	11. W	16. Au
2. Ge	7. Zr	12. Ta	17. Pt
3. Th	8. U	13. Be	18. V
4. Co	9. Cs	14. Tl	19. Li
5. Ti	10. Se	15. Mo	20. Sb

(Consult comprehensive works on quantitative analysis.)

Part 3. Measurement of one constituent in a sample.

1. Fe (German silver)	11. SiO_2 (soap)
2. K_2O (fertilizer)	12. Se (soils)
3. CO_2 (beer)	13. Al (baking powder)
4. Caffeine (tea)	14. V (steel)
5. P (brass)	15. TNT (explosives)
6. pH (water)	16. Available CaO (lime)
7. Dextrin (fruits)	17. Lipoids (wheat flour)
8. Free C (rubber goods)	18. Albumin (urine)
9. Lignin (plants)	19. $(C_2H_5)_4Pb$ (gasoline)
10. Dissolved O_2 (water)	20. Sugar (honey)

(Consult works on applied analysis.)

Part 4. Complete analysis of commercial materials.

1. Ammonium hydroxide	11. Silicate rocks
2. Vinegar	12. Ethyl ether
3. Lime	13. Baking powder
4. Lubricating oil	14. Coffee
5. Leather	15. Soap
6. Coal	16. Dow metal
7. Peanut butter	17. Aluminum alloys
8. Calcium carbide	18. Varnish
9. Flue gas	19. Ice cream
10. Hydrogen peroxide	20. White paint

(Consult works on applied analysis.)

Assignments for Library Problem 11

Part 1. Books on industrial chemistry subjects.

1. Alloy steels
2. Nuclear fuels
3. Industrial wastes
4. Leather
5. Acetylene
6. Latex
7. Bleaching
8. Catalysis
9. Ceramics
10. Process industries
11. Nuclear engineering
12. Magnesium alloys
13. Alkaloids
14. Ceramics
15. Rubber chemicals
16. Cement
17. Unit operations
18. Sodium
19. Carbon blacks
20. Carbohydrates

(Consult catalogues and lists of books.)

Part 2. Products having brand names.

1. Adeps lanae
2. Derris
3. Slate flour
4. Vine black
5. Argols
6. Degras
7. Saponin
8. Carrotin
9. Drop black
10. Soap bark
11. Japan colors
12. Cryolith
13. Hypernic
14. Smalt
15. Copra
16. Keratin
17. Antichlors
18. Button-lac
19. Divi divi
20. Egg-yolk oil

(Consult works listed in Chapter 10, page 192.)

Part 3. Manufacturers of chemical equipment.

1. Centrifuges
2. Electrolytic cells
3. Centrifugal pumps
4. Tubular filters
5. Freeze dryers
6. Ion exchangers
7. Carbon analyzers
8. Fluid agitators
9. Gas absorbers
10. Scrubbers
11. Air classifiers
12. Roll crushers
13. Blenders
14. Stills
15. Spray dryers
16. Air heaters
17. Heat exchangers
18. Grinding mills
19. Filter presses
20. Screen separators

(Consult works listed in Chapter 10, page 192; see also current advertising.)

Part 4. Scientific names of commercial chemicals.

1. Benzycin
2. Gardan
3. Elcovar
4. Holtite
5. Carbolon
6. Federine
7. Guantal
8. Edinol
9. Homorenon
10. Gelite
11. Alrose
12. Click
13. Hexamo
14. Hypol
15. Fixin
16. Dynax
17. Harbyline
18. Bondura
19. Cromodine
20. Flomine

(Consult dictionaries, encyclopedias, and works listed in Chapter 10, page 192.)

Part 5. Commercial laboratory equipment.

1. Direct-reading balance
2. Gas analyzers (I.R.)
3. Vapor fractometers
4. $X-Y$ plotter
5. Computers
6. Hygrometers
7. Jaw crushers
8. Automatic titrators
9. Metal polishers
10. Mortar grinder
11. Thermo-recording balance
12. Humidity controllers
13. Mass spectrometers
14. Scintillation counters
15. Electrophoresis apparatus
16. Penetrometer, ASTM
17. Beckmann thermometers
18. Refractometer, Abbé
19. Engler viscosimeter
20. Kjeldahl digestor

(Consult catalogues of chemical supply houses.)

Part 6. Bibliographies on commercial subjects.

1. Alkylation
2. Elastomers
3. Halogenation
4. Plastics
5. Wood
6. Adsorption
7. Evaporation
8. Size reduction
9. Colloids and surface behavior
10. Mass transfer
11. Fermentation
12. Fibers
13. Less-common metals
14. Polymerization
15. Pyrolysis of coal
16. Crystallization
17. Flotation
18. Heterogeneous catalysis
19. Fluid dynamics
20. Thermodynamics

(Consult annual reviews in *Industrial and Engineering Chemistry*.)

Part 7. Dealers in industrial chemicals.

1. Acetal
2. Allyl bromide
3. Beryllium oxide
4. Citronellol
5. Tungstophosphoric acid
6. Benzidine sulfate
7. Chromium fluoride
8. Sebacic acid
9. Amyl mercaptan
10. Brucine
11. Diethyl malate
12. Tobias acid
13. Bismuth trioxide
14. Isopropyl ether
15. Acrolein
16. Barium bromide
17. Cadmium tungstate
18. Diphenyl phthalate
19. Decyl alcohol
20. Calcium molybdate

(Consult works listed in Chapter 10, page 192.)

Part 8. Location of chemical manufacturers.

1. Los Angeles, Calif.
2. Grand Rapids, Mich.
3. Cleveland, Ohio
4. Seattle, Wash.
5. Denver, Colo.
6. Indianapolis, Ind.
7. Boston, Mass.
8. Dallas, Tex.
9. Milwaukee, Wis.
10. Birmingham, Ala.
11. Des Moines, Iowa
12. Elizabeth, N.J.
13. Philadelphia, Pa.
14. Knoxville, Tenn.
15. Atlanta, Ga.
16. Louisville, Ky.
17. Shreveport, La.
18. Charleston, S.C.
19. Brooklyn, N.Y.
20. Hartford, Conn.

(Consult works listed in Chapter 10, page 192.)

Part 9. Commercial methods of manufacture.

1. Acrylic acid
2. 1,3-Butadiene
3. Carbon monoxide
4. Cyclohexane
5. Amylene
6. Carbon black
7. Dextrin
8. Anthranol
9. Cadmium borate
10. Chrome alum
11. Ethyl mercaptan
12. Barium titanate
13. Cetylamine
14. Fluorescein
15. Aluminum acetate
16. Calcium lactate
17. Copper laurate
18. Ammonium carbamate
19. Boric acid
20. Diphenyl oxide

(Consult works on industrial chemistry.)

Part 10. History of chemical industries.

1. Hydrogenation of oils
2. Chemicals by fermentation
3. Elastomers (synthetic)
4. Soybean-oil industry
5. Antiknock substances
6. Phosphors
7. Glass-fiber materials
8. Butadiene rubber
9. Production of U^{235}
10. Mylar film
11. Catalytic cracking
12. Fluorination of hydrocarbons
13. Amination reactions
14. Artificial radioactivity
15. Jet fuels
16. Sulfonated-oil detergents
17. Liquid-oxygen explosives
18. Antibiotics
19. Magnesium alloys
20. Dacron fiber

(Consult *Chemical Abstracts* and periodicals on industrial chemistry.)

Assignments for Library Problem 12

Part 1. Annual reviews of foreign industrial developments.

1. Glass
2. Electrodeposition
3. Petroleum
4. Antibiotics
5. Leather
6. Control of pests
7. Enzymes
8. Ceramics
9. Fuel
10. Explosives
11. Rubber
12. Synthetic fibers
13. Plastics
14. Sugars
15. Corrosion of metals
16. Tar and tar products
17. Intermediates and dyestuffs
18. Photographic materials
19. Cellulosic fibers
20. Essential oils

(Consult review serials.)

Part 2. Sources of raw materials.

1. Caramel
2. Gelatin
3. Lecithin
4. Chromite
5. Hide glue
6. Agar
7. Canada balsam
8. Ball clay
9. Graphite
10. Menthol
11. Fish meal
12. Hemlock extract
13. Fire clay
14. Guano
15. Colors, earth
16. Cochineal
17. Copra
18. Gilsonite
19. Dried blood
20. Clove oil

(Consult works listed in Chapter 10, page 192.)

Part 3. Composition of, and general information regarding, industrial commodities.

1. Antiperspiration cream
2. Fireproofing paper
3. Herbicides
4. Capsule composition
5. Antique-green oxidizer
6. Lipsticks
7. Pine-oil emulsion
8. Mustard ointment
9. Insulating wax
10. Raspberry oil
11. Butterscotch fudge
12. Blue drawing crayons
13. Boiler compounds
14. Red fire
15. Orange sherbet
16. Green-fire composition
17. Sausage-marking ink
18. Sash-cord impregnant
19. Dynamo-brush lubricant
20. Liquid soap for dogs

(Consult dictionaries and encyclopedias.)

Part 4. Commercial grades of industrial materials.

1. Acetone
2. Aluminum sulfate
3. Aniline
4. Phenol
5. Phosphoric acid
6. Amyl acetate
7. Benzaldehyde
8. Acetamide
9. Ammonium sulfate
10. Arsenic trioxide
11. Citric acid
12. Aluminum chloride
13. Antimony trichloride
14. Benzene
15. Isopropyl alcohol
16. Ammonium carbonate
17. Acetyl chloride
18. Hydrofluoric acid
19. Aqueous ammonia
20. Barium carbonate

(Consult works listed in Chapter 10, page 192.)

Part 5. Commercial uses of chemicals.

1. Adipic acid
2. Barium titanate
3. Chrome alum
4. Acetin
5. Antimony tetroxide
6. Carnauba wax
7. Ethyl mercaptan
8. Almond oil
9. Cadmium borate
10. Copper erucate
11. Acrolein
12. Bismuth oxyiodide
13. Formamide
14. Ferric oleate
15. Anthranilic acid
16. Cerium tungstate
17. Ethyl silicate
18. Alumina
19. Calcium lactate
20. Activated charcoal

(Consult works listed in Chapter 10, page 192.)

Part 6. Manufacturers' industrial literature.

1. Ball mills
2. Gyratory crushers
3. Air filters
4. Rod mills
5. Cyclone separators
6. Rotary kilns
7. Insulated vats
8. Blade mixers
9. Electrolytic cells
10. Monel equipment
11. Impact pulverizers
12. Centrifugal pumps
13. Bottle fillers
14. Rubber-lined tanks
15. Rotary cutters
16. Hammer mills
17. Tantalum equipment
18. Steam-jacketed kettles
19. Turboblowers
20. Calcining furnaces

(Consult works listed in Chapter 10, page 192; see also late issues of periodicals on industrial chemistry.)

Part 7. Miscellaneous industrial information.

1. Acetal
2. Acetic anhydride
3. Arsenic acid
4. Chloroplatinic acid
5. Fluosilicic acid
6. Sodium fluoride
7. Allyl alcohol
8. Acetamide
9. Acetone
10. Boric acid
11. Chromic acid
12. Perchloric acid
13. Sulfuric acid
14. n-Amyl alcohol
15. Acetanilid
16. Glycine
17. Phenol
18. Hydrobromic acid
19. Lithium chloride
20. Diacetone alcohol

(Consult works listed in Chapter 10, page 192.)

Part 8. Specifications.

1. Acetic anhydride	8. Ethyl ether	15. Glycocoll
2. Barium chlorate	9. Benzoyl chloride	16. Bromine
3. Chloroform	10. Calcium oxide	17. Citric acid
4. Arsenic trioxide	11. Barium sulfate	18. Benzidine
5. Calcium bromide	12. Brucine	19. Calcium acetate
6. Dextrose	13. Glycerol	20. Ceric sulfate
7. Hydrogen peroxide	14. Cobalt acetate	

(Consult "ASTM Standards 1955"; "Federal Specifications"; "Pharmacopeia of the United States"; Rosin, "Reagent Chemicals and Standards"; "U.S. Government Specifications Directory"; Wichers, "Reagent Chemicals"; and *Advances in Chemistry Series*.[1])

Part 9. Chemically resistant materials.

1. Acetic acid, 10 per cent	7. Glycerol	15. NH_3, aqueous
2. $HClO_4$, 60 per cent	8. Benzene	16. SO_2, liquid
3. $SnCl_4$	9. Aniline	17. HCl, 35 per cent
4. Methanol	10. KOH, fused	18. Acetone
5. KOH, alcohol solution	11. Chloroform	19. Ammonium fluoride
6. HF, gaseous	12. Chloroacetic acid	20. Milk
	13. Formaldehyde	
	14. NaOCl	

(Consult works on the chemical properties of materials and monographs on corrosion.)

Assignments for Library Problem 13[2]

1. Algol yellow GC	11. Diamine fast orange EG
2. Fast scarlet 2G salt	12. Indanthrene brown RRD
3. Oxydiamogen OB	13. Radiogen red GS
4. Sulphon yellow R	14. Zambesi black V
5. Celliton fast rubine 3B	15. Fast Bordeaux GP salt
6. Fast red KB salt	16. Indanthrene olive green B
7. Naphthol AS-SW	17. Palatine fast pink BN
8. Cotonerol	18. Chlorantine fast red 6BLL
9. Fast red PDC base	19. Cellitazol AZN
10. Solantine orange 4G	20. Pontamine navy blue DB

[1] *No. 10*, p. 449 (1954).

[2] Various instructors in specialized fields of chemistry wish to have their students go into more detail than the rather general previous problems, such as Probs. 7 and 8 in organic chemistry. Problem 13 is included as an example of one kind of specialized assignment in organic chemistry. Similar problems could be devised for other special subjects or broader fields, such as agricultural chemistry or biochemistry.

(This problem covers items of general interest on dyes. Consult works likely to contain such information.)

Assignments for Library Problem 14

Part 1. Common ores.

1. Li	6. Mn	11. Ni	16. Cr
2. As	7. Fe	12. Rh	17. Cs
3. Be	8. Sr	13. Tl	18. Ge
4. Ti	9. Zr	14. Sn	19. Ta
5. Ce	10. Ag	15. Sb	20. W

(Consult general works on metallurgy and encyclopedias.)

Part 2. Methods of treating ores.

1. Beryl	8. Apatite	15. Horn silver
2. Cobaltite	9. Tourmaline	16. Azurite
3. Willemite	10. Spinel	17. Argentite
4. Franklinite	11. Orpiment	18. Monazite
5. Orthoclase	12. Melaconite	19. Zincite
6. Realgar	13. Gadolinite	20. Biotite
7. Titanite	14. Vanadinite	

(Consult works on production metallurgy.)

Part 3. Uses of alloys.

1. Alneon	8. Dowmetal F	15. Dumet
2. Maxtensile	9. Elastuf	16. Cromovan
3. Magnel	10. Alcoa 17S	17. Si steel
4. Mn bronze	11. Elinvar	18. Monel metal
5. Al bronze	12. W carbide	19. Naval brass
6. Antimonial lead	13. Everdur	20. Zr steel
7. Nickelene	14. Teledium	

(Consult metallurgical treatises, encyclopedias, and "Metals Handbook.")

Part 4. Books on metallurgical subjects.

1. Tungsten	8. Art bronze	15. Cyanidation
2. Zirconium	9. Amalgams	16. Beryllium
3. Blast furnaces	10. Casehardening	17. Stainless steels
4. Cast iron	11. Cutting tools	18. Copper refining
5. Powder metallurgy	12. Bearing metals	19. Blast-furnace slags
6. Chromium plating	13. Coke	20. Coloring metals
7. Physical metallurgy	14. X-ray testing	

(Consult lists of books on metallurgy and *Chemical Abstracts*.[1])

Part 5. Composition of alloys.

1. Acieral
2. Kromal
3. Circle "C"
4. Dimondite
5. Firex
6. Ideor
7. Lumdie
8. Alniloy
9. Copan
10. Cobalt steel
11. DM
12. Furbaloi
13. Jewell alloy
14. Magnalite
15. Fechral
16. Chromidium
17. Defirust
18. Elinvar
19. Harcus
20. Kiski

(Consult "Metals Handbook" and Woldman, "Engineering Alloys."[2])

Part 6. Equilibrium diagrams (alloys).

1. Ag-Sn
2. As-Pb
3. Be-Cu
4. Nb-Fe
5. Cr-W
6. Ag-Au-Pd
7. Be-Cu-Ni
8. Cd-Sb-Sn
9. Fe-Mn-Si
10. Mo-Ni-Si
11. Al-Ni
12. Au-Zn
13. Bi-Hg
14. Cd-Sb
15. Cu-Zr
16. Al-Fe-Si
17. C-Fe-V
18. Cu-Ni-Zn
19. Mg-Mn-Zn
20. Pb-Sn-Zn

(Consult "Metals Handbook" and abstracting journals.)

Part 7. Physical properties of alloys.

1. B.T.G. steel
2. Blue chip
3. Cromovan
4. Glowray
5. Jalcase 1
6. Mangonic
7. Ry-Ax
8. Armco iron
9. Rytense AA
10. Durodi
11. Hecla
12. Konel
13. Neloy
14. Special 8T
15. Avesta 393
16. Corronil
17. Ferry
18. Immadium V
19. Lesco "18-8"
20. Regular

(Consult Woldman, "Engineering Alloys.")

Part 8. Corrosion resistance.

1. Mg alloys: salt water
2. Si-Fe alloys: HCl, aqueous
3. Ni: salt solutions
4. Mg: acids
5. Pb: H_2SO_4
6. Cr alloys: HCl, aqueous
7. Ni: H_3PO_4
8. Al: salt solutions
9. Fe: basic solutions
10. Pt: fused $K_2S_2O_7$
11. Sn: acetic acid
12. Cr alloys: HNO_3, aqueous
13. Cu: food products
14. Sn plate: strawberries
15. Mo alloys: HCl, aqueous
16. Ni: atmosphere

[1] Sec. 9.

[2] Published by American Society for Metals, Cleveland, Ohio, 1954.

17. Cu: waters
18. Pb: neutral solutions

19. Cu: HClO$_4$
20. Monel metal: H$_2$SO$_4$

(Consult works on corrosion.)

Part 9. Current prices.

1. Steel bars
2. Ferrochrome
3. Cobalt oxide
4. Zr
5. Co
6. Ferromolybdenum
7. Te

8. Bessemer pig iron
9. Ti
10. Ni
11. Basic pig iron
12. Pt
13. Pyrites
14. Magnesite

15. Zn ore
16. Be ore
17. Si
18. Be-Cu
19. W
20. W ore

(Consult current market reports.)

Assignments for Library Problem 15

Part 1. General information on drugs.

1. Absinthium
2. Barbital
3. Calamus
4. Caulophyllum
5. Acriflavine
6. Bromural
7. Chineonal

8. Acitrin
9. Albargin
10. Carbromal
11. Chelidonium
12. Agaric acid
13. Cannabis
14. Cholesterin

15. Abonidine
16. Betol
17. Cascarilla
18. Alginic acid
19. Borneol
20. Capsicum

(Consult encyclopedias, "Merck's Index," and "Dispensatory of the United States.")

Part 2. Specifications for drugs and medicinals.

1. Acetanilid
2. Salicylic acid
3. Amidopyrine
4. Acetyltannic acid
5. Trichloroacetic acid
6. Alcohol
7. Silver nitrate
8. Phenacetin

9. Aconitine
10. Ammonia water
11. Boric acid
12. Aconite
13. Alum
14. Ammonium bro-
mide

15. Citric acid
16. Aloe
17. Zinc oxide
18. Aspirin
19. Wool fat
20. Amyl nitrite

(Consult "Merck's Index" and Rosin, "Reagent Chemicals and Standards.")

Part 3. Drug manufacturers (supply houses).

1. Thyroid
2. Amidopyrine
3. Bromural
4. Thymus
5. Blackleg antigen
6. Arsphenamine
7. Carbromal
8. Tetanus antitoxin
9. Anodyne
10. Carotene
11. Acne vaccine
12. Allantoin
13. Bandoline
14. Cascara compound
15. Adrenalin
16. Bone marrow
17. Placenta
18. Typhoid serum
19. Aminophyllin
20. Calisaya

(Consult works listed in Chapter 10, page 192.)

Part 4. Market prices.

1. Ephedrine sulfate
2. Viscysate
3. Nicotinic acid
4. Urease tablets
5. Styptysate
6. Thyroid glands
7. Sulfapyridine
8. Vitamin B_1
9. Diatussin
10. Mercurochrome
11. Solvogon powder
12. Anayodin pills
13. Flumerin
14. Digitalis tablets
15. Pregnacol
16. Alpha lobelin
17. Cod-liver oil
18. Gadusan
19. Activin
20. Hemaboloids

(Consult market reports in periodicals.)

Part 5. Composition (preparation) of drugs.

1. Bismuth cream
2. Glycerin jelly
3. Nasal drops
4. Astringent gargle
5. Boeck's lotion
6. Aseptic wax
7. Iodoform paint
8. Elixir of anise
9. Magma of $ZnSO_4$
10. Malliolis elixir
11. Benzoin inhalant
12. Antacid mixture
13. Bubeb mixture
14. Antiperiodic pills
15. Glycerite of guaiac
16. Antipruritic lotion
17. Almond emulsion
18. Anodyne liniment
19. Elixir of black-berry
20. Oleate of cocaine

(Consult "National Formulary" and other works listed in Chapter 10, page 192.)

Part 6. Methods of analysis (assay, purity tests).

1. Oil of chenopodium
2. Hydrastis
3. Magnesium citrate
4. Belladonna leaves
5. Calcium lactate
6. Nux vomica
7. Ammoniated mercury
8. Magnesium hydroxide
9. Benzaldehyde
10. Lime
11. Magnesium sulfate
12. Formaldehyde
13. Soluble barbital
14. Citrated caffeine
15. Cantharis
16. Oil of carraway
17. Jalap
18. Asafetida
19. Bismuth subnitrate
20. Capsicum

(Consult "National Formulary" and "Pharmacopeia of the United States.")

Assignments for Library Problem 16[1]

1. Magnesium sulfate
2. Methanol
3. Sodium carbonate
4. Ethyl chloride
5. Silver bromide
6. Acetylene
7. Sodium fluoride
8. Benzene
9. Aluminum
10. Trinitrotoluene
11. Calcium chloride
12. Aniline
13. Perchloric acid
14. Formaldehyde
15. Iodine
16. Isopropyl ether
17. Potassium dihydrogen phosphate
18. Sucrose
19. Lithium chloride
20. Quinone

(Consult appropriate reference works; see also *Journal of Chemical Education.*[2])

Assignments for Library Problem 17

This problem is devoted to miscellaneous items. Still others might be selected for those who have the time and interest.

Part 1. Biographical facts.

1. Wiley, Harvey
2. Gomberg, M.
3. Noyes, A. A.
4. Lamb, A. B.
5. Howe, H. E.
6. Whitmore, F. C.
7. Priestley, J.
8. Perkin, W. H.
9. Arrhenius, S.
10. Bragg, W. L.
11. Stieglitz, J.
12. Lundell, G. E. F.
13. Lewis, G. N.
14. Franklin, E. C.
15. Remsen, Ira
16. Noyes, W. A., Sr.
17. Hillebrand, W. F.
18. von Baeyer, A.
19. Gibbs, J. W.
20. Bogert, M. T.

(Consult biographical works, abstracting journals, histories of chemistry, and Soule, "Library Guide for the Chemist."[3])

Part 2. Abbreviations used in chemistry.

1. Abh.	6. Bd.	11. dch.	16. effy.
2. gasf.	7. Landw.	12. N.	17. Rec.
3. s.a.	8. cca.	13. fi.	18. gel.
4. hect.	9. Kem.	14. Leg.	19. mat.
5. P.A.	10. of.	15. schm.	20. Tfl.

[1] Information is most easily available for common chemicals.
[2] **10**:738 (1933).
[3] P. 25, 1938.

(Consult Crane, Patterson, and Marr, "A Guide to the Literature of Chemistry."[1])

Part 3. Summaries of contemporary knowledge.

1. Carcinogenic substances
2. Cracking catalysts
3. Isotopic tracers
4. Refining petroleum
5. Wood distillation
6. Zirconium
7. Statistical mechanics
8. Chemistry of cellulose
9. Solubility
10. Chemistry of dyestuffs
11. Radioactive fallout
12. Actinium-like metals
13. Structure of crystals
14. Shale oil
15. Corrosion of alloys
16. Industrial hydrogen
17. Chemistry of wood
18. Origin of spectra
19. Piezochemistry
20. Electrochemistry

(Consult monographs on chemistry.)

Part 4. Occurrence of chemical substances.

1. Ta
2. Tolu gum
3. F
4. Alabandite
5. P
6. K
7. Ti
8. Beryl
9. B
10. Sperrylite
11. Autunite
12. Thorianite
13. Sc
14. Fergusonite
15. Se
16. He
17. Li
18. Dechenite
19. Orangite
20. Spodumene

(Consult treatises and encyclopedias.)

Part 5. Popular publications (articles and books).

1. Smashing atoms
2. Modern dry-cleaning
3. Fluoridation of water
4. Carcinogenic agents
5. Artificial radioactivity
6. Diamonds in industry
7. Free radicals
8. Industrial wastes
9. Synthetic rubbers
10. The neutron
11. Sulfonated detergents
12. Dry ice
13. Powdered metals
14. Air conditioning
15. Gas chromatography
16. Water purification
17. Printing inks
18. Chain reactions
19. New chemical fibers
20. Plasticizers

(Consult "Readers' Guide" index, abstracting journals, and the less technical periodicals.)

[1] Appendix 2, 1957.

Part 6. Recipes for chemical products.

1. Expansion-joint filler
2. Mange cure
3. Butter substitute
4. Mayonnaise
5. Lipstick
6. Aquarium cement
7. Kola beverage
8. Apricot oil
9. Dry-cleaning fluid
10. Sunburn lotion
11. Envelope mucilage
12. Ginger-ale extract
13. Marshmallow
14. Hair tonic
15. Latex adhesive
16. Library paste
17. Vanilla flavoring
18. Pectin jellies
19. Red-rose soap
20. Deodorant spray

(Consult formularies.)

Part 7. Reactions of inorganic substances.

1. $BaO_2 + K_3Fe(CN)_6$
2. $H_2SO_4 + PCl_5$
3. $Br_2 + NH_3$
4. $HgNO_3 + SO_2 + H_2O$
5. $SO_2(OH)Cl + PCl_5$
6. $NaIO_3 + NaHSO_3$
7. $AgNO_3 + K_2S_2O_8 + H_2O$
8. $K_2TeO_3 + KOH + Cl_2$
9. $KMnO_4 + NO + H_2SO_4$
10. $HNO_3 + SnCl_2 + HCl$
11. $CoO + Ca(OCl)_2$
12. $NaClO_2 + KI + H_2O$
13. $CaS + CO_2 + H_2O$
14. $SO_2 + N_2O_3 + O_2 + H_2O$
15. $HBrO_3 + SO_2 + H_2O$
16. $N_2O_3 + (NH_4)_2SO_4$
17. $NaHSO_3 + SO_2 + Zn$
18. $N_2H_3I_3 + Zn(C_2H_5)_2$
19. $NH_2OH + ClHSO_3$
20. $CO(NH_2)_2 + H_2SO_4$

(Consult manuals of industrial chemistry and treatises on inorganic chemistry.)

Part 8. Experimental methods.

1. Acylation
2. Mercuration
3. Nitration, liquid phase
4. Alkylation
5. Chlorination, liquid phase
6. Fluorination
7. Arsonation
8. Reduction, NO_2 to $NHOH$
9. Reduction, COH to CH
10. Oxidation, CH_2OH to $COOH$
11. Dehydration
12. Hydrolysis, of nitrile
13. Addition, to $C{=}O$
14. Removal of HX
15. Resolution, d-, l- forms
16. Oxidation, CH_2 to $C{=}O$
17. Hydrolysis, of carbohydrate
18. Arylation
19. Sulfonation
20. Replacement, X by OR

(Consult treatises in the appropriate fields.)

Part 9. Methods of preparation.

1. SO_2Cl_2
2. $HOSO_2NO_2$
3. $Be(OH)_2$ (from beryl)
4. $CSCl_2$
5. $HOSO_2Cl$
6. Mg_3N_2
7. BiI_3
8. UCl_4
9. MoO_2Cl_2
10. $Ni(CO)_4$
11. Amyl nitrite
12. Triethyl phosphate
13. Phthalimide
14. Furan
15. Benzoin
16. $Pb(C_2H_5)_4$
17. Tetraethyl silicate
18. Pyrrole
19. Cyclohexene
20. Glycine

(Consult treatises in the appropriate fields.)

Assignments for Library Problem 18

Subjects for a Bibliography

1. Analysis by use of X rays
2. Determination of the composition of stars
3. Chemistry of lipsticks
4. Silicone resins
5. Structure of ice and snow crystals
6. Waterproofing paper
7. Distillery wastes
8. Sulfated alcohols
9. Hair-waving compounds
10. Dyeing of synthetic fibers
11. Molybdenum oxides as catalysts
12. Separations by columnar adsorption
13. Fluoride and tooth decay
14. Isotopes in experimental medicine
15. Ivy poisoning
16. Antioxidants for oils
17. Air pollution
18. Rocket fuels
19. Hay fever
20. Streptomycin

(Consult appropriate works of reference, such as encyclopedias and treatises. For much bibliographic work, abstracting journals are indispensable.)

Assignments for Library Problem 19

A report covering general information available may be prepared upon almost any chemical subject. However, not all subjects are equally suitable for student use, since beginners lack experience and perspective. Also the material on different subjects varies widely. In general, an assignment that is satisfactory for a bibliography in Problem 18 should be workable for a report. In any case a bibliography forms the basis of a report. For industrial chemistry, assignments such as those in Problem 16 may be desirable.

When one broadens report writing to include the preparation of manuscripts in a form suitable for publication as articles or books, so many details are involved that a weekly problem is insufficient for their consideration. Consequently, the author has expanded Problem 19 into a 1-hour semester's course on technical writing.

INDEX

Of many large volumes, the index is the best portion and the most useful.—*Wilmot.*

In this combined author, subject, and title index, subject entries are the most numerous. Authors are included when publications are well-known by their names. Specific titles are included for publications best known by their titles. Names appearing in footnotes or reference lists are omitted.

311

Date Due

Demco 293-5